A brief history of a never-ending numbe

Every year on March 14, mathematicians celebrate International π–Day. In 2005, a Japanese therapist recited more than 80,000 decimal places of pi from memory. There are books, poems, websites and even movies devoted to this remarkable number. What makes π (pi) so special?

π is the number obtained when the circumference of a circle is divided by its diameter. You will often see this ratio written as 3.14159, but there is more to π than that. However long or hard you try, you will never find its exact value. The decimal places of π go on forever, and with no discernible pattern.

The ancient Egyptians used a rough estimate of π in the building of their temples, but it was the Greeks who started the search for an increasingly accurate value. Fifteen hundred years ago, Chinese, Japanese and Indian mathematicians obtained ratios close to the one we use today, and five hundred years later, calculations made by Arab scholars spread from North Africa into Europe.

With the invention of the computer, the search for π really took off. In 2002, a supercomputer in Japan determined its value to more than 1 trillion decimal places.

Circles are everywhere in nature, and wherever circles are found, you will find π. From rainbows to DNA, from the structure of atoms to the motion of stars – all are described by equations involving π. It appears in other places, too, in fields as diverse as statistics, engineering and cosmology. Despite the fascination it holds for many, this never-ending number is much more than just a mathematical diversion.

diameter

circumference

$$\pi = \frac{\text{circumference}}{\text{diameter}}$$

π is the ratio of a circle's circumference to its diameter. It is a mathematical constant that appears in many equations involving circles and spheres

William Collins' dream of knowledge for all began with the publication of his first book in 1819. A self-educated mill worker, he not only enriched millions of lives, but also founded a flourishing publishing house.

Today, staying true to this spirit, Collins books are packed with inspiration, innovation and practical expertise. They place you at the centre of a world of possibility and give you exactly what you need to explore it.

Collins

DO MORE

Mixed Sources
Product group from well-managed forests and other controlled sources
www.fsc.org Cert no. SW-COC-1806
© 1996 Forest Stewardship Council

Published by Collins
An imprint of HarperCollinsPublishers
77–85 Fulham Palace Road,
Hammersmith,
London W6 8JB

Browse the complete Collins Education catalogue at
www.collinseducation.com

©HarperCollinsPublishers Limited 2006

10 9 8 7 6 5 4

ISBN-13: 978-0-00-775548-6

Paul Metcalf asserts his moral right
to be identified as the author of this work

British Library Cataloguing in Publication Data
A Catalogue record for this publication is available from the British Library

Cover design by White-Card, London
Text page design by Christina Newman
New artwork by Jerry Fowler

Printed and bound by Printing Express, Hong Kong

This high quality material is endorsed by Edexcel and has been through a rigorous quality assurance programme to ensure that it is a suitable companion to the specification for both learners and teachers.

This does not mean that its contents will be used verbatim when setting examinations nor is it to be read as being the official specification – a copy of which is available at **www.edexcel.org.uk**

Acknowledgements

The Authors and Publishers are grateful to the following for permission to reproduce copyright material:

Edexcel Ltd: p183 q9, q10, q11; p185 q20, q24; p187 q8; p188 q16, q17, q18

Edexcel Ltd accept no responsibility whatsoever for the accuracy or method of working in the answers given.

Inside Front Cover spread: Dave King © Dorling Kindersley, Courtesy of The Science Museum, London

Section spreads: pp12/13 Joerg Hartmannsgruber; pp56/57 © Frank Wattenberg, Department of Mathematical Sciences, United States Military Academy; pp98/99 Earth satellite image – Planetary Visions Ltd/ Science Photo Library; HK satellite image – CNES 1995 Distribution Spot Image/Science Photo Library; HK Harbour satellite image – Space Imaging/Science Photo Library; pp160/161 Joerg Hartmannsgruber

Photographs

Jupiterimages Corporation © 2006 pp16, 31, 40, 65, 102, 103, 112, 129, 133, 139, 152, 173

Every effort has been made to contact the holders of copyright material, but if any have been inadvertently overlooked, the Publishers will be pleased to make the necessary arrangements at the first opportunity.

IGCSE
MATHEMATICS

for Edexcel

by Paul Metcalf

Collins

GETTING THE BEST FROM THE BOOK AND THE CD-ROM

Welcome to IGCSE Maths for Edexcel. This textbook and the accompanying CD-ROM have been designed to help you understand all of the requirements needed to succeed in the IGCSE Maths for Edexcel course. The material from the syllabus has been covered in this book in the most useful order to aid learning, and you'll find a matching chart overleaf that details how the sections of this book correspond. The textbook also has some very useful features which have been designed to really help you understand all the aspects of Maths which you will need to know for this specification.

- Worked examples in the text take you through the techniques step-by-step to help you really understand.

- Banks of questions appear after every section to test your understanding of the work you've just covered.

- Throughout you will find hints to guide you past potential pitfalls.

IGCSE Maths for Edexcel is assessed in the following manner:

Examination Paper 3H – The Higher Tier – worth 50% of the marks.

AND

Examination Paper 4H – The Higher Tier – worth 50% of the marks.

Collins IGCSE Maths for Edexcel covers all of the topics and skills you will need to achieve success.

To help you through the course we have added a unique CD-ROM which may be used in class or by yourself as part of your private study. To allow you to really understand the subject as you progress through the course we have added the following features to the CD-ROM:

QUESTION BANK ON THE CD-ROM

'Practice makes perfect', the saying goes, and we have included a large bank of questions related to the Maths syllabus to help you understand the topics you will be studying.

Your teacher may be able to use this in class or you may want to try the questions in your private study sessions.

These questions will reinforce the knowledge you have gained in the classroom and through using the textbook and could also be used when you begin revising for your examinations. Don't try and do all the questions at once, though; the most effective way to use this feature is to try the questions every now and then, to test yourself. That way you can identify those areas where you need a little more work.

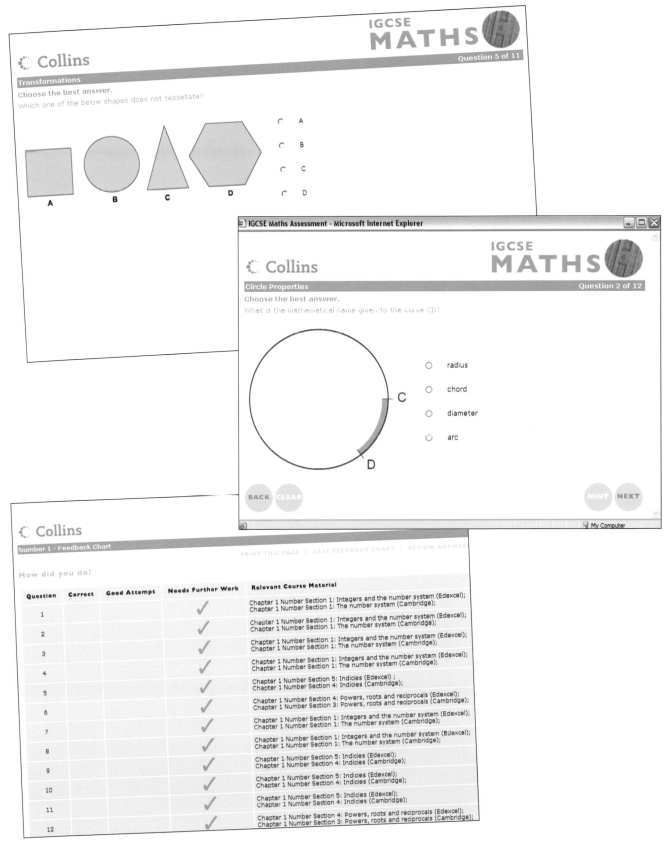

SUDOKU GAME

Sudoku, the crossword puzzle without words, has taken the world by storm. Literally translated, *su* means number and *doku* means place. Although no arithmetical skill is required, sudoku can develop logical reasoning skills – and provide an occasional relaxation!

There are 28000 Sudoku puzzles provided on the IGCSE Maths CD-ROM. The puzzle is a number grid consisting of 4, 6 or 9 boxes of 4, 6 or 9 squares. The objective is to fill the grid so that every column, every row and every box contains the digits 1 to 4, 1 to 6 or 1 to 9.

The puzzles are also provided at three levels of difficulty – Easy, Medium and Hard. To help make progress, you can choose to reveal a square at a time.

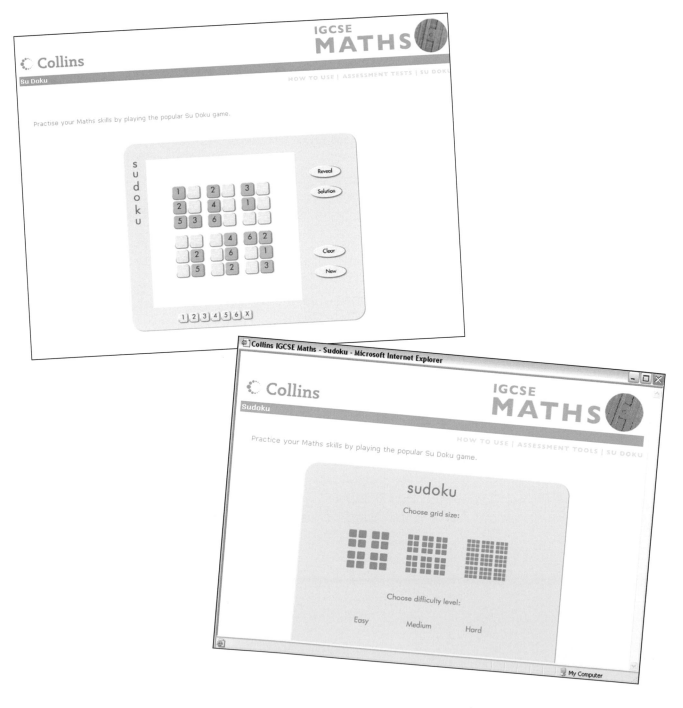

OPERATING SYSTEMS REQUIRED AND SET-UP INSTRUCTIONS.

Mac System requirements

500 MHz PowerPC G3 and later

Mac OS X 10.1.x and above

128MB RAM

Microsoft Internet Explorer 5.2, Firefox 1.x, Mozilla 1.x, Netscape 7.x and above, Opera 6, or Safari 1.x and above (Mac OS X 10.2.x only)

15 MB of free hard disc space.

To run the program from the CD
1 Insert the CD into the drive
2 When the CD icon appears on the desktop, double-click it
3 Double-click Collins IGCSE Maths.html

To install the program to run from the hard drive
1 Insert the CD into the drive
2 When the CD icon appears on the desktop, double-click it to open a finder window
3 Drag Collins IGCSE Maths.html to the desktop
4 Drag Collins IGCSE Maths Content to the desktop.

PC System requirements

450 MHz Intel Pentium II processor (or equivalent) and later

Windows 98/ME/NT/2000/XP

128MB RAM

Microsoft Internet Explorer 5.5, Firefox 1.x, Mozilla 1.x, Netscape 7.x and above, Opera 7.11 and above

15 MB of hard disc space

To run the program from the CD
1 Insert the CD into the drive
2 Double-click on the CD-ROM drive icon inside My Computer
3 Double-click on Collins IGCSE Maths.html

To install the program to run from the hard drive
1 Insert the IGCSE Maths disc into your CD-ROM drive
2 Double-click on the CD-ROM drive icon inside My Computer
3 Double-click on the SETUP.EXE

4 Follow onscreen instructions. These include instructions concerning the Macromedia Flash Player included   with and required by the program.
5 When the installation is complete, remove the CD from the drive.

Good luck with your IGCSE Maths studies. This book and the CD-ROM provide you with stimulating, interesting and motivating learning resources that we are sure will help you succeed in your course.

We have written this book in an order which we consider best for teaching and learning. The chapters therefore often cover more than one Objective from the Specification and in some places you will find the order of the topics differs sllightly from that in your Specification. We believe that by integrating some topics in this way, we have made them easier to understand and shown how one topic progresses into another. This chart will help you to see which Specification objectives are being covered in each chapter.

AO1 NUMBER AND ALGEBRA

Specification section		*Book chapters*
1	**Numbers and the number system**	
1.1	Integers	*Chapters 1 and 2*
1.2	Fractions	*Chapter 3*
1.3	Decimals	*Chapter 3*
1.4	Powers and roots	*Chapters 4, 5 and 6*
1.5	Set notation and language	*Chapter 7*
1.6	Percentages	*Chapters 8 and 9*
1.7	Ratio and proportion	*Chapter 10*
1.8	Degree of accuracy	*Chapters 11 and 12*
1.9	Standard form	*Chapter 13*
1.10	Applying number	*Chapters 8 and 9, etc.*
1.11	Electronic calculators	*Chapter 14*
2	**Equations, formulae and identities**	
2.1	Use of symbols	*Chapters 15 and 16*
2.2	Algebraic manipulations	*Chapters 16, 17 and 18*
2.3	Expressions and formulae	*Chapters 17, 18 and 19*
2.4	Linear equations	*Chapter 21*
2.5	Proportion	*Chapter 20*
2.6	Simultaneous linear equations	*Chapter 22*
2.7	Quadratic equations	*Chapter 23 (and 22)*
2.8	Inequalities	*Chapter 24*
3	**Sequences, functions and graphs**	
3.1	Sequences	*Chapter 25*
3.2	Functional notation	*Chapter 30*
3.3	Graphs	*Chapters 26, 27, 28 and 29*
3.4	Calculus	*Chapter 31*

AO2 SHAPE, SPACE AND MEASURES

Specification section	*Book chapters*
4 Geometry	
4.1 Angles and triangles	*Chapter 32*
4.2 Polygons	*Chapter 32*
4.3 Symmetry	*Chapters 41 and 42*
4.4 Measures	*Chapter 39*
4.5 Construction	*Chapter 33*
4.6 Circle properties	*Chapters 34 and 40*
4.7 Geometrical reasoning	*Chapter 32*
4.8 Trigonometry and Pythagoras' theorem	*Chapters 35, 36, 37 and 38*
4.9 Mensuration	*Chapter 39*
4.10 Similarity	*Chapter 39*
5 Vectors and transformation geometry	
5.1 Vectors	*Chapter 43*
5.2 Transformation geometry	*Chapter 42*

AO3 HANDLING DATA

Specification section	*Book chapters*
6 Statistics	
6.1 Graphical representation of data	*Chapters 44 and 45*
6.2 Statistical measures	*Chapters 46 and 47*
6.3 Probability	*Chapters 48, 49 and 50*

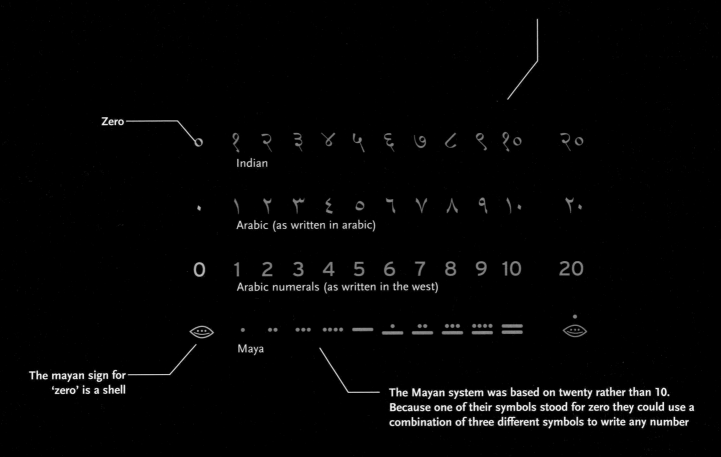

The number system we use today was developed in the third century BC in India. The signs may look different, but Indian and Arabic numerals and the numbers we use today are all the same system

Zero

Indian

Arabic (as written in arabic)

0 1 2 3 4 5 6 7 8 9 10 20

Arabic numerals (as written in the west)

Maya

The mayan sign for 'zero' is a shell

The Mayan system was based on twenty rather than 10. Because one of their symbols stood for zero they could use a combination of three different symbols to write any number

Nothing is important!

Have you ever thought about the way we write and use numbers? We use a place-value decimal system, with ten different symbols for the values zero to nine. The actual value of the numeral depends on its position – for example, '4' has different values in the numbers 45 and 436. Although the symbols we use are often called 'Arabic numerals' the system was actually first invented in India. They, along with the Chinese and the Mayan civilisations, realised how useful a figure for 'nothing' could be. The ancient Egyptians, Hebrews, Romans and Greeks did not have symbols for zero. But without zero how could we use our system to write the following sums?

2 508	30 001	740	300
+ 1 020	− 480	× 30	÷ 3
3 528	29 521	22 200	100

NUMBER

Roman numerals reflect the most natural method of
counting – on one's hands:
I, II, III symbolise one, two and three fingers. V could
represent a hand and X two hands. Without zero the
Romans needed different symbols for larger numbers and
used letters – L is 50, C is 100, D is 500, M is 1000

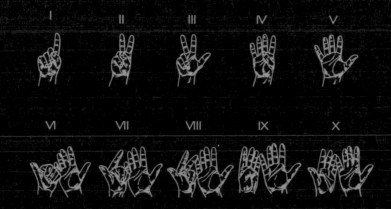

1 INTEGERS AND THE NUMBER SYSTEM

What are integers?

An **integer** is a whole number. It may be positive ($^+1$, $^+2$, $^+3$, ...) or negative ($^-1$, $^-2$, $^-3$, ...), or 0.

What are multiples?

The **multiples** of a number are the products in the multiplication tables.

Multiples of 5 are 5, 10, 15, 20, 25, 30, ...

Multiples of 6 are 6, 12, 18, 24, 30, 36, ...

The **lowest common multiple** of two or more numbers is the lowest (least) multiple that is common to all of the given numbers.

Worked example

Find the lowest common multiple of 3 and 5.

Multiples of 3:	3 , 6, 9, 12, 15, 18, 21, 24, 27, 30, ...
Multiples of 5:	5, 10, 15, 20, 25, 30, 35, 40, 45, ...
Common multiples of 3 and 5:	15, 30, 45, 60, ...

The lowest common multiple of 3 and 5 is 15.

HINTS

- Factors of a number come in pairs. For example:
  $24 = 1 \times 24$
  $= 2 \times 12$
  $= 3 \times 8$
  $= 4 \times 6$
  Factors of 24 are:
  1, 2, 3, 4, 6, 8, 12, 24.

. . . .

- Square numbers such as 16 always have an odd number of factors as one of the factor pairs is made up of the same factor, multiplied by itself.

What are factors?

The **factors** (divisors) of a number are numbers that divide *exactly* into that number (i.e. **without a remainder**). The number 1 and the number itself are *always* factors of the given number.

Factors of 8 are 1, 2, 4 and 8 because each of these divides exactly into 8.

Factors of 13 are 1 and 13 because each of these divides exactly into 13.

A number with exactly two factors is a **prime number**. The numbers 2, 3, 5, 7, 11, 13, 17, ... are all prime numbers.

Remember that the number **1 is not a prime number** because it has only one factor.

The **highest common factor** of two or more numbers is the highest factor which is common to all of the given numbers.

Worked example

Find the highest common factor of 16 and 24.

Factors of 16:	1, 2, 4, 8 and 16
Factors of 24:	1, 2, 3, 4, 6, 8, 12 and 24
Common factors of 16 and 24:	1, 2, 4 and 8

The highest common factor of 16 and 24 is 8.

What are prime factors?

A **prime factor** is a factor that is also a prime number.

All numbers can be written as a **product of prime factors**.

The number 15 can be written as 3×5 where 3 and 5 are prime factors.

The number 90 can be written as $2 \times 3 \times 3 \times 5$ where 2, 3 and 5 are prime factors.

You can find the prime factors of a number by rewriting it in **factor pairs**. Carry on doing this until all the factor pairs are prime numbers.

Worked example

Write 90 as a product of its prime factors.

```
          90
        /    \
=    9    ×   10
    / \      /  \
= 3 × 3 × 2 × 5
```

or alternatively,

```
      90                        90
     /  \                      /  \
    3   30          or        2   45
       /  \                      /  \
      3   10                    3   15
         /  \                      /  \
        2    5                    3    5
```

So $90 = 3 \times 3 \times 2 \times 5$ or $90 = 2 \times 3^2 \times 5$

QUESTIONS

Q1 From the numbers in the grid below write down:
   a) a multiple of 7
   b) a factor of 10
   c) a factor of 51
   d) a square number bigger than 10
   e) a prime number bigger than 16
   f) a prime number that is even
   g) a number that is a multiple of 3 and also a multiple of 7.

1	2	3	4	5
6	7	8	9	10
11	12	13	14	15
16	17	18	19	20
21	22	23	24	25

Q2 Write 264 as a product of its prime factors.

Q3 **a)** Express these numbers as products of their prime factors.
   (i) 56
   (ii) 84
   b) Find the highest common factor of 56 and 84.

Answers are on page 190.

More questions on the CD ROM

2 DIRECTED NUMBERS

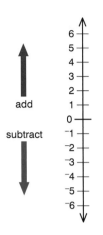

add

subtract

HINT

- When two signs appear together (e.g. 5 − ⁻4), replace them with one sign, using these rules.

  + + gives +

  + − gives −

  − + gives −

  − − gives +

  (−1) + (−2) is the same as ⁻1 − 2 as + − gives −.

  (+2) − (⁻3) is the same as ⁺2 + 3 as − − gives +.

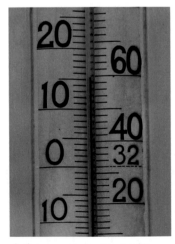

A thermometer using positive and negative numbers

More questions on the CD ROM

What are directed numbers?

A directed number has a + or − sign in front of it.

You will see directed numbers used in temperature scales, where negative numbers show temperatures below freezing.

Adding and subtracting directed numbers

To add or subtract directed numbers, find the starting position, then move up or down the number line. On a horizontal number line, move right or left.

Worked example

$2 + 3 = {}^+5$	Start at $^+2$ and move up 3 places to $^+5$.
$4 - 7 = {}^-3$	Start at $^+4$ and move down 7 places to $^-3$.
$^-3 + 6 = {}^+3$	Start at $^-3$ and move up 6 places to $^+3$.
$^-1 - 4 = {}^-5$	Start at $^-1$ and move down 4 places to $^-5$.

Multiplying and dividing directed numbers

To multiply or divide directed numbers, multiply or divide the numbers and then attach the sign according to these rules.

If the signs are the same, the answer will be positive.

If the signs are opposite, the answer will be negative.

So: and:

$$+ \times + = + \qquad - \times - = + \qquad\qquad + \div + = + \qquad - \div - = +$$

$$+ \times - = - \qquad - \times + = - \qquad\qquad + \div - = - \qquad - \div + = -$$

Worked example

$^+3 \times {}^-4 = {}^-12$	As $+ \times - = -$.
$^-6 \div {}^+2 = {}^-3$	As $- \div + = -$.
$^-4 \div {}^-8 = {}^+\frac{1}{2}$	As $- \div - = +$ and $\frac{4}{8} = \frac{1}{2}$.

QUESTIONS

Q1 Work these out.

a) $^-2 + 8$ b) $^-9 + 3$ c) $^-2 - 5$

d) $^+7 - {}^+2$ e) $^-3 - {}^-4$ f) $^-11 + {}^-2$

g) $^-10 - {}^-4$

Q2 Work these out.

a) $^-3 \times {}^+2$ b) $^+7 \times {}^-3$ c) $^-6 \times {}^-5$

d) $^+12 \div {}^+3$ e) $^+16 \div {}^-2$ f) $^-10 \div {}^+4$

g) $^-4 \times {}^+3 \times {}^-1$

Answers are on page 190.

3 FRACTIONS AND DECIMALS

The parts of a fraction

The top part of a fraction is called the **numerator** and the bottom part of a fraction is called the **denominator**.

Equivalent fractions

You can find equivalent fractions by multiplying or dividing the numerator and denominator by the same number.

$$\overset{\times 2}{\frac{1}{2}} = \frac{2}{4} \qquad \overset{\times 10}{\frac{3}{4}} = \frac{30}{40} \qquad \overset{\times 3}{\frac{4}{7}} = \frac{12}{21} \qquad \overset{\div 2}{\frac{160}{200}} = \frac{80}{100} \qquad \overset{\div 3}{\frac{9}{12}} = \frac{3}{4}$$

Cancelling fractions

You can express a fraction in its **lowest terms** or **simplest form** by making the numerator and the denominator as small as possible. Both numerator and denominator must be integers. The process of reducing fractions to their lowest terms is called **cancelling down** or **simplifying**.

One number as a fraction of another

To find one number as a fraction of another, write the numbers as a fraction, with the first number as the numerator and the second as the denominator.

Worked example

Write 55¢ as a fraction of 80¢.

55¢ as a fraction of 80¢ $= \frac{55}{80} = \frac{11}{16}$ so 55¢ is $\frac{11}{16}$ of 80¢.

Worked example

Write 4 mm as a fraction of 8 cm.

You must first ensure that the units are the same.

8 cm = 80 mm

4 mm as a fraction of 80 mm $= \frac{4}{80} = \frac{1}{20}$

So 4 mm is $\frac{1}{20}$ of 8 cm.

Addition and subtraction

To add (or subtract) fractions, make sure they have the same denominator.

Worked example

Add $\frac{2}{7} + \frac{4}{7}$.

$$\frac{2}{7} + \frac{4}{7} = \frac{6}{7}$$

Subtract $\frac{7}{8} - \frac{1}{5}$.

$$\frac{7}{8} - \frac{1}{5} = \frac{35}{40} - \frac{8}{40} = \frac{27}{40}$$

Writing both fractions with a denominator of 40.

Mixed numbers

A mixed number is made up of a whole number part and a fractional part, such as $1\frac{1}{5}$ or $5\frac{13}{20}$.

Any mixed number can be converted to an **improper fraction** (or **top-heavy fraction**).

$$1\frac{1}{5} = 1 + \frac{1}{5} = \frac{5}{5} + \frac{1}{5} = \frac{6}{5} \qquad \text{where } 1 = \frac{5}{5}$$

$$5\frac{13}{20} = 5 + \frac{13}{20} = \frac{100}{20} + \frac{13}{20} = \frac{113}{20} \qquad \text{where } 5 = \frac{100}{20}$$

Worked example

Add $1\frac{1}{5} + 5\frac{13}{20}$.

$$1\frac{1}{5} + 5\frac{13}{20} = \frac{6}{5} + \frac{113}{20} = \frac{24}{20} + \frac{113}{20}$$

$$= \frac{137}{20} = 6\frac{17}{20}$$

Converting to improper fractions and writing both fractions with a denominator of 20.

Rewriting as a mixed number.

$$\frac{6}{5} \overset{\times 4}{\underset{\times 4}{=}} \frac{24}{20}$$

Multiplication of fractions

To multiply fractions, multiply the numerators and multiply the denominators.

Worked example

Work out $\frac{4}{7} \times \frac{2}{11}$.

$$\frac{4}{7} \times \frac{2}{11} = \frac{4 \times 2}{7 \times 11}$$

$$= \frac{8}{77}$$

When working with mixed numbers you *must* convert to improper fractions first.

Worked example

Work out $1\frac{1}{5} \times 6\frac{2}{3}$.

$$1\frac{1}{5} \times 6\frac{2}{3} = \frac{6}{5} \times \frac{20}{3} \quad \text{Converting to top-heavy fractions.}$$

$$= \frac{6 \times 20}{5 \times 3} \quad \text{Multiplying the numerators and multiplying the denominators.}$$

$$= \frac{120}{15} = 8$$

Worked example

Find $\frac{2}{5}$ of 100.

$\frac{2}{5}$ of $100 = \frac{2}{5} \times \frac{100}{1}$ Writing 100 as a top-heavy fraction.

$= \frac{\cancel{200}^{40}}{\cancel{5}} \cdot \frac{40}{1}$ Cancelling.

$= 40$

> ## HINT
>
> - Alternatively, you can cancel the fractions.
>
> $$\frac{2 \times \cancel{100}}{\cancel{5} \times 1} = \frac{2 \times 20}{1 \times 1}$$
>
> $$= \frac{40}{1} = 40$$

Division of fractions

To divide one fraction by another, multiply the first fraction by the **reciprocal** of the second fraction.

Worked example

Work out $\frac{3}{7} \div \frac{1}{7}$.

$\frac{3}{7} \div \frac{1}{7} = \frac{3}{\cancel{7}} \times \frac{\cancel{7}}{1}$ Multiplying by the reciprocal and cancelling the fractions.

$= 3$

Changing decimals to fractions

You can change a decimal to a fraction by considering place value as follows.

Worked example

Change 0.459 to a fraction.

$0.459 = 0$ units and 4 tenths and 5 hundredths and 9 thousandths

$0.459 = 0 + \frac{4}{10} + \frac{5}{100} + \frac{9}{1000}$

$= \frac{400}{1000} + \frac{50}{1000} + \frac{9}{1000}$ Writing the fractions with a common denominator of 1000.

$= \frac{459}{1000}$

Changing fractions to decimals

Alternatively you can use division to change a fraction to a decimal.

Worked example

Change $\frac{1}{4}$ to a decimal.

$\frac{1}{4} = 1 \div 4$

$= 0.25$

Worked example

Change $\frac{4}{15}$ to a decimal.

$\frac{4}{15} = 4 \div 15$

$= 0.266\,666\,6 \ldots$

Note that the decimal in the example above carries on for ever. It is a **recurring decimal**.

In the decimal $0.2\dot{6}$ the dot over the 6 tells you that the number carries on infinitely.

If a group of numbers repeats infinitely then you can use two dots to show the repeating numbers.

$0.\dot{2}\dot{7} = 0.27\ 27\ 27\ 27\ ...$

$0.\dot{1}4285\dot{7} = 0.142857\ 142857\ ...$

What are recurring decimals?

In recurring decimals, part of the decimal fraction is repeated indefinitely.

Recurring decimals are all rational numbers as they can be expressed as fractions.

0.266 666 666 ...	written $0.2\dot{6}$	$= \frac{4}{15}$
0.142 857 142 857 ...	written $0.\dot{1}42\ 85\dot{7}$	$= \frac{1}{7}$
0.272 727 27 ...	written $0.\dot{2}\dot{7}$	$= \frac{3}{11}$

CONVERTING RECURRING DECIMALS

Worked example

Change $0.\dot{8}$ to a fraction.

Notice that	$10 \times 0.\dot{8} = 8.888\ 888\ 8...$	Multiplying both sides by 10.
and	$1 \times 0.\dot{8} = 0.888\ 888\ 8...$	
Subtracting:	$9 \times 0.\dot{8} = 8$	$8.888\ 888\ 8... - 0.888\ 888\ 8...$
and	$0.\dot{8} = \frac{8}{9}$	Dividing both sides by 9.
So	$0.\dot{8} = \frac{8}{9}$	

HINT

- Now check this by putting $\frac{8}{9}$ into your calculator.

Worked example

Convert $14.\dot{2}\dot{3}$ to a mixed number.

A mixed number consists of a whole number part and a fractional part.
In this question you can split the number up and deal with the recurring decimal or else proceed as shown previously.

Notice that	$100 \times 14.\dot{2}\dot{3} = 1423.232\ 323\ ...$	Multiplying both sides by 100.
and	$1 \times 14.\dot{2}\dot{3} = 14.232\ 323\ ...$	
Subtracting:	$99 \times 14.\dot{2}\dot{3} = 1409$	$1423.232\ 323\ ... - 14.232\ 323\ ...$
and	$14.\dot{2}\dot{3} = \frac{1409}{99}$	Dividing both sides by 99.
	$= 14\frac{23}{99}$	Converting back to a mixed number.
So	$14.\dot{2}\dot{3} = 14\frac{23}{99}$	

QUESTIONS

Q1 Work out $3\frac{1}{4} - 1\frac{1}{5}$.

Q2 Work out $\frac{3}{4} \times \frac{2}{5}$.

Q3 Work out $4\frac{4}{5} \div 1\frac{1}{15}$.

Q4 Change 0.162 to a fraction.

Q5 Raj said, 'I've got three-quarters of a tin of paint.'
Mei said, 'I've got four-sixths of a tin of paint and my tin of paint is the same size as yours.'

Who has got more paint, Mei or Raj?

Explain your answer.

Q6 Write a fraction that is equivalent to the recurring decimal $0.2\dot{5}\dot{3}$.

Q7 Change $0.8\dot{3}\dot{5}$ to a fraction.

Q8 Convert the recurring decimal $0.5\dot{3}$ to a fraction. Give your answer in the smallest form.

More questions on the CD ROM

Answers are on page 191.

4 POWERS, ROOTS AND RECIPROCALS

Powers and roots

Multiplying a number by itself one or more times gives a **power** of the first number. The base number is a **root** of the power.

$5 \times 5 = 5^2 = 25$
5^2 is 5 raised to the **power** of 2 or 5 **squared**.
5 is the **square root** of 25.

What are squares and cubes?

A **square number** is formed by multiplying a number by itself.

The square of 8 is $8 \times 8 = 64$ so 64 is a square number.

A **cube number** is formed when another number is multiplied by itself and then multiplied by itself again.

The cube of 5 is $5 \times 5 \times 5 = 125$ so 125 is a cube number.

Square roots and cube roots

The **square root** of a number is the number which, when squared, gives the first number.

The square root of 36 is 6, because $6 \times 6 = 36$.
The square root of 36 is also $^-6$, because $^-6 \times {}^-6 = 36$.

The sign $\sqrt[2]{}$ or $\sqrt{}$ is used to denote the square root so $\sqrt{36} = 6$ or $\sqrt{36} = {}^-6$, which you usually write as $\sqrt{36} = \pm6$.

Remember that **the square root of a number may be positive or negative**.

You can use the $\boxed{\sqrt{}}$ key on your calculator to find the square root of a number, but it will only give the positive square root.

The **cube root** of a number such as 27 is the number which, when cubed, gives the first number (27).

The cube root of 27 is 3 because $3 \times 3 \times 3 = 27$.

The sign $\sqrt[3]{}$ is used to denote the cube root so $\sqrt[3]{27} = 3$.

You can find a cube root on a calculator if you have a key marked $\boxed{\sqrt[3]{}}$.

Reciprocals

To find the **reciprocal** of a number you divide 1 by that number.

You can find the reciprocal of any non-zero number by converting the number to a fraction and turning the fraction upside-down.

■ The reciprocal of $\frac{2}{3}$ is $\frac{3}{2}$ and the reciprocal of 10 is $\frac{1}{10}$.

With a calculator you can find the reciprocal of a number by using the $\boxed{^{1}/_{x}}$ or $\boxed{x^{-1}}$ key.

You may need to use the $\boxed{\text{INV}}$ or $\boxed{\text{2ndF}}$ or $\boxed{\text{SHIFT}}$ key with it.

QUESTIONS

Q1 Work out $\sqrt{36}$, $\sqrt{10}$.

Q2 Work out $\sqrt[3]{4096}$, $\sqrt[3]{-10}$.

Q3 Work out the reciprocals of $\frac{3}{4}$, 15, $1\frac{1}{5}$.

More questions on the CD ROM

Answers are on page 191.

5 INDICES

Rules for indices

When you multiply a number by itself, use the following shorthand.

$5 \times 5 = 5^2$ Say, '5 to the power 2 (or 5 squared).'

$5 \times 5 \times 5 = 5^3$ Say, '5 to the power 3 (or 5 cubed).'

In general, you write the shorthand like this:

5^4 ← power
← base

and you say it as 'five to the power four'.

The power (or **index**) tells you how many times to multiply the base number.

5^4 tells you to multiply together 4 (the power or index) 'lots' of 5 (the base number).

$5^4 = 5 \times 5 \times 5 \times 5$

Similarly 4^7 tells you to multiply together 7 'lots' of 4.

$4^7 = 4 \times 4 \times 4 \times 4 \times 4 \times 4 \times 4$

HINT

• You are multiplying the base number by itself, not by the index.

How to multiply numbers with indices

You can multiply numbers with indices like this.

$3^4 = 3 \times 3 \times 3 \times 3$ $3^5 = 3 \times 3 \times 3 \times 3 \times 3$

So $3^4 \times 3^5 = (3 \times 3 \times 3 \times 3) \times (3 \times 3 \times 3 \times 3 \times 3)$

$= 3 \times 3 \times 3 \times 3 \times 3 \times 3 \times 3 \times 3 \times 3$

$= 3^9$

To multiply two numbers with indices **when their bases are the same** you just add their indices.

$3^4 \times 3^5 = 3^{4+5} = 3^9$ and $12^4 \times 12^6 = 12^{4+6} = 12^{10}$

HINT

• In general: $a^m \times a^n = a^{m+n}$

How to divide numbers with indices

You can divide numbers with indices like this.

$$6^7 \div 6^4 = \frac{6 \times 6 \times 6 \times \cancel{6} \times \cancel{6} \times \cancel{6} \times \cancel{6}}{\cancel{6} \times \cancel{6} \times \cancel{6} \times \cancel{6}} = 6 \times 6 \times 6 = 6^3$$

To divide two numbers with indices **when their bases are the same** you just subtract their indices.

$6^7 \div 6^4 = 6^{7-4} = 6^3$ and $15^9 \div 15^3 = 15^{9-3} = 15^6$

HINT

• In general: $a^m \div a^n = a^{m-n}$

Negative powers

From the above it follows that:

$$7^4 \div 7^6 = 7^{4-6} = 7^{-2} \quad \text{and} \quad 7^4 \div 7^6 = \frac{\overset{1}{7} \times \overset{1}{7} \times \overset{1}{7} \times \overset{1}{7}}{7 \times 7 \times \underset{1}{7} \times \underset{1}{7} \times \underset{1}{7} \times \underset{1}{7}} = \frac{1}{7^2}$$

So $7^{-2} = \frac{1}{7^2}$

HINT

- In general: $a^{-m} = \frac{1}{a^m}$

- In general: $a^{-1} = \frac{1}{a}$

Zero powers

Using the same ideas as before:

$$5^4 \div 5^4 = 5^{4-4} = 5^0 \quad \text{and} \quad 5^4 \div 5^4 = \frac{\overset{1}{5} \times \overset{1}{5} \times \overset{1}{5} \times \overset{1}{5}}{\underset{1}{5} \times \underset{1}{5} \times \underset{1}{5} \times \underset{1}{5}} = 1$$

$5^0 = 1, 6^0 = 1, 100^0 = 1, 645.321^0 = 1$ and so on.

HINT

- Any number raised to the power zero is equal to 1.
- In general: $a^0 = 1$

Rules for fractional indices

Using the fact that

$a^m \times a^n = a^{m+n}$, you can see that:

$a^{\frac{1}{2}} \times a^{\frac{1}{2}} = a^{\frac{1}{2}+\frac{1}{2}} = a^1 = a$

so any number raised to the power $\frac{1}{2}$ means $\sqrt[2]{}$ or $\sqrt{}$ $\quad a^{\frac{1}{2}} = \sqrt{a}$

$a^{\frac{1}{3}} \times a^{\frac{1}{3}} \times a^{\frac{1}{3}} = a^{\frac{1}{3}+\frac{1}{3}+\frac{1}{3}} = a^1 = a$

so any number raised to the power $\frac{1}{3}$ means $\sqrt[3]{}$ $\quad a^{\frac{1}{3}} = \sqrt[3]{a}$

Similarly:

$a^{\frac{1}{n}} = \sqrt[n]{a}$

CALCULATIONS WITH FRACTIONAL INDICES

Worked example

Evaluate the following.

a) $49^{\frac{1}{2}}$

$49^{\frac{1}{2}} = \sqrt{49}$

$\qquad = 7$

b) $3125^{\frac{1}{5}}$

$3125^{\frac{1}{5}} = \sqrt[5]{3125}$

$\qquad = 5$

Worked example

Evaluate $216^{\frac{2}{3}}$.

$216^{\frac{2}{3}} = (216^{\frac{1}{3}})^2$

$\qquad = 6^2$ as $216^{\frac{1}{3}} = 6$

$\qquad = 36$

Alternatively, you can use: $216^{\frac{2}{3}} = (216^2)^{\frac{1}{3}} = 46\,656^{\frac{1}{3}} = 36$
although this is rather longwinded.

QUESTIONS

Q1 Find the value of the following.
  a) 9^3 **b)** 4^{-2} **c)** 6^1

Q2 Calculate these, giving your answers in index form where possible.
  a) $3^{11} \times 3^{12}$ **b)** $8^6 \div 8^4$ **c)** $13^4 \div 13^4$ **d)** $4^3 \times 5^2$

Q3 Work out the value of each expression.
  a) $(2^2)^3$ **b)** $(\sqrt{3})^2$ **c)** $\sqrt{2^4 \times 9}$

Q4 Evaluate these.   **a)** $36^{\frac{1}{2}}$ **b)** $64^{\frac{1}{3}}$ **c)** $10\,000^{\frac{1}{4}}$

Q5 Evaluate these.   **a)** $125^{\frac{2}{3}}$ **b)** $125^{-\frac{2}{3}}$

Q6 What is the value of n if $4^n = \frac{1}{2}$?

Q7 Work these out.   **a)** 4^0 **b)** 3^{-2} **c)** $16^{\frac{3}{2}}$

Q8 $x = 2^p, y = 2^q$
  a) Express these in terms of x and/or y.
     (i) 2^{p+q} **(ii)** 2^{2q} **(iii)** 2^{p-1}

  $xy = 32, 2xy^2 = 32$
  b) Find the value of p and the value of q.

More questions
on the CD ROM

Answers are on page 192.

6 RATIONAL AND IRRATIONAL NUMBERS

What are rational and irrational numbers?

A rational number can be expressed in the form $\frac{p}{q}$ where p and q are integers.

Rational numbers include $\frac{1}{5}$, $0.\dot{3}$, 7, $\sqrt{9}$, $\sqrt[3]{64}$.

Irrational numbers include $\sqrt{2}$, $\sqrt{3}$, $\sqrt[3]{20}$, π, π^2.

Irrational numbers involving square roots are also called **surds**. Surds can be multiplied and divided.

Worked example

Work these out.

a) $\sqrt{3} \times \sqrt{3}$ **b)** $\sqrt{2} \times \sqrt{8}$ **c)** $\frac{\sqrt{48}}{\sqrt{12}}$ **d)** $\frac{\sqrt{30}}{\sqrt{6}}$

a) $\sqrt{3} \times \sqrt{3} = \sqrt{3 \times 3} = \sqrt{9} = 3$ **b)** $\sqrt{2} \times \sqrt{8} = \sqrt{2 \times 8} = \sqrt{16} = 4$

c) $\frac{\sqrt{48}}{\sqrt{12}} = \sqrt{\frac{48}{12}} = \sqrt{4} = 2$ **d)** $\frac{\sqrt{30}}{\sqrt{6}} = \sqrt{\frac{30}{6}} = \sqrt{5}$

Worked example

Simplify the following.

a) $\sqrt{72}$ **b)** $\sqrt{5} + \sqrt{45}$ **c)** $\frac{1}{\sqrt{5}}$ **d)** $(3 - \sqrt{2})^2$

a) $\sqrt{72} = \sqrt{36 \times 2} = \sqrt{36} \times \sqrt{2} = 6 \times \sqrt{2}$

$= 6\sqrt{2}$ As $6 \times \sqrt{2}$ is usually written $6\sqrt{2}$.

b) $\sqrt{5} + \sqrt{45} = \sqrt{5} + \sqrt{9 \times 5} = \sqrt{5} + (\sqrt{9} \times \sqrt{5})$

$= \sqrt{5} + (3 \times \sqrt{5}) = \sqrt{5} + 3\sqrt{5} = 4\sqrt{5}$

c) $\frac{1}{\sqrt{5}} = \frac{1}{\sqrt{5}} \times \frac{\sqrt{5}}{\sqrt{5}} = \frac{\sqrt{5}}{5}$ As $(\sqrt{5})^2$ is 5.

d) $(3 - \sqrt{2})^2 = 3 \times 3 - 3\sqrt{2} - 3\sqrt{2} + \sqrt{2}\sqrt{2}$

$= 9 - 6\sqrt{2} + 2$

$= 11 - 6\sqrt{2}$

QUESTIONS

Q1 Which of these are rational numbers?

$3^{\frac{1}{2}}$ $(\sqrt{3})^2$ π^{-2} $\sqrt{5\frac{1}{4}}$ $\sqrt{6\frac{1}{4}}$

Write each of the rational numbers in the form $\frac{p}{q}$ where p and q are integers.

Q2 Simplify the following expressions, leaving your answers in surd form.

a) $\sqrt{5} \times \sqrt{15}$ **b)** $\sqrt{5} + \sqrt{20}$ **c)** $\frac{1}{\sqrt{7}}$

Q3 Simplify $(4 + \sqrt{3})(4 - \sqrt{3})$.

Q4 Work this out. $\dfrac{(5 + \sqrt{3})(5 - \sqrt{3})}{\sqrt{22}}$

Give your answer in its simplest form.

More questions on the CD ROM

Q5 **a)** Express $\dfrac{10}{\sqrt{5}}$ in the form $k\sqrt{5}$ where k is an integer.

b) Express $(5 + \sqrt{3})^2$ in the form $a + b\sqrt{3}$ where a and b are integers.

Answers are on page 193.

7 SETS AND SET NOTATION

What is a set?

A set is a collection of items such as letters, numbers, objects, etc.

e.g. a, e, i, o, u   is the set of vowels – the set is a finite set with 5 members or elements.

1, 2, 3, ... is the set of positive integers – the set is an infinite set.

dog, cat, fish, rabbit ....is the set of household pets.

Sets can be described, e.g. the set of vowels or listed, e.g. a, e, i, o, u.

We often use curly brackets to identify sets.

Here the list includes 5 members or elements which are separated by commas

{set of vowels} = {a, e, i, o, u}

Notation

You need to know the following notation for sets:

$\mathscr{E}$ is the universal set

$\emptyset$ is the empty (or null) set ← This is also sometimes written as { }

$\in$ means 'is a member of'

$\cap$ means 'intersect'

$\cup$ means 'union'

$\subset$ means 'is a subset of'

A′   is the complement of A′ meaning everything outside of A

n(A)   is the number of members or element in set A

e.g. if $\mathscr{E}$ is the universal set of all lower case letters and A is the set of vowels

i.e. if $\mathscr{E}$ = {all lower case letters}, A = {vowels} and B = {s, q, u, a, r, e}

then A = {a, e, i, o, u}
      A $\cap$ B = {a, e, u}
      A $\cup$ B = {a, e, i, o, q, r, s, u}
      A′ $\cap$ B = {s, q, r}
      A $\cap$ B′ = {i, o}
      A′ = {consonants}
      u $\in$ A
      v $\in$ A′
      n (A) = 5
      n (A′) = 21
      A $\cap$ {p, q, r, s, t} = $\emptyset$
      {a, e, i} $\subset$ A

Worked example

Given that $\mathscr{E}$ = {Positive integers}

        A = {Prime numbers}

        B = {Even numbers less than 12}

        C = {Factors of 12}

        D = {Multiples of 3}

a) List the elements of

   (i)   A ∩ B

   (ii) C ∩ D

   (iii) B ∩ D′

   (iv) B ∪ C

b) Which of the following are true?

   (i)   1 ∈ A

   (ii) 12 ∈ B

   (iii) n(C) = 6

   (iv) B ∩ D = ∅

Before answering this question, it is a good idea to list the elements of each set:

A = {Prime numbers} = {2, 3, 5, 7, 11, 13, …}   *This is an infinite set*

B = {Even numbers less than 12} = {2, 4, 6, 8, 10} *12 is not less than 12*

C = {Factors of 12} = {1, 2, 3, 4, 6, 12}   *Remember that factors come in pairs*

D = {Multiples of 3} = {3, 6, 9, 12, 15, 18, …}   *This is an infinite set*

a)

   (i)   A ∩ B = {2, 3, 5, 7, 11, 13, …} ∩ {2, 4, 6, 8, 10} = {2}

   (ii) C ∩ D = {1, 2, 3, 4, 6, 12} ∩ {3, 6, 9, 12, 15, 18, …} = {3, 6, 12}

   (iii) B ∩ D′ = {2, 4, 6, 8, 10} ∩ {1, 2, 4, 5, 7, 8, 10, 11, 13, 14,…} = {2, 4, 8, 10}

   (iv) B ∪ C = {2, 4, 6, 8, 10} ∪ {1, 2, 3, 4, 6, 12} = {1, 2, 3, 4, 6, 8, 10, 12}

b)

These are all the positive integers which are not multiples of 3

   (i)   1 ∈ A is FALSE as 1 is not a prime number.

   (ii) 12 ∈ B is FALSE as 12 is not less than 12.

   (iii) n(C) = 6 is TRUE as there are 6 elements in C.

   (iv) B ∩ D = ∅ is FALSE as 6 is a member of B ∩ D.

Venn diagrams

Set notation can be shown diagrammatically by making use of a Venn diagram.

In a Venn diagram, the rectangular box represents the Universal set ($\mathscr{E}$).

Other sets are usually represented by circles as follows:

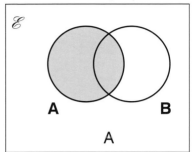

A

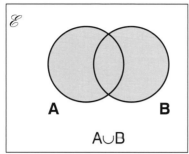

A∪B

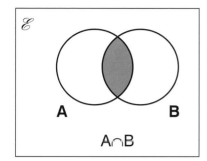

A∩B

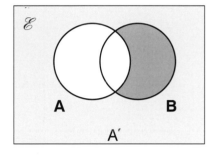

A′

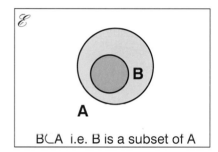

B⊂A i.e. B is a subset of A

Venn diagrams can also be used to show the number of elements in each set

From this diagram

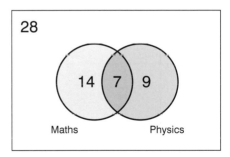

14 + 7 = 21 students take mathematics

7 + 9 = 16 students take physics

14 students take mathematics but not physics

9 students take physics but not mathematics

7 students take mathematics and physics

28 students do not take mathematics or physics

Worked example

Given that $\mathscr{E}$ = {x: x is an integer and 1≤ x <15}

x: x means "x is such that" so that in this case x is such that x is an integer and 1≤ x <15

E = {Even numbers}

F = {Factors of 12}

a) Copy the Venn diagram and fill in each member of $\mathscr{E}$ in the correct region

b) Write down the value of n(E∩F′)

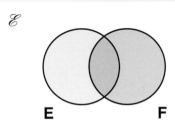

a) Listing the elements of each set:

$\mathscr{E}$ = {Positive integers less than 15} = {1, 2, 3, 4, ...14}

E = {Even numbers} = {2, 4, 6, 8, 10, 12, 14}   *remember that these must be members of $\mathscr{E}$*

F = {Factors of 12} = {1, 2, 3, 4, 6, 12}

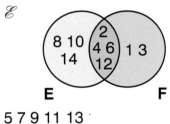

b) E∩F′ = {2, 4, 6, 8, 10, 12, 14} ∩ {5, 7, 8, 9, 10, 11, 13, 14}

E∩F′ = {8, 10, 14}

n(E∩F′) = 3

Remember that F′ is the complement of F so everything outside F but in the universal set belongs to F′.

Worked example

There are 30 pupils in a class and 3 of them do not take any language.

15 pupils take French and 19 pupils take German.

How many pupils take both French and German?

Completing a Venn diagram to show the situation more clearly

$\mathscr{E}$ = 30

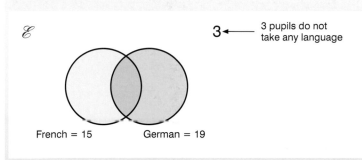

The number of pupils shown on the diagram is 15 + 19 + 3 = 37

But there are only 30 pupils in the class, so 7 pupils are being counted twice.

These 7 pupils are the pupils who take both French and German

$\mathscr{E}$ = 30

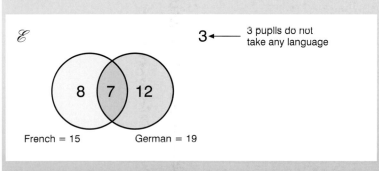

The diagram confirms that 7 pupils take French and German.

QUESTIONS

Q1 Given that $\mathscr{E}$ = {Positive integers}
                   A = {Even numbers less than 16}
                   B = {Factors of 15}
                   C = {Multiples of 3}

     a) List the elements of   **(b)** Which of the following are true?
         (i) $B \cap C$ **(i)** $16 \in A$
         (ii) $A \cap B$ **(ii)** $n(C) = 4$
         (iii) $A' \cap B$ **(iii)** $A \cap B \cap C = \varnothing$
         (iv) $A \cup B$ **(iv)** $B \subset A'$

Q2 Given that $\mathscr{E}$ = {x: x is an integer and $1 \le x < 15$}
F = {Factors of 12}
M = {Multiples of 3}

a) Copy the Venn diagram and fill in each member of $\mathscr{E}$ in the correct region.

b) Write down the value of $n(F \cap M')$.

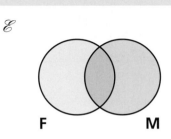

Q3 Copy the Venn diagram.

Use your diagram to shade the region represented by A'∩B.

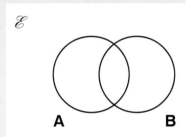

Q4 In the Venn diagram, the numbers of elements in different regions is shown.

a) Given that n($\mathscr{E}$) = 50 calculate $n(A \cap B \cap C)$

b) Use the diagram to find
   (i) $n(C)$
   (ii) $n(A \cap B)$
   (iii) $n((A \cup B)')$

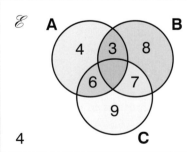

Q5 In the Venn diagram, the numbers of students taking biology (B), chemistry (C) and physics (P) are shown:

6 students study physics, chemistry and biology.
10 students study biology and chemistry.
7 students study biology and physics.

a) How many students study chemistry altogether?
Given that there are 50 students altogether:
b) how many students study physics only.

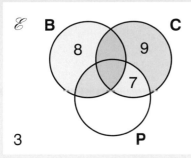

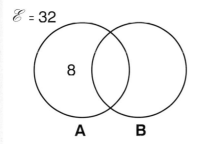

Q6 $n(\mathscr{E}) = 32$, $n(A') = 20$ and $n(A \cap B') = 8$.

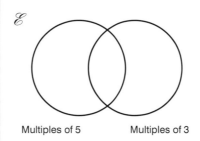

Find

(i) $n(A)$,   **(ii)** $n(A \cap B)$.

Q7 The universal set, $\mathscr{E}$ = {whole numbers}

A = {Multiples of 5}

B = {Multiples of 3}

Sets A and B are represented by the circles in the Venn diagram.

Multiples of 5   Multiples of 3

a) (i) On the diagram, shade the region that represents the set
$A \cap B'$
(ii) Write down **three** members of the set $A \cap B'$

C = {Multiples of 10}

b) (i) On the diagram draw a circle to represent the set C.
(ii) Write down **three** members of the set $A \cap B \cap C'$

Answers are on page 193.

8 PERCENTAGES

What is a percentage?

A percentage is a number of parts per 100.

- 50% means 50 parts per 100 or $\frac{50}{100} = \frac{1}{2}$ in its lowest terms.

Changing percentages, fractions and decimals

PERCENTAGES TO FRACTIONS

To change a percentage to a fraction, divide by 100.

Worked example

Change **68%** to a fraction.

$68\% = \frac{68}{100}$

$\qquad = \frac{17}{25}$ Cancelling down to the lowest terms.

Worked example

Change $45\frac{1}{2}\%$ to a fraction.

$45\frac{1}{2}\% = \frac{45}{100}$

$\qquad = \frac{90}{200}$ Multiplying top and bottom by 2 to give integers on the top and bottom.

PERCENTAGES TO DECIMALS

To change a percentage to a decimal, divide by 100.

Worked example

Change **68%** to a decimal.

$68\% = 68 \div 100$
$\qquad = 0.68$

Worked example

Change $72\frac{3}{4}\%$ to a decimal.

$72\frac{3}{4}\% = \frac{72}{100}$

$\qquad = \frac{291}{400}$ Multiplying top and bottom by 4 to remove the fraction on the top.

$\qquad = 291 \div 400$

HINT

- As $72\frac{3}{4} = 72.75$, you could just divide 72.75 by 100 to get the same result.

FRACTIONS TO PERCENTAGES

To change a fraction to a percentage, multiply by 100.

Worked example

Change $\frac{1}{4}$ to a percentage.

$\frac{1}{4} = \frac{1}{4} \times 100\%$
$\quad = 25\%$

DECIMALS TO PERCENTAGES

To change a decimal to a percentage, multiply by 100.

Worked example

Convert 0.2 to a percentage.

$0.2 = 0.2 \times 100\%$
$\quad = 20\%$

Worked example

Change 0.005 to a percentage.

$0.005 = 0.005 \times 100\%$
$\quad\quad = 0.5\%$

Comparing percentages, fractions and decimals

To compare and order percentages, fractions and decimals, change them all into percentages.

Worked example

Place the following in order of size, starting with the smallest.

$65\%, \frac{3}{5}, 0.62, 63.5\%, \frac{3}{4}, 0.7$

65%	65%
$\frac{3}{5} = \frac{3}{5} \times 100\% = 60\%$	60%
$0.62 = 0.62 \times 100\% = 62\%$	62%
63.5%	63.5%
$\frac{3}{4} = \frac{3}{4} \times 100\% = 75\%$	75%
$0.7 = 0.7 \times 100\% = 70\%$	70%

So the order is $\frac{3}{5}, 0.62, 63.5\%, 65\%, 0.7, \frac{3}{4}$ (smallest to highest).

Expressing one number as a percentage of another

To express one number as a percentage of another, write the first number as a fraction of the second and convert the fraction to a percentage.

Worked example

Write 55¢ as a percentage of 88¢.

55¢ as a fraction of 88¢ $= \frac{55}{88}$.

$\frac{55}{88} = \frac{55}{88} \times 100\%$ Converting the fraction to a percentage.

$\quad = 62.5\%$

Worked example

Write 2 feet as a percentage of 5 yards.

First you must ensure that the units are the same.

5 yards = 15 feet   As 1 yard = 3 feet

So the problem becomes 'write 2 feet as a percentage of 15 feet'.

2 feet as a fraction of 15 feet $= \frac{2}{15}$.

$\frac{2}{15} = \frac{2}{15} \times 100\%$ Converting the fraction to a percentage.

$\quad = 13.333\,333\ldots\%$

$\quad = 13.3\%$ (3 s.f.)

Finding a percentage of an amount

To find a percentage of an amount, find 1% of the amount and then multiply to get the required amount.

Worked example

Calculate 50% of $72.

1% of $\$72 = \$\frac{72}{100}$

$= \$0.72$

50% of $\$72 = 50 \times \$0.72$

$= \$36$

Worked example

An investment valued at $2000 shows an increase of 6% one year.
What is the new value of the investment?

To find 6% of $2000, first find 1%.

1% of $\$2000 = \$20$

So 6% of $\$2000 = 6 \times \$20$

$= \$120$

The new value of the investment is $2000 + $120 = $2120

An alternative method uses the fact that after a 6% increase, the new amount will be 100% of the original amount + 6% of the original amount.

$100\% + 6\% = 106\%$ of the original amount

The new value of the investment is 106% of $2000.

1% of $\$2000 = \$20$

106% of $\$2000 = 106 \times \$20$

$= \$2120$ (as before)

or $1.06 \times \$2000 = \$2120$

HINT

- 106% is equivalent to a multiplier of $1.06 \left(\frac{106}{100}\right)$.

Worked example

A trailer valued at $8000 depreciates by 9% each year. What is the value of the trailer after:

a) one year **b)** two years?

After a depreciation of 9%, the new amount

$= 100\%$ of the original amount $- 9\%$ of the original amount

$= 91\%$ of the original amount

a) After one year, the value of the trailer is 91% of $8000.

1% of $\$8000 = \$80$

91% of $\$8000 = 91 \times \$80$

$= \$7280$

or $0.91 \times \$8000 = \$7280$

b) After the second year, the value of the trailer is 91% of $7280.

1% of $\$7280 = \$72.80$

91% of $\$7280 = 91 \times \$72.80$

$= \$6624.80$

or $0.91 \times \$7280 = \$6624.80$

HINT

- 91% is equivalent to a multiplier of $0.91\left(\frac{91}{100}\right)$.

Percentage change

To work out the percentage change, work out the increase or decrease and add or subtract it from the original amount.

$$\text{Percentage change} = \frac{\text{change}}{\text{original amount}} \times 100\%$$

where the change might be an increase, decrease, profit, loss, error, etc.

Worked example

A company produces 78 000 parts one year and 79 950 the following year. Calculate the percentage increase.

$$\text{Percentage increase} = \frac{\text{increase}}{\text{original amount}} \times 100\%$$

Increase $= 79\,950 - 78\,000 = 1950$

$$\text{Percentage increase} = \frac{1950}{78\,000} \times 100\% = 2.5\%$$

Worked example

A car valued at $3200 is sold for $2950. What is the percentage loss?

$$\text{Percentage loss} = \frac{\text{decrease}}{\text{original amount}} \times 100\%$$

Loss $= \$3200 - \$2950 = \$250$

$$\text{Percentage loss} = \frac{250}{3200} \times 100\% = 7.8125\%$$

$\qquad = 7.81\%$ or 7.8% to an appropriate degree of accuracy.

QUESTIONS

Q1 There are 800 students at Mandela School. 45% of these 800 students are girls.
  a) Work out 45% of 800.

  There are 176 students in Year 10.

  b) Write 176 out of 800 as a percentage.

Q2 The price of a bathroom suite is advertised as $2800. A discount of 5.5% is agreed for a speedy sale. What is the final cost of the bathroom suite?

Q3 A weighing machine records a weight of 6 kg when the actual weight is 6.005 kg. What is the percentage error on the actual weight?

Q4 In July 2002, the population of Egypt was 69 million.
By July 2003, the population of Egypt has increased by 2%.

Work out the population of Egypt in July 2003.

Q5 Krishnan used 611 units of electricity.
The first 182 units cost $0.0821 per unit.
The remaining units cost $0.0704 per unit.
Tax is added at 5% of the total amount.

Complete Krishnan's bill.

182 units at $0.0821 per unit	$_____
429 units at $0.0704 per unit	$_____
Total amount	$_____
Tax at 5% of the total amount	$_____
Amount to pay	$_____

More questions on the CD ROM

Answers are on page 194.

9 REVERSE PERCENTAGES

What is a reverse percentage?

When an amount is increased or decreased by a given percentage, the result is a new amount. Use the technique of reverse percentages to:

find the original amount after a percentage change
find the percentage by which the amount was changed.

Using reverse percentages

Worked example

A CD system costs $282 including sales tax at $17\frac{1}{2}$%. What is the cost of the CD system without the sales tax?

CD player

117.5% of the cost of the CD system = $282

$282 represents 117.5% (100% + 17.5%) of the cost of the CD system.

$$1\% \text{ of the cost of the CD system} = \$\frac{282}{117.5}$$

$$= \$2.40$$

$$100\% \text{ of the cost of the CD system} = 100 \times \$2.40$$

$$= \$240$$

The CD system costs $240 without the sales tax.

Worked example

A washing machine is advertised at $335.75 after a price reduction of 15%. What was the original price of the washing machine?

$335.75 represents 85% of the original price (100% − 15%).

$$\text{So } 85\% \text{ of the original price} = \$335.75$$

$$1\% \text{ of the original price} = \$\frac{335.75}{85}$$

$$= \$3.95$$

$$100\% \text{ of the original price} = 100 \times \$3.95$$

$$= \$395$$

The original price of the washing machine was $395.

QUESTIONS

Q1 The price of a holiday is reduced by 5% to $361. What was the original cost of the holiday?

More questions on the CD ROM

Q2 A car is sold for $5225 after a depreciation of 45% of the original purchase price. Calculate the original purchase price of the car.

Answers are on page 195.

10 RATIOS AND PROPORTIONAL DIVISION

How do you use ratios?

You can use a ratio to compare one quantity to another quantity.
Ratios work in a similar way to fractions.

Worked example

In a box there are 12 lemons and 16 oranges. Write this as a ratio comparing the number of lemons to the number of oranges.

The ratio of the number of lemons to the number of oranges is 12 to 16.

You write this as 12 : 16.

The order is important in ratios.

The ratio of the number of oranges to the number of lemons is 16 to 12 or 16 : 12.

Equivalent ratios

Equivalent ratios are ratios that are equal to each other.

The following ratios are all equivalent to 2 : 5.

$$2 : 5 = 4 : 10 = 6 : 15 = 8 : 20 = ...$$

Equivalent ratios can be found by multiplying or dividing both sides of the ratio by the same number. You can use this method to obtain the ratio in a form where both sides are integers.

$1 : 2 = 2 : 4$	$3 : 7 = 15 : 35$	$16 : 20 = 4 : 5$
$0.5 : 5 = 1 : 10$	$\frac{3}{11} : \frac{4}{11} = 3 : 4$	$12.5 : 15 = 5 : 6$

Cancelling ratios

A ratio can be expressed in its **simplest form** or **lowest terms** by making both sides of the ratio as small as possible. Remember that both sides of the ratio must be integers.

Worked example

Write each of these ratios in its simplest form.

a) 10 : 15   b) 121 : 44   c) $4 : \frac{1}{4}$ d) 2.5 : 0.5

a) $10 : 15 = 2 : 3$	b) $121 : 44$	c) $4 : \frac{1}{4} = 16 : 1$	d) $2.5 : 0.5 = 5 : 1$
Dividing both sides by 5.	$= 11 : 4$ Dividing both sides by 11.	Multiplying both sides by 4 to get integer values.	Multiplying both sides by 2 to get integer values.

Worked example

Express the ratio 40¢ to $2 in its simplest form.

You must ensure that the units are the same.

$2 = 200¢

Then the ratio is 40 : 200 = 1 : 5 in its simplest form.

Worked example

Two lengths are in the ratio 4 : 5. If the first length is 60 cm, what is the second length?

The ratio is 4 : 5.

4 : 5 = 1 : 1.25	Dividing both sides by 4 to make an equivalent ratio, in the form 1 : n.
= 1 × 60 : 1.25 × 60	Multiplying both sides by 60 to find an equivalent ratio in the form 60 : m.
= 60 cm : 75 cm	As 1.25 × 60 = 75

So the second length is 75 cm.

Proportional parts

To share an amount into proportional parts, add up the individual parts and divide the amount by this number to find the value of one part.

Worked example

Divide $50 between two sisters in the ratio 3 : 2. How much does each get?

Number of parts = 3 + 2 = 5

Value of each part = $50 ÷ 5 = $10

The sisters receive $30 (3 parts at $10 each) and $20 (2 parts at $10 each).

HINT

- It is useful to check that the separate amounts add up to the original amount
(i.e. $30 + $20 = $50).

QUESTIONS

Q1 Express the ratio of 5 km to 600 m in its simplest form.

Q2 Express the ratio 2 : 5 in the form 1 : n.

Q3 Express the ratio $\frac{1}{3} : \frac{1}{4}$ in its simplest form.

Q4 Three children raise money for a charity. The amounts they each raise are in the ratio 2 : 3 : 7. The total amount raised is $72. How much does each child raise?

Answers are on page 195.

More questions on the CD ROM

11 DEGREES OF ACCURACY

Decimal places

Any number can be rounded to a given number of **decimal places** (written d.p.).

Significant figures

Any number can be rounded to a given number of **significant figures** (written s.f.).

Use the following rules.

Count along the digits to the required number of significant figures.

Look at the **next digit** (to the right) in the number.
If its value is less than 5, leave the digit before it as it is.
If its value is 5 or more, increase the digit before it by 1.

Replace all the digits to the right, but before the decimal point, by zeros, to keep the number at its correct size.

Digits to the right after the decimal point can just be left out.

Worked example
Round 7638.462 to the number of significant figures shown.

6 s.f. 7638.462 = 7638.46 (6 s.f.)

5 s.f. 7638.462 = 7638.5 (5 s.f.)

4 s.f. 7638.462 = 7638 (4 s.f.)

3 s.f. 7638.462 = 7640 (3 s.f.) Fill with 0s to keep the number at its correct size.

2 s.f. 7638.462 = 7600 (2 s.f.) Fill with 0s to keep the number at its correct size.

1 s.f. 7638.462 = 8000 (1 s.f.) Fill with 0s to keep the number at its correct size.

Use the following rules.

Count along the digits to the required number of decimal places.

Look at the **next digit** (to the right) in the number.
If its value is less than 5 leave the digit before it as it is.
If its value is 5 or more, increase the digit before it by 1.

Leave out all the digits to the right.

Worked example
Round 6.427 509 3 to the number of decimal places shown.

6 d.p.   6.427 509 3 = 6.427 509 (6 d.p.)

5 d.p.   6.427 509 3 = 6.427 51 (5 d.p.)

4 d.p.   6.427 509 3 = 6.4275 (4 d.p.)

3 d.p.   6.427 509 3 = 6.428 (3 d.p.)

2 d.p.   6.427 509 3 = 6.43 (2 d.p.)

1 d.p.   6.427 509 3 = 6.4 (1 d.p.)

HINT

• Numbers to the left of the decimal point are not affected by this rounding process.

Why use estimates?

Estimation and approximation are important elements of the non-calculator examination paper. You will be required to give an estimation by rounding numbers to convenient approximations, usually one significant figure.

Rounding

Worked example

Estimate the value of $\frac{40.68 + 61.2}{9.96 \times 5.13}$.

Rounding each of these figures to 1 s.f. gives $\frac{40 + 60}{10 \times 5} = \frac{100}{50} = 2$

Using a calculator, the actual answer is 1.993 940 7... so the answer is a good approximation.

Worked example

Estimate the value of $\frac{\sqrt{98.6}}{2.13^3 + 1.88}$.

Rounding these figures to 1 s.f. gives $\frac{\sqrt{00}}{2^3 + 2} = \frac{10}{8 + 2} = \frac{10}{10} = 1$

Using a calculator, the actual answer is 0.860 195 766 ...

QUESTIONS

Q1 Write each of the following correct to 3 s.f., 2 s.f. and 1 s.f.
   a) 174.9   **b)** 699.06

Q2 Write 0.8006 correct to 3 d.p., 2 d.p. and 1 d.p.

Estimate the value of each of these expressions.

Q3 $\dfrac{3.87 \times 5.07^3}{5.16 \times 19.87}$

Q4 $\dfrac{2.78 + \pi}{\sqrt{5.95 \times 6.32}}$

Q5 $\dfrac{59.96}{40.21 + 19.86} + \sqrt{80.652}$

More questions on the CD ROM

Answers are on page 195.

12 UPPER AND LOWER BOUNDS

What are upper and lower bounds?

If a weight is given as 10 grams to the nearest gram, then the actual weight will lie in the interval 9.5 grams to 10.499 999... grams as all values in this interval will be rounded to 10 grams to the nearest gram. The weight 10.499 999... grams is usually written as 10.5 g although it is accepted that 10.5 g would be rounded to 11 g (to the nearest gram).

The value 9.5 g is called the **lower bound** as it is the lowest value which would be rounded to 10 g, while 10.5 g is called the **upper bound**.

Working with bounds

Worked example

A rectangle measures 10 cm by 6 cm, where each measurement is given to the nearest cm. Write down an interval approximation for the area of a rectangle.

The lower bound (minimum area) = $9.5 \times 5.5 = 52.25$ cm^2
The upper bound (maximum area) = $10.5 \times 6.5 = 68.25$ cm^2
The interval approximation = 52.25 cm^2 to 68.25 cm^2

Worked example

To the nearest whole number, the value of p is 215 and the value of q is 5.
Calculate the maximum and minimum values of the following expressions.

a) $p + q$ **b)** $p - q$ **c)** $p \times q$ **d)** $p \div q$

$p_{min} = 214.5$ $p_{max} = 215.5$ $q_{min} = 4.5$ $q_{max} = 5.5$

a) For $p + q$
maximum = $215.5 + 5.5 = 221$
minimum = $214.5 + 4.5 = 219$

b) For $p - q$
maximum = $215.5 - 4.5 = 211$
minimum = $214.5 - 5.5 = 209$

c) For $p \times q$
maximum = $215.5 \times 5.5 = 1185.25$
minimum = $214.5 \times 4.5 = 965.25$

d) For $p \div q$
maximum = $215.5 \div 4.5 = 47.888 \ldots$
minimum = $214.5 \div 5.5 = 39$

HINT

- For the maximum value of $p - q$, work out $p_{max} - q_{min}$.

- For the minimum value of $p - q$, work out $p_{min} - q_{max}$.

- For the maximum value of $p \div q$, work out $p_{max} \div q_{min}$.

- For the minimum value of $p \div q$, work out $p_{min} \div q_{max}$.

QUESTIONS

Q1 The length of a square is 5.2 cm, correct to two significant figures. Find the maximum and minimum values for its area.

Q2 A sports car costs $18 700 and a family car costs $17 300, both prices being given to the nearest $100. What is the least possible difference in price between the two cars?

Q3 The diagram shows a triangle ABC. Angle ABC is exactly 90°.
AB = 83 mm correct to 2 significant figures.
BC = 90 mm correct to 1 significant figure.
a) Calculate the upper bound for the area of triangle ABC.

Angle CAB = $x°$.

b) Calculate the lower bound for the value of tan $x°$.

Diagram not drawn accurately

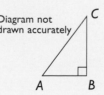

More questions on the CD ROM

Answers are on page 196.

13 STANDARD FORM INVOLVING POSITIVE AND NEGATIVE INDICES

What is standard form?

Standard form is a short way of writing very large and very small numbers. You must always write standard form numbers in the form:

$$A \times 10^n$$

where A is a number from 1 to 10 and n is an integer which tells you how many times to multiply by 10 (if n is positive) or divide by 10 (if n is negative).

A may take the value 1, but it must *always* be less than 10.

Very large numbers

Worked example

Write 35 000 in standard form.

Place the decimal point so A is a number from 1 to 10 and find n.

3.5 0 0 0   so $A = 3.5$ and $n = 4$.

$35\ 000 = 3.5 \times 10^4$

HINT

- In standard form, n is positive for large numbers (e.g. $3.5 \times 10^4 = 35\ 000$) and n is negative for small numbers (e.g. $4.78 \times 10^{-7} = 0.000\ 000\ 478$).

Very small numbers

Worked example

Write 0.000 000 478 in standard form.

Place the decimal point so A is a number from 1 to 10 and find n.

0 0 0 0 0 0 0 0 4.78   so $A = 4.78$ and $n = {}^-7$.

$0.000\ 000\ 478 = 4.78 \times 10^{-7}$

Adding and subtracting numbers in standard form

To add (or subtract) numbers in standard form **when the powers are the same**, proceed as shown in the next example.

Worked example

Work out $(4.18 \times 10^{11}) + (3.22 \times 10^{11})$.

$$
\begin{aligned}
(4.18 \times 10^{11}) + (3.22 \times 10^{11}) &= (4.18 + 3.22) \times 10^{11} \\
&= 7.4 \times 10^{11}
\end{aligned}
$$

To add (or subtract) numbers in standard form **when the powers are *not* the same** you need to **convert the numbers to ordinary form**.

Worked example

Work out $(8.42 \times 10^6) + (6 \times 10^7)$.

$(8.42 \times 10^6) + (6 \times 10^7) = 8\,420\,000 + 60\,000\,000$ Converting to ordinary form.
$= 68\,420\,000$
$= 6.842 \times 10^7$ Converting back to standard form.

HINT

- Your calculator will deal with numbers in standard form, if you use the EXP or EE or × 10ˣ key.

Multiplying and dividing numbers in standard form

Use the rules of indices to multiply (or divide) numbers in standard form. (See Chapter 3: Indices.)

Worked example

Work out $(8.5 \times 10^3) \times (4.2 \times 10^7)$.

$(8.5 \times 10^3) \times (4.2 \times 10^7) = (8.5 \times 4.2) \times (10^3 \times 10^7)$ Collecting powers of 10.

$= 35.7 \times 10^{3+7}$
Using the rules of indices where $a^m \times a^n = a^{m+n}$

$= 35.7 \times 10^{10}$

$= 3.57 \times 10^{11}$
Writing 35.7 as 3.57×10^{11} to get the final answer in standard form.

Worked example

Work out $(6.3 \times 10^5) \div (2.1 \times 10^8)$.

$(6.3 \times 10^5) \div (2.1 \times 10^8) = (6.3 \div 2.1) \times (10^5 \div 10^8)$
Collecting powers of 10 together.

$= 3 \times 10^{5-8}$
Using the rules of indices where $a^m \div a^n = a^{m-n}$.

$= 3 \times 10^{-3}$

QUESTIONS

Q1 **a)** The distance from the Earth to the Moon is 250 000 miles. Write this number in standard form.
b) The weight of a hydrogen atom is given as 0.000 000 000 000 000 000 001 67 milligrams. Write this number in standard form.

Q2 **a)** **(i)** Write 40 000 000 in standard form.
(ii) Write 3×10^{-5} as an ordinary number.
b) Work out the value of $3 \times 10^{-5} \times 40\,000\,000$ giving your answer in standard form.

Q3 Work these out without a calculator, then use a calculator to check your answers.
a) $(2.69 \times 10^5) - (1.5 \times 10^5)$ **b)** $(4.31 \times 10^{-4}) + (3.5 \times 10^{-4})$
c) $(6 \times 10^3) \times (4 \times 10^{-2})$ **d)** $(3 \times 10^{11}) \div (6 \times 10^4)$

Q4 Light travels at 3×10^5 kilometres per second (km/s). How far does it travel in one year?
Give your answer in kilometres, using standard index form.

More questions on the CD ROM

Answers are on page 196.

14 Using a calculator

What can my calculator do?

Make sure you know how to use your calculator.

Read the user manual.

The following functions are to be found on most calculators, but your manual will provide further information.

You may need to use `INV` or `2ndF` or `SHIFT` to access some of the functions.

Key	Explanation
`C`	Cancel – cancels only the last number entered.
`AC`	All cancel – cancels all of the data entered.
x^2	Calculates the square of the number.
x^3	Calculates the cube of the number.
$\sqrt{}$	Calculates the square root of the number.
$\sqrt[3]{}$	Calculates the cube root of the number.
$1/x$ or x^{-1}	Calculates the reciprocal of the number.
`+/-`	Reverses the sign by changing positive numbers to negative numbers and negative numbers to positive numbers.
x^y	This is the power key. To enter 3^6 you key in `3` x^y `6`
`EXP` or `EE`	This is the standard-form button. To enter 3.2×10^7 you key in `3` `.` `2` `EXP` `7` The display will show 3.2 ^{07} or 3.2 07
a^b/c	This is the fraction key (not all calculators have this key). To enter $\frac{3}{4}$ key in `3` a^b/c `4`. 3⌐4 in the display means $\frac{3}{4}$. To enter $1\frac{3}{4}$ key in `1` a^b/c `3` a^b/c `4`. 1⌐3⌐4 in the display means $1\frac{3}{4}$.
`Min` or `STO`	Stores the displayed value in the memory.
`MR` or `RCL`	Recalls the value stored in the memory.
`M+`	Adds the displayed value to the number in the memory.
`M−`	Subtracts the displayed value from the number in the memory.
`Mode`	Gives the mode for calculations – refer to your user manual.
`DRG`	Gives the units for angles (degrees, radians or grads). Your calculator should normally be set to degrees.

QUESTIONS

Use your calculator to work these out.

Q1 5.1^2

Q2 $\sqrt[3]{41.3}$

Q3 2^{-5}

Q4 $(2.5 \times 10^3) \div 5$

Q5 $(2.1 \times 10^{-3}) + (4.62 \times 10^{-2})$

Q6 $\frac{4}{7} \div \frac{8}{9}$

Q7 $2\frac{1}{5} \times \frac{5}{9}$

Q8 Use your calculator to work out the value of:

$$\frac{6.27 \times 4.52}{4.81 \times 9.63}$$

   a) Write down all the figures on your calculator display.

   b) Write your answer to part a) to an appropriate degree of accuracy.

Q9 **a)** Use your calculator to work out:

$$\frac{(6.2 - 3.9)^2}{1.25}$$

   Write down all the figures on your calculator display.

   b) Put brackets into each expression so that each statement is true.

   (i) $14.5 - 2.6 \times 4.5 - 3.6 = 49.95$

   (ii) $14.5 - 2.6 \times 4.5 - 3.6 = 10.71$

Answers are on page 197.

More questions
on the CD ROM

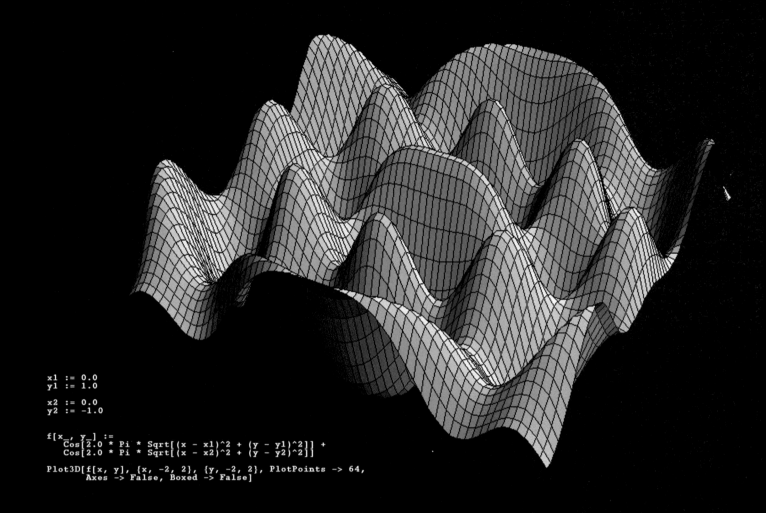

```
x1 := 0.0
y1 := 1.0

x2 := 0.0
y2 := -1.0

f[x_, y_] :=
    Cos[2.0 * Pi * Sqrt[(x - x1)^2 + (y - y1)^2]] +
    Cos[2.0 * Pi * Sqrt[(x - x2)^2 + (y - y2)^2]]

Plot3D[f[x, y], {x, -2, 2}, {y, -2, 2}, PlotPoints -> 64,
    Axes -> False, Boxed -> False]
```

Putting X and Y together to make Z

At around 1850 BC, in Ancient Egypt, mathematicians could solve problems with one unknown, but at this time algebra was limited by the fact that problem solving was 'rhetorical' – problems had to be stated and solved verbally without any recourse to writing. As the understanding of numbers grew, and systems for writing complex equations were evolved, the Babylonians, Greeks, Hindus, Arabs and Europeans all made contributions to the development of algebra. Algebra progressed from the 'rhetorical' stage, through 'syncopated' – where abbreviations were used to write down problems, allowing symbols to stand for unknown numbers – to the fully-fledged 'symbolic' system we know today.

ALGEBRA

15 Use of symbols

What is an expression?

An **algebraic expression** is a collection of algebraic terms along with their + and − signs.

Like terms

Like terms are numerical multiples of the same algebraic quantity. For example, $3x$, ^-5x, $\frac{1}{2}x$ and $0.55x$ are all like terms because they are all multiples of the same algebraic quantity, x.

Worked example

Collect together the like terms from the following list.

x	$3x$	y
^-6x	xy^2	$3ab$
^-3y	xy	^-4xy
$\frac{1}{3}y$	x^2y	$7ab$
^-2ba	yx^2	$-\frac{3}{4}xy^2$

Like terms are numerical multiples of the same algebraic quantity.

x, $3x$, ^-6x are all terms in x

y, ^-3y, $\frac{1}{3}y$ are all terms in y

xy^2, $-\frac{3}{4}xy^2$ are all terms in xy^2

$3ab$, $7ab$, ^-2ba are all terms in ab where $^-2ba = {}^-2ab$

xy, ^-4xy are all terms in xy

x^2y, yx^2 are all terms in x^2y where $yx^2 = x^2y$

In algebraic terms involving more than one letter, it is useful to write them in alphabetical order, so that $3ba$ is written $3ab$ and $14zxy$ is written $14xyz$, etc.

Adding, subtracting, multiplying and dividing

You can add or subtract like terms. The process of adding and subtracting like terms in an expression or equation is called **simplifying**.

Worked example

Simplify the following expression.

$3x + 2y - 7z + 4x - 3y$

$3x + 2y - 7z + 4x - 3y$

$\quad = 3x + 4x + 2y - 3y - 7z$ Putting like terms together, *along with the signs in front of them.*

$\quad = 7x - 1y - 7z$ Adding and subtracting like terms.

$\quad = 7x - y - 7z$ Rewriting $1y$ as y.

Worked example

Simplify the following expression.

$4p + 3pq - 3p + 8qp - 2r$

$4p + 3pq - 3p + 8qp - 2r$	
$= 4p - 3p + 3pq + 8qp - 2r$	Putting like terms together, *along with the signs in front of them.*
$= 4p - 3p + 3pq + 8pq - 2r$	Writing $8qp$ as $8pq$ since $p \times q$ is the same as $q \times p$.
$= p + 11pq - 2r$	

You can also simplify terms or expressions by multiplying or dividing. When you are dividing terms, you can simplify them by cancelling.

Worked example

Simplify the following expressions.

a) $3f \times 4g$

b) $8pq^2 \div 2pq$

a)	$3f \times 4g = 3 \times f \times 4 \times g$	
	$= 12 \times f \times g$	Multiplying $3 \times 4 = 12$.
	$= 12fg$	Rewriting without the $\times$ signs.
b)	$8pq^2 \div 2pq = \dfrac{8 \times p \times q \times q}{2 \times p \times q}$	Writing as a fraction with $q^2 = q \times q$.
	$= \dfrac{^{4}\cancel{8} \times \cancel{p} \times q \times \cancel{q}}{_{1}\cancel{2} \times \cancel{p} \times \cancel{q}}$	Cancelling.
	$= 4q$	Rewriting without the $\times$ signs.

QUESTIONS

Q1 Simplify the following expressions.

   a) $3a + 6b - 2a - 5c$

   b) $5x + 7y - 3xy + 2x + 2yx$

   c) $x^3 + 3x^2 - 4x - 9x^2 + 7x - 2$

   d) $3x \times 4y \times 2z$

   e) $5a \times 2a^2$

   f) $(4abc)^2 \times a^2 b$

   g) $8mn^3 \div 4n$

Answers are on page 197.

More questions on the CD ROM

16 ALGEBRAIC INDICES

What are the rules?

You should recall that, in general:

$$a^m \times a^n = a^{m+n}$$

$$a^m \div a^n = a^{m-n}$$

$$a^{-m} = \frac{1}{a^m}$$

$$a^0 = 1 \qquad \text{Remember: any number to the power 0 is 1.}$$

$$a^{1/n} = \sqrt[n]{a}$$

Using the rules

Worked example

Simplify these expressions.

a) $a^2 \times a^5$ **b)** $b^7 \div b^7$ **c)** $c^4 \times c \times c^{11}$ **d)** $(d^2)^3$ **e)** $e^{1/5} \times e^{2/5}$

a) $a^2 \times a^5 = a^{2+5} = a^7$

b) $b^7 \div b^7 = b^{7-7} = b^0 = 1$

c) $c^4 \times c \times c^{11} = c^{4+1+11} = c^{16}$ As $c = c^1$.

d) $(d^2)^3 = d^2 \times d^2 \times d^2 = d^{2+2+2} = d^6$

e) $e^{1/5} \times e^{2/5} = a^{1/5+2/5} = a^{3/5}$

In general

$$(a^m)^n = a^{m \times n}$$

QUESTIONS

Q1 Simplify these expressions.

a) $x^4 \times x$ 　　　　　 **b)** $(y^3)^2$

c) $(2a^4)^3$ 　　　　　 **d)** $d^{12} \div d^9$

e) $6x^7 \div 3x^4$ 　　　 **f)** $3x^6 \div 9x^8$

g) $(2x^{1/3})^3$ 　　　　 **h)** $\dfrac{x^{1/2} \times x^{3/4}}{x^{1/3}}$

Q2 Find the values of the letters in these equations.

a) $3^x = 81$

b) $2^{3y} = 64$

c) $5^{2x+1} = 125$

More questions
on the CD ROM

Answers are on page 197.

17 Expanding and Factorising

What do the words mean?

Brackets are used to group algebraic terms. The process of removing brackets from an expression (or an equation) is called **expanding** and the process of rewriting an expression (or an equation) so that it includes terms in brackets is called **factorising**.

Expanding brackets

When expanding brackets in an expression, you must multiply all the terms inside the brackets by the term just before the bracket.

HINT

- You must take care, when expanding brackets, to multiply every term in the brackets by the term outside the brackets.

Worked example

Expand the following expression.
$3(5a - 2b)$

$$3(5a - 2b) = 3 \times 5a + 3 \times {}^-2b$$
$$= 15a - 6b$$

Worked example

Expand the following expression.
${}^-7(a + 2b - 3c)$

$${}^-7(a + 2b - 3c) = {}^-7 \times a - 7 \times 2b - 7 \times {}^-3c$$
$$= {}^-7a - 14b + 21c \quad \text{Remembering that } {}^-7 \times {}^-3c = {}^+21c.$$

Worked example

Expand and simplify the following expression.
$5(p + 2q) + 2(p - 5q)$

$$5(p + 2q) + 2(p - 5q) = 5 \times p + 5 \times 2q + 2 \times p + 2 \times {}^-5q$$
$$= 5p + 10q + 2p - 10q$$
$$= 7p + 0q$$
$$= 7p$$

Worked example

Expand and simplify the following expression.
$4a(b - c) - 3b(a - c)$

$$4a(b - c) - 3b(a - c) = 4a \times b + 4a \times {}^-c - 3b \times a - 3b \times {}^-c$$
The term outside the second bracket is ${}^-3b$.
$$= 4ab - 4ac - 3ab + 3bc$$
Writing $3ba$ as $3ab$ and remembering that ${}^-3b \times {}^-c = {}^+3bc$.
$$= 1ab - 4ac + 3bc$$
$$= ab - 4ac + 3bc \quad \text{As } 1ab \text{ is usually written } ab.$$

Factorising expressions into brackets

To factorise an expression, you need to look for terms that have **common factors**. Then you rewrite the expression with the factors outside brackets. Remember that common factors of two (or more) terms are factors that appear in both (or all) of the terms.

Worked example

Factorise $5a - 15$.

To factorise the expression, write it as a term inside brackets, with common factors taken outside the brackets.

$5a - 15 = 5(a - 3)$ 　　　　　5 is a common factor, as
$5a = 5 \times a$ and $15 = 5 \times 3$.

Worked example

Factorise $9xy + 33yz$.

$9xy + 33yz = 3y(3x + 11z)$ 　　　$3y$ is a common factor as
$9xy = 3y \times 3x$ and $33yz = 3y \times 11z$.

Worked example

Factorise $pq^3 - p^2q$.

$pq^3 - p^2q = pq(q^2 - p)$ 　　　pq is a common factor as
$pq^3 = pq \times q^2$ and $p^2q = pq \times q$.

Binomial expressions

A binomial expression consists of two terms such as $(a + b)$ or $(5x - 2z)$.

To expand the product of two binomial expressions, you must multiply each term in the first expression by each term in the second expression.

$$(a + b)(c + d) = a \times (c + d) + b \times (c + d)$$
$$= a \times c + a \times d + b \times c + b \times d$$
$$= ac + ad + bc + bd$$

			Product
F = First		$(a + b)(c + d)$	$a \times c$
O = Outsides		$(a + b)(c + d)$	$a \times d$
I = Insides		$(a + b)(c + d)$	$b \times c$
L = Last		$(a + b)(c + d)$	$b \times d$

Worked example

Expand $(x + 3)(x + 5)$.

$$(x + 3)(x + 5) = x \times x + x \times 5 + 3 \times x + 3 \times 5$$
$$= x^2 + 5x + 3x + 15$$
$$= x^2 + 8x + 15$$

Worked example

Expand $(3x - 1)(4x - 5)$.

$$(3x - 1)(4x - 5) = 3x \times 4x + 3x \times {}^-5 + {}^-1 \times 4x + {}^-1 \times {}^-5$$
$$= 12x^2 - 15x - 4x + 5 \quad \text{Remembering that } {}^-1 \times {}^-5 = {}^+5.$$
$$= 12x^2 - 19x + 5$$

You can use the reverse process to write a quadratic as a product of brackets, as shown in the following worked example.

Worked example

Factorise $x^2 + 5x + 6$.

You know that $x^2 + 5x + 6 = (x \quad)(x \quad)$ Since $x \times x = x^2$ as required.

Look for pairs of numbers that multiply together to give ${}^+6$.

Possibilities include:

$${}^+1 \times {}^+6 \quad (x + 1)(x + 6) = x^2 + 6x + 1x + 6$$
$$= x^2 + 7x + 6$$

$${}^-1 \times {}^-6 \quad (x - 1)(x - 6) = x^2 - 6x - 1x + 6$$
$$= x^2 - 7x + 6$$

$${}^+2 \times {}^+3 \quad (x + 2)(x + 3) = x^2 + 2x + 3x + 6$$
$$= x^2 + 5x + 6$$

$${}^-2 \times {}^-3 \quad (x - 2)(x - 3) = x^2 - 2x - 3x + 6$$
$$= x^2 - 5x - 6$$

and the correct solution is:

$$(x + 2)(x + 3) = x^2 + 2x + 3x + 6$$
$$= x^2 + 5x + 6.$$

An alternative method is to look at pairs of numbers that multiply together to give ${}^+6$ (i.e. with product ${}^+6$) and add to give ${}^+5$ (i.e. with sum ${}^+5$).

Numbers	Product	Sum	
${}^+1$ and ${}^+6$	${}^+6$	${}^+7$	✗
${}^-1$ and ${}^-6$	${}^+6$	${}^-7$	✗
${}^+2$ and ${}^+3$	${}^+6$	${}^+5$	✔
${}^-2$ and ${}^-3$	${}^+6$	${}^-5$	✗

From this, you can quickly see the numbers you need.

Again, the correct solution is $(x + 2)(x + 3)$.

Worked example

Factorise $x^2 + x - 12$.

You know that $x^2 + x - 12 = (x \quad)(x \quad)$ Since $x \times x = x^2$ is required.

You now need to look at pairs of numbers that multiply together to give $^-12$.

Possibilities include:

$^-1 \times {}^+12$	$(x - 1)(x + 12) = x^2 - 1x + 12x - 12$	$= x^2 + 11x - 12$
$^+1 \times {}^-12$	$(x + 1)(x - 12) = x^2 + 1x - 12x - 12$	$= x^2 - 11x - 12$
$^-2 \times {}^+6$	$(x - 2)(x + 6) = x^2 - 2x + 6x - 12$	$= x^2 + 4x - 12$
$^+2 \times {}^-6$	$(x + 2)(x - 6) = x^2 + 2x - 6x - 12$	$= x^2 - 4x - 12$
$^-3 \times {}^+4$	$(x - 3)(x + 4) = x^2 - 3x + 4x - 12$	$= x^2 + x - 12$
$^+3 \times {}^-4$	$(x + 3)(x - 4) = x^2 + 3x - 4x - 12$	$= x^2 - x - 12$

So the correct solution is:

$(x - 3)(x + 4) = x^2 - 3x + 4x - 12 = x^2 + x - 12$.

HINT

- $(x - 3)(x + 4)$ can be written as $(x + 4)(x - 3)$, which also gives $x^2 + x - 12$.

Again, using the alternative method, look for numbers with product $^-12$ and sum $^+1$.

Numbers	Product	Sum	
$^-1$ and $^+12$	$^-12$	$^+11$	✗
$^+1$ and $^-12$	$^-12$	$^-11$	✗
$^-2$ and $^+6$	$^-12$	$^+4$	✗
$^+2$ and $^-6$	$^-12$	$^-4$	✗
$^-3$ and $^+4$	$^-12$	$^+1$	✔
$^+3$ and $^-4$	$^-12$	$^-1$	✗

The correct solution is $(x - 3)(x + 4)$.

Algebraic fractions

Algebraic fractions can often be simplified by factoring.

Worked example

Simplify fully the expression $\dfrac{x^2 - 16}{2x^2 + 7x - 4}$.

Factorising the numerator: $x^2 - 16 = (x - 4)(x + 4)$

Remember the difference of two squares, where $x^2 - 16 = x^2 - 4^2$.

Factorising the denominator: $2x^2 + 7x - 4 = (2x - 1)(x + 4)$

Combining these: $\dfrac{x^2 - 16}{2x^2 + 7x - 4} = \dfrac{(x - 4)(x + 4)^1}{(2x - 1)(x + 4)^1}$ Cancelling the $(x + 4)$ factors.

$$= \dfrac{x - 4}{2x - 1}$$

QUESTIONS

Q1 Expand and simplify these expressions.
   a) $5x - (3y + 4x)$

   b) $5(a + b - 2c) - 2(a - 2b + 3c)$

   c) $a(2a + b) - 2b(a - b^2)$

Q2 Factorise these expressions completely.
   a) $4x^2 - 6x$ **b)** $2lw + 2wh + 2hl$ **c)** $5x^2y - 10xy^2$

Q3 **a)** Simplify these expressions.
      (i) $3a + 4b - 2a - b$ **(ii)** $5x^2 + 2x - 3x^2 - x$

   b) Expand the brackets.
      (i) $4(2x - 3)$ **(ii)** $p(q - p^2)$

   c) Expand and simplify $5(3p + 2) - 2(5p - 3)$.

Q4 Expand and simplify these expressions.
   a) $(x + 1)(x + 4)$

   b) $(3y - 5)(2y - 7)$

   c) $(3x + 1)^2$

Q5 Factorise these expressions completely.
   a) $x^2 + 6x + 8$

   b) $x^2 - x - 2$

   c) $x^2 - 7x - 18$

Q6 **a)** Expand and simplify $(x + y)^2$.
   b) Hence or otherwise find the value of $3.47^2 + 2 \times 3.47 \times 1.53 + 1.53^2$.

Q7 Solve the equation $\dfrac{1}{x} + \dfrac{3x}{x - 1} = 3$.

Q8 Solve the equation
   $$\dfrac{2}{x + 1} + \dfrac{3}{x - 1} = \dfrac{5}{x^2 - 1}.$$

More questions
on the CD ROM

Answers are on page 198.

59

18 CHANGING THE SUBJECT

What are the rules?

You can rearrange (or **transpose**) a formula in exactly the same way as you solve an equation. To maintain the balance of the formula you must make sure that whatever you do to one side of the formula you also do to the other side of the formula.

Using the rules

For the formula $S = \frac{D}{T}$, S is called the **subject** of the formula. The formula can be rearranged to make D or T the subject as follows.

$$S = \frac{D}{T}$$

$S \times T = D$ Multiplying both sides of the formula by T.

$D = S \times T$ or $D = ST$ Turning the formula round so that D is the subject of the formula.

Or, from $D = ST$:

$$\frac{D}{S} = T$$ Dividing both sides of the formula by S.

$$T = \frac{D}{S}$$ Turning the formula around so that T is the subject.

Worked example

Make x the subject of the formula $y = 3x + 2$.

$y = 3x + 2$

$y - 2 = 3x$ Subtracting 2 from both sides.

$\frac{y - 2}{3} = x$ Dividing both sides of the formula by 3.

$x = \frac{y - 2}{3}$ Turning the formula around so that x is the subject.

Worked example

Make x the subject of the formula $p = \frac{xy}{x - y}$.

$p = \frac{xy}{x - y}$

$p(x - y) = xy$ Multiplying both sides by $(x - y)$.

$px - py = xy$ Expanding the brackets.

$px = xy + py$ Adding py to both sides, to try to isolate terms in x.

$px - xy = py$ Collecting terms in x on one side only.

$x(p - y) = py$ Factorising the left-hand side with x outside the bracket.

$x = \frac{py}{p - y}$ Dividing both sides by $(p - y)$ to make x the subject.

QUESTIONS

Q1 Rewrite the following with the letter indicated in brackets as the subject.

   a) $C = 2\pi r$ (r) **b)** $v = u + at$ (u)

   c) $v = u + at$ (a) **d)** $A = \pi r^2$ (r)

   e) $V = \pi r^2 h$ (h) **f)** $V = \pi r^2 h$ (r)

   g) $I = \dfrac{PRT}{100}$ (T)

Q2 Rearrange the formula $a = \dfrac{m}{b^2}$ to make b the subject.

Q3 Rearrange the formula $r = \sqrt{\dfrac{s}{s+t}}$ to make s the subject.

Q4 A formula states $x = \dfrac{1 - t^2}{1 + t^2}$.

   a) Find the value of x when $t = \frac{1}{2}$.

   b) Rearrange the formula to make t the subject.

Q5 This rule can be used to work out the number of litres of paint needed to cover the walls of a room, using the length, width and height, in metres, of the room.

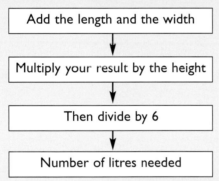

Add the length and the width
↓
Multiply your result by the height
↓
Then divide by 6
↓
Number of litres needed

A room has a length of L metres, width W metres and height H metres. N litres of paint are needed to cover the walls of the room.

   a) Find a formula for N in terms of L, W and H.

The perimeter of the room is P metres.

   b) Find a formula for N in terms of P and H.

More questions
on the CD ROM

Answers are on page 199.

19 SUBSTITUTION

What is substitution?

Substitution means replacing the letters in a formula or expression by the given numbers.

Worked example

Find the value of:

a) $3x + 4y - 5z$ where $x = 3, y = 7$ and $z = {}^-4$

b) $3ab + ac^2 - \dfrac{b}{c}$ where $a = 2, b = {}^-10$ and $c = 5$.

a) Substituting $x = 3, y = 7$ and $z = {}^-4$ in $3x + 4y - 5z$:

$$3x + 4y - 5z = 3 \times 3 + 4 \times 7 - 5 \times {}^-4$$

$$= 9 + 28 - {}^-20 \qquad \text{Remember that } - (-) = +.$$

$$= 9 + 28 + 20$$

$$= 57$$

b) Substituting $a = 2, b = {}^-10$ and $c = 5$ in $3ab + ac^2 - \dfrac{b}{c}$:

$$3ab + ac^2 - \frac{b}{c} = 3 \times 2 \times {}^-10 + 2 \times 5 \times 5 - \frac{{}^-10}{5}$$

$$= {}^-60 + 50 - {}^-2 \quad \text{Remember that } - (-) = +.$$

$$= {}^-60 + 50 + 2$$

$$= {}^-8$$

HINT

- Remember: $3x$ means $3 \times x$, $4y$ means $4 \times y$ and $5z$ means $5 \times z$.

HINT

- Remember:
$ac^2 = a \times c \times c$
so only the c is squared.

QUESTIONS

Q1 The surface area, A, of a closed cone is given by $A = \pi r l + \pi r^2$ where r is the radius of the base and l is the slant height.
Find the surface area of a cone with radius 3 cm and slant height 8 cm, giving your answer in terms of π.

Q2 Given that $\dfrac{1}{u} = \dfrac{1}{f} - \dfrac{1}{v}$, find the value of u when:

  a) $f = 4$ and $v = 8$

  b) $f = 3$ and $v = 5$.

More questions on the CD ROM

Answers are on page 200.

20 PROPORTION

How do you write proportions in maths?

With **direct proportion** as one variable increases, the other increases and as one decreases, the other one decreases.

With **inverse proportion** as one variable increases, the other decreases and as one decreases, the other one increases.

If y is proportional to x then $y \propto x$ or $y = kx$.
If y is inversely proportional to x then $y \propto \dfrac{1}{x}$ or $y = \dfrac{k}{x}$.

The value of k is a constant and k is called the constant of proportionality.

Worked example

Rewrite these statements, using the $\propto$ sign and the constant of proportionality.

a) y varies directly as x cubed.

b) s is proportional to the square root of t.

c) v varies inversely as the square of w.

d) p is inversely proportional to the cube root of q.

a) $y \propto x^3$ or $y = kx^3$ **b)** $s \propto \sqrt{t}$ or $s = k\sqrt{t}$

c) $v \propto \dfrac{1}{w^2}$ or $v = \dfrac{k}{w^2}$ **d)** $p \propto \dfrac{1}{\sqrt[3]{q}}$ or $p = \dfrac{k}{\sqrt[3]{q}}$

Worked example

Given that a varies directly as the cube of b and $a = 4$ when $b = 2$, find the value of k and the value of a when $b = 3$.

If a varies directly as the cube of b then $a \propto b^3$ or $a = kb^3$.

Since we know that $a = 4$ when $b = 2$, then: $4 = k \times 2^3$
$$4 = k \times 8$$
$$\text{so } k = \tfrac{1}{2}$$

The equation is $a = \tfrac{1}{2}b^3$.

When $b = 3$ then $a = \tfrac{1}{2} \times 3^3 = \tfrac{1}{2} \times 27 = 13.5$.

QUESTIONS

Q1 Given that T is proportional to the positive square root of W and $T = 36$ when $W = 16$:
     a) calculate T when W is 100   **b)** calculate W when T is 18.

Q2 If V varies inversely as the cube of Y and $V = \tfrac{3}{8}$ when $Y = 2$, find the value of V when:
     a) $Y = 3$ **b)** $Y = 10$.

Q3 y is directly proportional to the square of x. When $x = 4$, $y = 25$.
     a) Find an expression for y in terms of x.
     b) Calculate y when $x = 2$.   **c)** Calculate x when $y = 9$.

More questions
on the CD ROM

Answers are on page 200.

21 Solving Equations

What is an equation?

An **algebraic equation** is made up of two algebraic expressions separated by an equals sign. The equals sign provides a balance between the two algebraic expressions. To maintain the balance of an equation, you must make sure that whatever you do to one side you also do to the other side.

$$x + 8 = 11$$
$$x + 8 - 8 = 11 - 8 \qquad \text{Subtracting 8 from both sides.}$$
$$x = 3$$

$$x - 2.5 = 3$$
$$x - 2.5 + 2.5 = 3 + 2.5 \qquad \text{Adding 2.5 to both sides.}$$
$$x = 5.5$$

$$4x = 12$$
$$\frac{4x}{4} = \frac{12}{4} \qquad \text{Dividing both sides by 4.}$$
$$x = 3$$

$$\frac{x}{5} = 3.2$$
$$\frac{x}{5} \times 5 = 3.2 \times 5 \qquad \text{Multiplying both sides by 5.}$$
$$x = 16$$

Worked example

Solve the following equations.

a) $4x + 5 = 17$ **b)** $9x - 1 = 7x + 14$ **c)** $6(2x + 5) = 48$

a)
$$4x + 5 = 17$$
$$4x = 17 - 5 \qquad \text{Subtracting 5 from both sides.}$$
$$4x = 12$$
$$x = \frac{12}{4} \qquad \text{Dividing both sides by 4.}$$
$$x = 3$$

b)
$$9x - 1 = 7x + 14 \qquad \text{This equation has the unknown on both sides.}$$
$$9x = 7x + 14 + 1 \qquad \text{Adding 1 to both sides.}$$
$$9x = 7x + 15$$
$$9x - 7x = 15 \qquad \text{Subtracting } 7x \text{ from both sides.}$$
$$2x = 15$$
$$x = \frac{15}{2} \qquad \text{Dividing both sides by 2.}$$
$$x = 7\tfrac{1}{2} \text{ or } 7.5$$

c)
$$6(2x + 5) = 48$$
$$6 \times 2x + 6 \times 5 = 48 \qquad \text{Expanding the brackets.}$$
$$12x + 30 = 48$$
$$12x = 48 - 30 \qquad \text{Subtracting 30 from both sides.}$$
$$12x = 18$$
$$x = \frac{18}{12} \qquad \text{Dividing both sides by 12.}$$
$$x = 1\tfrac{1}{2} \text{ or } 1.5$$

Worked example

Find three consecutive numbers with a sum of 15.

To solve a problem like this, call one of the numbers x. Then, as the numbers are consecutive, the other two numbers are $(x + 1)$ and $(x + 2)$.

If the sum is 15 then $x + (x + 1) + (x + 2) = 15$.

$$x + x + 1 + x + 2 = 15$$

$3x + 3 = 15$	Collecting like terms.
$3x = 15 - 3$	Subtracting 3 from both sides.
$3x = 12$	
$x = \frac{12}{3}$	Dividing both sides by 3.
$x = 4$	

Having found the answer, now interpret it. The consecutive numbers were x, $(x + 1)$ and $(x + 2)$ so the required numbers are 4, $(4 + 1)$ and $(4 + 2)$ or 4, 5 and 6.

HINT

- You can apply the same method to solve equations in a variety of number problems.

HINT

- You should now check your solutions to make sure that they are correct.

Worked example

A group of people shared a pay-out of \$45 000 equally, and each of them received \$5000. How many people shared the money?

You need to form an equation and solve it. Let the number of people be x.

$$\frac{45\,000}{x} = 5000$$

$45\,000 = 5000x$	Multiplying both sides by x.
$\frac{45\,000}{5000} = x$	Dividing both sides by 5000.
$9 = x$	
$x = 9$	Reversing the answer to get x on the left.

Nine people shared the pay-out.

Lottery tickets in Thailand

QUESTIONS

Q1 Solve the following equations.

a) $3x + 4.5 = 15$ b) $20x = 30$ c) $\frac{27}{z} = 3$

d) $3y + 5 = 25 - y$ e) $4(2x - 3) = 44$

f) $4x + 1 = 3(x + 2)$ g) $\frac{y + 3}{10} = 3$

h) $6(x - 2) - 2(2x + 1) = 0$

Q2 Find three consecutive numbers with a sum of 78.

Q3 The angles of a triangle are $x°$, $2x°$ and $(3x + 30)°$. Find the value of x.

Q4 Fatimah buys eight cups and eight mugs. A cup costs \$$x$ and a mug costs \$$(x + 2)$.

a) Write down an expression, in terms of x, for the total cost, in pounds, of eight cups and eight mugs.

The total cost of eight cups and eight mugs is \$72.

b) (i) Express this information as an equation in terms of x.
(ii) Solve your equation to find the cost of a cup and the cost of a mug.

Answers are on page 201.

More questions
on the CD ROM

22 SIMULTANEOUS EQUATIONS

What are simultaneous equations?

A pair of simultaneous equations is a pair of equations in **two unknowns.**
Both equations are correct at the same time, or simultaneously.
Simultaneous equations are usually solved by **graphical** or **algebraic**
methods.

Graphical solution

To solve the equations graphically, plot the two lines. The coordinates of
the point of intersection give the solution of the simultaneous equations.

Algebraic solution

There are two algebraic methods for solving simultaneous equations.

SUBSTITUTION METHOD
Rewrite one equation to make one of the unknowns the subject. Then you
can **substitute** this expression into the second equation and solve it.

Worked example

Solve these simultaneous equations.
$x + 2y = 5$
$3x - 2y = 7$

Using $x + 2y = 5$ you can write:
$$x = 5 - 2y \quad \text{Making } x \text{ the subject of the equation.}$$
Substitute this value of x into the second equation.

$$
\begin{aligned}
3x - 2y &= 7 \\
3(5 - 2y) - 2y &= 7 &&\text{Substituting } x = 5 - 2y. \\
15 - 6y - 2y &= 7 &&\text{Expanding the brackets.} \\
8 &= 8y &&\text{Collecting like terms on each side.} \\
y &= 1
\end{aligned}
$$

Now use $x = 5 - 2y$ with $y = 1$ to find x.
$x = 5 - 2y$
$x = 5 - 2 \times 1 \qquad$ As $y = 1$.
$x = 3$

ELIMINATION METHOD

Add or subtract the equations, or multiples of them, to **eliminate** one of the unknowns. Then solve the resulting equation.

Worked example

Solve these simultaneous equations.

$x + 2y = 5$
$3x - 2y = 7$

$x + 2y = 5$
$3x - 2y = 7$

If you add the left-hand sides of the equations then y will be eliminated.

The sum of the two left-hand sides must equal the sum of the two right-hand sides.

$$(x + 2y) + (3x - 2y) = 5 + 7 \quad \text{or} \qquad x + 2y = 5$$
$$x + 2y + 3x - 2y = 12 \qquad\qquad + 3x - 2y = 7$$
$$4x = 12 \qquad\qquad\qquad 4x \quad = 12$$
$$x = 3 \qquad\qquad\qquad\quad x = 3$$

Substituting for y in the first equation:

$x + 2y = 5$
$3 + 2y = 5$ As $x = 3$.
    $2y = 2$ Subtracting 3 from both sides.
      $y = 1$ Dividing both sides by 2.

Harder simultaneous equations

You would generally use the substitution method when solving simultaneous equations involving mixed linear and quadratic equations.

Worked example

Solve these simultaneous equations.

$y = x + 4$
$y = x^2 + 2$

Use the second equation.

$$y = x^2 + 2$$
$$(x + 4) = x^2 + 2 \qquad\qquad \text{Substituting } y = x + 4.$$
$$0 = x^2 + 2 - x - 4 \quad \text{Collecting terms on one side.}$$
$$x^2 - x - 2 = 0 \qquad\qquad\qquad \text{Simplifying to obtain a quadratic equation.}$$
$$(x + 1)(x - 2) = 0 \qquad\qquad \text{Factorising the quadratic.}$$

Either $x = {}^-1$ or $x = 2$.
If $x = {}^-1$ then $y = 3$.   As $y = x + 4$.
If $x = 2$ then $y = 6$.   Again, as $y = x + 4$.

The solutions are $x = {}^-1, y = 3$ and $x = 2, y = 6$.

Worked example

Solve these simultaneous equations.

$$y = x + 1 \qquad x^2 + y^2 = 25$$

Use the second equation.

$$x^2 + y^2 = 25$$
$$x^2 + (x + 1)^2 = 25 \qquad \text{Substituting } y = x + 1.$$
$$x^2 + x^2 + 2x + 1 = 25 \qquad \text{Expanding the brackets.}$$
$$2x^2 + 2x - 24 = 0 \qquad \text{Collecting the terms on one side.}$$
$$x^2 + x - 12 = 0 \qquad \text{Dividing both sides by 2.}$$
$$(x + 4)(x - 3) = 0 \qquad \text{Factorising the quadratic.}$$

Either $x = {}^-4$ or $x = 3$.

If $x = {}^-4$ then $y = {}^-3$. \qquad As $y = x + 1$.

If $x = 3$ then $y = 4$. \qquad Again, as $y = x + 1$.

The solutions of the simultaneous equations are $x = {}^-4, y = {}^-3$ and $x = 3, y = 4$.

QUESTIONS

Q1 Solve the following simultaneous equations by:
  i) the graphical method
  ii) the substitution method
  iii) the elimination method.

  a) $x + 3y = 10$
  $2x - 3y = 2$

  b) $x = 5y - 3$
  $3x - 8y = 12$

  c) $x - 1 = y$
  $3x + 4y = 6$

Q2 Solve these simultaneous equations.
  $6x - 2y = 33$
  $4x + 3y = 9$

Q3 Find two numbers with a sum of 36 and a difference of 4.

Q4 The cost of two skirts and a shirt is $32.50 while the cost of one skirt and two shirts is $41.00. What is the cost of a skirt and a shirt?

Q5 Solve the simultaneous equations.
  a) $y = 11x - 2$ \qquad **b)** $x + y = 7$
  $y = 5x^2$ \qquad\qquad $x^2 + y^2 = 25$

Q6 Raneen said that the line $y = 6$ cuts the curve $x^2 + y^2 = 25$ at two points.

  a) By eliminating y, show that Raneen is incorrect.

  b) By eliminating y, find the solutions to these simultaneous equations.

  $x^2 + y^2 = 25 \qquad y = 2x - 2$

More questions
on the CD ROM

Answers are on page 202.

23 QUADRATIC EQUATIONS

What do the symbols mean?

Quadratic equations are equations of the form $ax^2 + bx + c = 0$ where $a \neq 0$. You can solve quadratic equations in a number of ways but this chapter introduces three methods:

solution by factors

solution by formula

solution by iteration

Solution by factors

If the product of two numbers is zero then one or both of the numbers must be zero.

If $ab = 0$ then either $a = 0$ or $b = 0$ or both $a = 0$ and $b = 0$.
You can apply this fact to the solution of quadratic equations.

The factor method is most appropriate when the quadratic factorises. This method gives exact solutions.

Worked example

Solve the quadratic equation $(x - 3)(x + 1) = 0$.

Since the product of the two factors is zero then one or both of the factors must be zero so:

either $(x - 3) = 0$ which implies that $x = 3$
or $(x + 1) = 0$ which implies that $x = {}^-1$.

The solutions of the equation $(x - 3)(x + 1) = 0$ are $x = 3$ and $x = {}^-1$.

Worked example

Solve the quadratic equation $x^2 + 4x - 21 = 0$.

Factorising the left-hand side of the equation:

$x^2 + 4x - 21 = (x \quad)(x \quad)$ You need to look for numbers that, when multiplied
$ = (x - 3)(x + 7)$ together, give ${}^-21$ and that, when added, give 4.
 Try ${}^+1$ and ${}^-21$ ${}^-1$ and ${}^+21$
 ${}^+3$ and ${}^-7$ ${}^-3$ and ${}^+7$

The only pair to satisfy the equation is ${}^-3$ and ${}^+7$.

The quadratic equation can be written $(x - 3)(x + 7) = 0$.

Since the product of the two factors is zero then one or both of the factors must be zero so:

either $(x - 3) = 0$ which implies that $x = 3$
or $(x + 7) = 0$ which implies that $x = {}^-7$.

The solutions of the equation $x^2 + 4x - 21 = 0$ are $x = 3$ and $x = {}^-7$.

HINT

- This formula for solving quadratic equations will be given in the examination so you do not need to memorise it but you do need to know how to use it correctly.

Solution by formula

As an alternative to completing the square, you can use the formula:

$$x = \frac{-b \pm \sqrt{b^2 - 4ac}}{2a}$$

to solve any quadratic of the form $ax^2 + bx + c = 0$.

The formula method is most appropriate when the quadratic does not factorise. Answers will normally be given 3 s.f.

Worked example

Solve the equation $x^2 + 3x - 2 = 0$, giving your answer to an appropriate degree of accuracy.

Comparing the given quadratic with the general form $ax^2 + bx + c = 0$:

$a = 1, b = 3, c = {}^-2$.

Substituting these values in the formula:

$$x = \frac{{}^-b \pm \sqrt{b^2 - 4ac}}{2a}$$

$$x = \frac{{}^-3 \pm \sqrt{3^2 - 4 \times 1 \times {}^-2}}{2 \times 1}$$

$$x = \frac{{}^-3 \pm \sqrt{9 - {}^-8}}{2}$$

$$x = \frac{{}^-3 \pm \sqrt{17}}{2}$$

$$x = \frac{{}^-3 \pm 4.123\,105\,626}{2}$$

HINT

- The answer $\dfrac{{}^-3 \pm \sqrt{17}}{2}$ is the same as the answer obtained in the example above.

$$x = \frac{{}^-3 + 4.123\,105\,626}{2} \quad \text{or} \quad x = \frac{{}^-3 - 4.123\,105\,626}{2}$$

$$x = \frac{1.123\,105\,626}{2} \quad \text{or} \quad x = \frac{{}^-7.123\,105\,626}{2}$$

$$x = 0.561\,552\,813 \quad \text{or} \quad x = {}^-3.561\,552\,813$$

$$x = 0.562 \text{ (3 s.f.)} \quad \text{or} \quad x = {}^-3.56 \text{ (3 s.f.)}$$

Solution by iteration

Iteration involves using an initial value (usually denoted by x_1) to find successive solutions (x_2, x_3, x_4, ...). Each solution is based on the previous solution to improve the accuracy, so that x_{n+1} is calculated from x_n, using the given iterative formula.

Iterative formulae can be used as an alternative method for solving quadratic equations. The iterative formula can be found by rearranging the equation.

Worked example

Solve the quadratic equation $x^2 - 5x + 1 = 0$ by using an iterative formula.

$x^2 - 5x + 1 = 0$

$x^2 + 1 = 5x$ Adding $5x$ to both sides.

$5x = x^2 + 1$ Turning the equation around.

$x = \frac{1}{5}(x^2 + 1)$ Dividing both sides by 5.

Now, writing this as an iterative formula:

$x_{n+1} = \frac{1}{5}(x_n^2 + 1)$

Using a starting value of $x = 0.25$

$x_2 = \frac{1}{5}(0.25^2 + 1) = 0.2125$

$x_3 = \frac{1}{5}(0.2125^2 + 1) = 0.2090\,3125$

$x_4 = 0.2087\,38812$

$x_5 = 0.2087\,14378$

The solution is 0.2087 correct to 4 decimal places.

Any equation can give rise to a number of different iterative formulae, although they are not always of any use in solving the quadratic. In the above example $x_{n+1} = \frac{1}{5}(x_n^2 + 1)$ provides a solution to the quadratic whereas $x_{n+1} = 5 - \frac{1}{x_n}$ will not, as successive iterations will diverge.

QUESTIONS

Q1 Solve the following quadratic equations.

    a) $(x - 5)(x - 7) = 0$ **b)** $(x - 6)(2x + 1) = 0$

    c) $x^2 + 4x - 5 = 0$

Q2 Write down quadratic equations with solutions as follows.

    a) $x = 2$ and $x = 5$ **b)** $x = {}^-3$ and $x = \frac{1}{5}$

Q3 Solve $x^2 - 5x + 2 = 8$.

Q4 The length of a rectangle is 4 centimetres more than its width. The area of the rectangle is 96 square centimetres. What are the length and the width of the rectangle?

Q5 Solve the following quadratic equations by using the formula

$$x = \frac{{}^-b \pm \sqrt{b^2 - 4ac}}{2a}.$$

    a) $x^2 + 2x - 1 = 0$ **b)** $2x^2 = 10x - 4$

Q6 The length of a room is 4 metres longer than its width. Find the dimensions of the room if the area is 32 square metres.

Q7 Use the iteration $x_{n+1} = 10 + \frac{1}{x_n}$ with $x_1 = 5$ to find a root of the equation $x^2 - 10x - 1 = 0$ correct to four decimal places.

Q8 A sequence is given by $x_{n+1} = \frac{6}{x_n + 5}$.

The first term, x_1, of the sequence is 3.

    a) Find the next three terms.

    b) What do you think is the value of x_n as n becomes very large? Write down this value.

    c) Show that the quadratic equation which the sequence above is intended to solve is $x^2 + 5x - 6 = 0$.

    d) Solve this quadratic equation.

More questions on the CD ROM

Answers are on page 203.

24 INEQUALITIES AND GRAPHS

What do the symbols mean?

The solution of the inequality $x < 5$ can take many values such as 4, π, $\sqrt{2}$, $2\frac{1}{2}$, 0, $-3\frac{1}{4}$, $-100\,000$. You can show such inequalities on a number line.

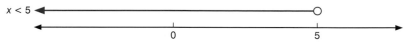

The open circle, $\bigcirc$, at the end of the line shows that the value 5 is not included as $x < 5$.

The solid circle, $\bullet$, is used to show that the number is included, as shown below for $x \leqslant 5$.

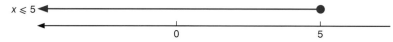

Solving inequalities

You can solve inequalities in exactly the same way as you would equalities (i.e. equations) except that **when you multiply or divide by a negative number you must reverse the inequality sign.**

Worked example

Solve the following inequalities and show each solution on a number line.

a) $3y + 5 < 17$ **b)** $^-10c > 5$ **c)** $5 - 8m \leqslant 13$
d) $4x < 5x + 2$ **e)** $2 \leqslant \frac{2}{3}(x + 5) \leqslant 6$

a) $3y + 5 < 17$

$\quad 3y < 12$ Subtracting 5 from both sides.
$\quad y < 4$ Dividing both sides by 3.

b) $^-10c > 5$

$\quad c < \frac{5}{^-10}$ Dividing both sides by $^-10$ and reversing the sign.
$\quad c < ^-\frac{1}{2}$ Cancelling and taking the sign to the front.

c) $5 - 8m \leqslant 13$

$\quad ^-8m \leqslant 8$ Subtracting 5 from both sides.
$\quad m \geqslant ^-1$ Dividing both sides by $^-8$ and reversing the sign.

d) $4x < 5x + 2$

$\quad ^-x < 2$ Subtracting 5x from both sides.
$\quad x > ^-2$ Multiplying both sides by $^-1$ and reversing the sign.

e) $2 \leqslant \frac{2}{3}(x + 5) \leqslant 6$

This inequality actually represents two separate inequalities.
i.e. $2 \leqslant \frac{2}{3}(x + 5)$ and $\frac{2}{3}(x + 5) \leqslant 6$

$\quad 2 \leqslant \frac{2}{3}(x + 5) \leqslant 6$
$\quad 6 \leqslant 2(x + 5) \leqslant 18$ Multiplying both sides (of both inequalities) by 3.
$\quad 3 \leqslant x + 5 \leqslant 9$ Dividing both sides (of both inequalities) by 2.
$\quad ^-2 \leqslant x \leqslant 4$ Subtracting 5 from both sides (of both inequalities).

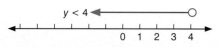

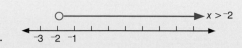

Graphing inequalities

You can show inequalities on a graph by replacing the inequality sign by an equals (=) sign and drawing the line. This will divide the graph into two regions. You need to decide which of these regions is required.

You should usually shade out the region that is not required, although some examination questions ask you to shade the required region. You must make it clear to the examiner which is your required region, by labelling it as appropriate.

You also need to make clear whether the line is included (i.e. the inequality is ⩽ or ⩾), or excluded (i.e. the inequality is < or >). Use a solid line if the line is included, or a dotted line if it is not included.

Worked example

Draw graphs of these lines.

$x = 2$ $y = 4$ $y = 6 - x$

On your graph, label the region where the points (x, y) satisfy the inequalities:

$x \geqslant 2$ $y < 4$ $y \leqslant 6 - x$.

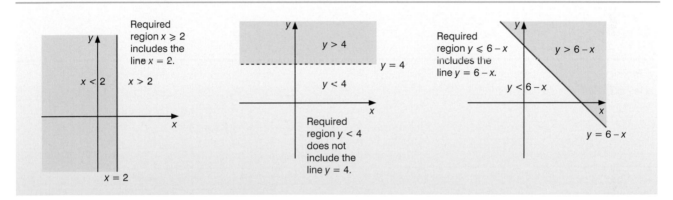

Now combining the graphs:

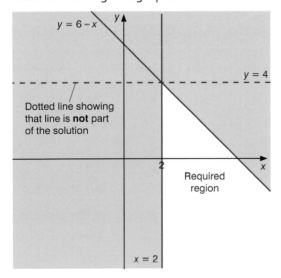

QUESTIONS

Q1 Solve these inequalities.
  a) $4x + 2 \leqslant 17 - x$ **b)** $18 - 6x < 3 - 3x$

Q2 n is an integer.
  a) Write down the values of n that satisfy the inequality $-2 < n \leqslant 3$.

  b) Solve the inequality $3x + 2 \leqslant 4$.

Q3 Write down the inequalities illustrated in the unshaded parts of the diagrams below.

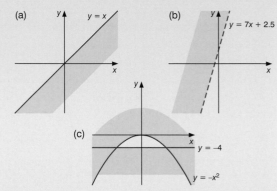

Q4 Draw a set of axes, with each axis labelled from 0 to 10. Label the region represented by these inequalities.
  $x \geqslant 2$ $y \geqslant 1$ $x + y \leqslant 9$

What is the maximum value of $x + y$ which satisfies all of these conditions?

Q5 **a)** On the grid below, draw straight lines and use shading to show the region R that satisfies these inequalities.

$x \geqslant 2$
$y \geqslant x$
$x + y \leqslant 6$

The point P, with coordinates (x, y), lies inside the region R. x and y are integers.

  b) Write down the coordinates of all the points in R with coordinates that are both integers.

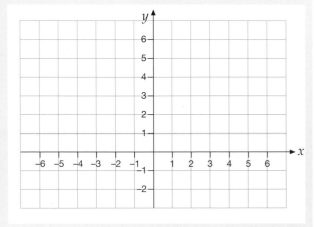

Q6 Show, by shading on the grid, the region which satisfies all three of these inequalities.

$x \geqslant 1$
$y \geqslant x$
$x + 2y \leqslant 6$

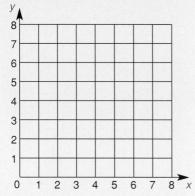

More questions on the CD ROM

Answers are on page 205.

25 PATTERNS AND SEQUENCES

What is a sequence?

A **sequence** is a set of numbers that follow a particular rule. The word **term** is often used to describe the numbers in the sequence. In the following sequence, the first term is 7, the second term is 9, the third term is 11, and so on.

7, 9, 11, 13, 15, 17, ...

The **general form** of the terms is called the **nth term**, and this gives the value of any term in the sequence. If you are given a sequence in which the nth term is $2n + 5$ then:

	first term (where $n = 1$) gives	$2 \times 1 + 5 = 7$
	second term (where $n = 2$) gives	$2 \times 2 + 5 = 9$
	third term (where $n = 3$) gives	$2 \times 3 + 5 = 11$
Similarly:	50th term (where $n = 50$) gives	$2 \times 50 + 5 = 105$
and	1000th term (where $n = 1000$) gives	$2 \times 1000 + 5 = 2005$

Sequence rules

Most number sequences involve adding/subtracting or multiplying/dividing in the rule for finding one term from the one before it. Once you have found the term-to-term rule, you can use it to find subsequent terms.

Worked example

Find the sequence rule and find the next three terms of these sequences.

a) 1, 6, 11, 16, 21, ...   **b)** 243, 81, 27, 9, 3, ...

c) 1, 4, 13, 40, 121, ...

---

a)
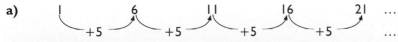

$$\begin{array}{ccccccccc} 1 & & 6 & & 11 & & 16 & & 21 & \dots \\ & +5 & & +5 & & +5 & & +5 & & \dots \end{array}$$

The rule for moving from term to term is $+ 5$.
The next three terms are 26, 31 and 36.

b)

$$\begin{array}{ccccccccc} 243 & & 81 & & 27 & & 9 & & 3 & \dots \\ & \div 3 & & \div 3 & & \div 3 & & \div 3 & & \dots \end{array}$$

The rule for moving from term to term is $\div 3$.
The next three terms are 1, $\frac{1}{3}$ and $\frac{1}{9}$.

c)

$$\begin{array}{ccccccccc} 1 & & 4 & & 13 & & 40 & & 121 & \dots \\ & \times 3 + 1 & & \times 3 + 1 & & \times 3 + 1 & & \times 3 + 1 & & \dots \end{array}$$

The rule for moving from term to term is $\times 3 + 1$.
The next three terms are 364, 1093 and 3280.

FINDING TERMS

You can use the term-to-term method shown above for finding subsequent terms of a sequence but it would be rather time-consuming if you needed to find the 100th term or the 500th term etc.

The following method gives you the *n*th term of a linear sequence.

Worked example

Find the *n*th term of the following linear sequences.

a) 3, 7, 11, 15, ...

b) 12, 9, 6, 3, ...

a)
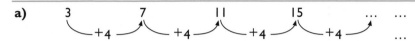

The difference between terms is 4, so use 4 as the multiplier.

You can construct a table as follows.

Term number			1	2	3	4
Sequence			3	7	11	15
Try 4 × (term number)			4	8	12	16
Difference			−1	−1	−1	−1

The difference is always equal to −1.

So try 4 × (term number) − 1.   3   7   11   15

So the *n*th term is 4 × *n* − 1 or 4*n* − 1.

b)

The difference between terms is ⁻3, so use ⁻3 as the multiplier.

You can construct a table as follows.

Term number			1	2	3	4
Sequence			12	9	6	3
Try (−3) × (term number)			−3	−6	−9	−12
Difference			15	15	15	15

The difference is always equal to 15.

So try (⁻3) × (term number) + 15.   12   9   6   3

So the *n*th term is ⁻3 × *n* + 15 or ⁻3*n* + 15 or 15 − 3*n*.

Special sequences

You should be able to recognise the following special sequences of numbers.

1, 4, 9, 16, 25, ...	square numbers
1, 3, 6, 10, 15, ...	triangle numbers
1, 8, 27, 64, 125, ...	cube numbers
2, 3, 5, 7, 11, 13, 17, ...	prime numbers

Another sequence that you should know is the **Fibonacci sequence**. Each term after the second is found by adding the two previous terms.

1, 1, 2, 3, 5, 8, 13, 21, ...

So 3rd term = 1st term + 2nd term
4th term = 2nd term + 3rd term   etc.

QUESTIONS

Q1 Write down the first five terms of each of the following sequences, for which the nth term is given.

a) $2n + 1$

b) $3n - 8$

c) $n^2 - 3n$

d) $\dfrac{n}{n + 1}$

Q2 Write down the nth term of the sequence 3, 8, 13, 18, 23, ...

Q3 There are the first five terms of an arithmetic sequence.
6, 11, 16, 21, 26

Find an expression, in terms of n, for the nth term of the sequence.

Q4 The nth term of a sequence is given by $\dfrac{4n}{n + 1}$.

a) Write down the value of the 10th term.

b) Write down the value of the 100th term.

c) What happens to the values of the sequence as n increases in size?

Answers are on page 206.

More questions
on the CD ROM

26 INTERPRETING GRAPHS

You need to understand how to read graphs and be familiar with interpreting them. They can be presented in many different contexts.

Conversion graphs

Worked example

Draw a conversion graph to show the relationship between miles and kilometres, given that a distance of 5 miles is approximately 8 kilometres.

Use your graph to find:

a) how many kilometres there are in 15 miles

b) how many kilometres there are in 8 miles

c) how many miles there are in $32\frac{1}{2}$ kilometres.

The first requirement is to draw the graph, using the fact that 5 miles is approximately 8 kilometres. This means that a distance of:

5 miles is approximately 8 kilometres

10 miles is approximately 16 kilometres

20 miles is approximately 32 kilometres   etc.

As this is a straight-line graph, you should just need three points (two points for the line and one point as a check) to draw the graph. It is also helpful to note that 0 miles is equal to 0 kilometres so the straight line should pass through the origin.

The question asks you to 'use your graph' to find answers to the questions asked and so it is important to show the examiner how you arrived at your solutions and convince them that you did not just calculate the answers.

From the graph:

a) there are approximately 24 kilometres in 15 miles

b) there are approximately 12.8 kilometres in 8 miles
(Remembering that each small square is 1 kilometre on this scale.)

c) there are approximately 20.3 miles in $32\frac{1}{2}$ kilometres.
(Remembering that each small square is 1 mile on this scale.)

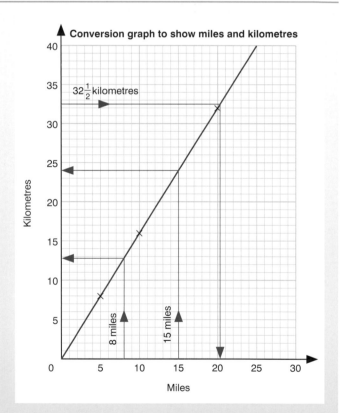

Conversion graph to show miles and kilometres

Travel graphs

Worked example

A salesperson leaves home at 1030 hours and their distance from home is shown on the graph below.

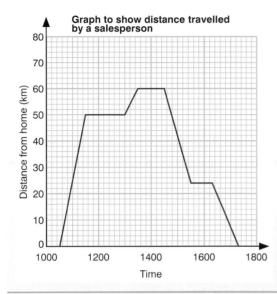

Use the graph to answer the following questions.

a) How many kilometres are travelled before the first stop?

b) How long does it take to reach the first stop?

c) How far is the salesperson away from home at 1600 hours?

d) What time does the salesperson arrive back at home?

e) How far does the salesperson travel between 1200 hours and 1600 hours?

f) What is the average speed of the salesperson between 1030 hours and 1130 hours?

g) What is the average speed of the salesperson between 1300 hours and 1330 hours?

---

a) The salesperson travels 50 kilometres before the first stop.

b) The first stop is after $1\frac{1}{2}$ hours (from 1130 hours to 1300 hours).

c) The salesperson is 24 kilometres away from home at 1600 hours.

d) The salesperson arrives back home at 1718 hours. (Remembering that each small square represents $\frac{1}{5}$ hour or 12 minutes.)

e) The salesperson travels 10 km + 36 km = 46 km.

f) Between 1030 hours and 1130 hours:

distance travelled = 50 km

time taken = 1 hour

so speed = 50 kilometres per hour

(speed = distance ÷ time)

g) Between 1300 hours and 1330 hours:

distance travelled = 10 km

time taken = $\frac{1}{2}$ hour

so speed = 20 kilometres per hour   (speed = distance ÷ time)

QUESTIONS

Q1 The cooking instructions for roasting a piece of meat are given as:
40 minutes per kilogram plus 25 minutes.

Draw a graph and use it to find:

a) how long a piece of meat weighing 2 kilograms would take to cook
b) how long a piece of meat weighing 1.4 kilograms would take to cook
c) the weight of a piece of meat which takes $1\frac{1}{2}$ hours to cook.

Q2 Jodi went on a trip by cycle from his home.
The diagram shows his distance/time graph.

a) At what times was Jodi 6 km from home?
b) Where was Jodi after 120 minutes?
c) Between what times was Jodi moving fastest?
d) Calculate Jodi's speed during the first 20 minutes of his trip. Give your answer in kilometres per hour.
e) At what time had Jodi cycled 14 km?

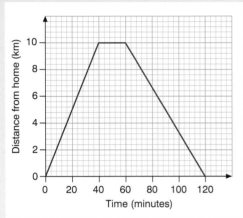

Q3 The graph on the right shows the journeys of two cyclists travelling between two places that are 25 kilometres apart.

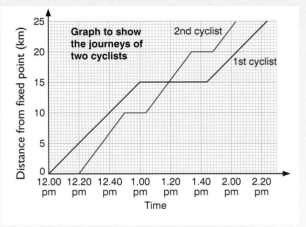

Use the graph to answer the following questions.

a) How many kilometres does the first cyclist travel before the first stop?

b) What is the average speed of the first cyclist over this first part of the journey?

c) How long does this first cyclist stop?

d) At what time does the second cyclist overtake the first cyclist?

e) What is the speed of the second cyclist at this time?

f) What time does the second cyclist arrive at the destination?

g) What is the greatest distance between the two cyclists?

Q4 P, Q and R are three stations on a railway line.

PQ = 26 kilometres

QR = 4 kilometres

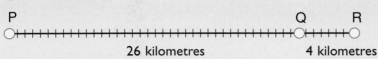

A passenger train leaves P at 12:00. It arrives at Q at 12:30. Information about the journey is shown in the travel graph on the right.

The passenger train stops at Q for 10 minutes. It then returns to P at the same speed as on its journey from P to Q.

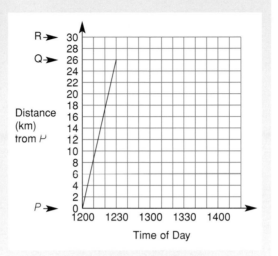

a) Copy the graph and complete the travel graph for this train.

A goods train leaves R at 12:00. It arrives at P at 13:00.

b) On the same graph, draw the travel graph for the goods train.

c) Write down the distance from P of the point where the goods train passes the passenger train.

Answers are on page 207.

More questions on the CD ROM

27 LINEAR GRAPHS AND COORDINATES

What do the words mean?

Coordinates are used to locate points on a graph.

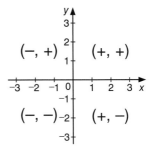

Negative coordinates can be used by extending the *x*-axis and *y*-axis in the negative directions, dividing the graph into four quadrants.

A **linear graph** is one in which the points can be joined to give a straight line.

Linear graphs and midpoints

The midpoint of a given line can be found by making use of a diagram or else using a formula.

The midpoint of (x, y_1) and (x_2, y_2) is

$$\left(\frac{x_1 + x_2}{2}, \frac{y_1 + y_2}{2} \right)$$

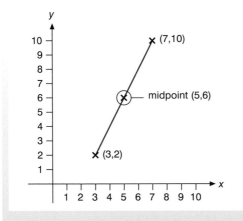

Worked example

Calculate the midpoint of the line joining the points (3, 2) and (7, 10)
Sketch the two points (3, 2) and (7, 10) on a graph.

Alternatively, using the formula:

The midpoint of (3, 2) and (7, 10) $= \left(\dfrac{3 + 7}{2}, \dfrac{2 + 10}{2} \right)$

$= (5, 6)$ as before

Linear graphs and gradients

Linear graphs are straight lines.

The gradient of the line is defined as:

$$\frac{\text{vertical distance}}{\text{horizontal distance}}$$

Gradients can be either positive or negative, depending on their direction of slope.

positive gradient

negative gradient

Worked example

Calculate the gradients of the lines joining the points:

a) (3, 2) and (7, 10)   **b)** (⁻8, 5) and (2, ⁻1).

a) Sketch the two points (3, 2) and (7, 10) on a graph.

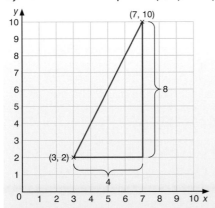

$$\text{Gradient} = \frac{\text{vertical distance}}{\text{horizontal distance}}$$

$$= \frac{8}{4}$$

$$= 2$$

b) Sketch the two points (⁻8, 5) and (2, ⁻1) on a graph.

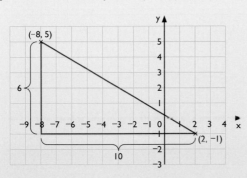

$$\text{Gradient} = \frac{\text{vertical distance}}{\text{horizontal distance}}$$

$$= -\frac{6}{10}$$

$$= -\frac{3}{5}$$

The negative sign is important as it tells you which way the graph is sloping. This graph is sloping down, from left to right.

All linear graphs can be written in the form $y = mx + c$ where m is the **gradient** of the line and c is the cut-off on the y-axis. This is where the line **intersects** the y-axis (also called the y-**intercept**).

Worked example

Sketch the following straight-line graphs.

a) $y = 2x - 1$ **b)** $y + 3x = 3$

You can easily sketch the graphs if you compare their equations with the general form $y = mx + c$ where m is the gradient and c is the cut-off on the y-axis (i.e. the y-intercept).

a) For $y = 2x - 1$:

$m = 2$ and $c = {}^-1$

So the gradient is 2 and the cut-off on the y-axis is ⁻1.

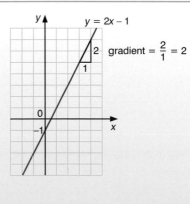

gradient $= \frac{2}{1} = 2$

b) For $y + 3x = 3$, rearrange the formula to get it in the form $y = mx + c$.

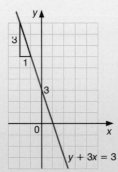

gradient $= \frac{^-3}{1}$

$= {}^-3$

$y = 3 - 3x$ Subtracting 3x from both sides.
$y = {}^-3x + 3$ Rewriting in the required form.

$m = {}^-3$ and $c = 3$

So the gradient is ⁻3 and the cut-off on the y-axis is 3.

QUESTIONS

Q1 On the same set of axes, sketch the following lines.

    a) $y = \frac{1}{2}x + 5$ **b)** $y = \frac{1}{2}x + 3$ **c)** $y = \frac{1}{2}x - 2$

What can you say about the lines?

Q2 On the same set of axes, sketch the following graphs.

    a) $y + 3x = 5$ **b)** $x = 2y + 6$

Q3 What are the coordinates of the midpoint of the line joining $(5, 3)$ and $(-6, 4)$?

Q4 What is the gradient of the line joining $(5, 3)$ and $(-6, 4)$?

Q5 Write down the equations of the straight-line graphs shown on this grid.

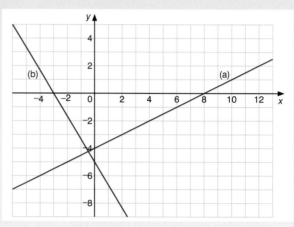

Q6 ABCD is a rectangle and A is the point $(0, 1)$, C is the point $(0, 6)$.
The equation of the straight line through A and B is $y = 2x + 1$. Find the equation of the straight line through C and D.

Diagram not drawn accurately

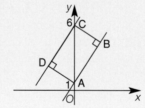

Q7 A straight line has the equation $y = \frac{1}{2}x + 1$. The point P lines on the straight line. P has a y-coordinate of 5.

    a) Find the x-coordinate of P.

    b) Write down the equation of a different straight line that is parallel to $y = \frac{1}{2}x + 1$.

Answers are on page 208.

More questions on the CD ROM

28 QUADRATIC GRAPHS

What do the graphs look like?

Quadratic graphs all have the same basic shape, as illustrated below.

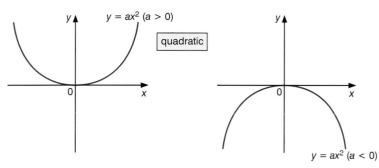

Quadratic graphs can be written in the form $y = ax^2 + bx + c$ (where a is non-zero). They all have approximately the same basic shape.

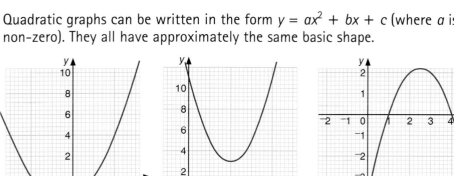

$y = x^2 + x - 2$ $\qquad$ $y = 2x^2 - 8x + 11$ $\qquad$ $y = {}^-x^2 + 5x - 4$

HINT

- When drawing quadratic graphs it is important that you join the points with a smooth curve rather than a series of straight lines.

Worked example

Draw the graph of $y = x^2 + 2x - 8$ and use it to solve the equation $x^2 + 2x - 8 = 0$.

HINT

- You should check your answers by substituting them into the equation to see if they are correct.

Drawing up a table of values:

x	$^-5$	$^-4$	$^-3$	$^-2$	$^-1$	0	1	2	3
$y = x^2 + 2x - 8$	7	0	$^-5$	$^-8$	$^-9$	$^-8$	$^-5$	0	7
Coordinates	$(^-5, 7)$	$(^-4, 0)$	$(^-3, ^-5)$	$(^-2, ^-8)$	$(^-1, ^-9)$	$(0, ^-8)$	$(1, ^-5)$	$(2, 0)$	$(3, 7)$

To solve the equation $x^2 + 2x - 8 = 0$ you need to consider the points that lie on the curve $y = x^2 + 2x - 8$ and on the line $y = 0$. Any points that satisfy both of these equations will also satisfy the equation $x^2 + 2x - 8 = 0$.

From the graph you can see that $x^2 + 2x - 8 = 0$ when the curve crosses the $y = 0$ line, giving $x = {}^-4$ and $x = 2$.

So $x = {}^-4$ and $x = 2$ satisfy the equation $x^2 + 2x - 8 = 0$.

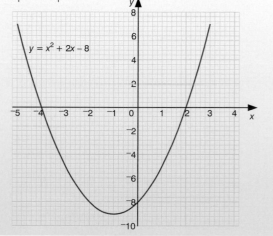

Worked example

Draw the graph of $y = 2x^2$ and use it to solve the equation $2x^2 - 5x - 3 = 0$.

Drawing up a table of values:

x	$^-2$	$^-1$	0	1	2	3	4
$y = 2x^2$	8	2	0	2	8	18	32
Coordinates	$(^-2, 8)$	$(^-1, 2)$	$(0, 0)$	$(1, 2)$	$(2, 8)$	$(3, 18)$	$(4, 32)$

To solve the equation $2x^2 - 5x - 3 = 0$ using $y = 2x^2$, rewrite the given equation as follows:

$2x^2 - 5x - 3 = 0$

$2x^2 = 5x + 3$ Adding $5x + 3$ to both sides.

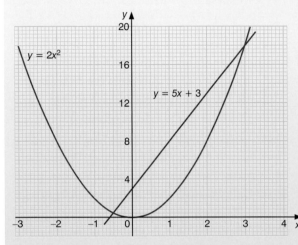

To solve the equation $2x^2 - 5x - 3 = 0$ you need to consider the points that lie on the curve $y = 2x^2$ and on the line $y = 5x + 3$. Any points that satisfy both of these equations will also satisfy the equation $2x^2 - 5x - 3 = 0$.

Draw the graph of $y = 2x^2$ from the table, and then draw the line $y = 5x + 3$.

From the graph you can see that where the two graphs $y = 2x^2$ and $y = 5x + 3$ cross, $x = ^-\frac{1}{2}$ and $x = 3$, so these values satisfy the equation $2x^2 - 5x - 3 = 0$.

Worked example

Draw the graph of $y = 3x - x^2$ for values of x from $x = ^-1$ to $x = 4$.

Use your graph to find:

a) the value of x when $3x - x^2$ is as large as possible

b) the values of x for which $3x - x^2$ is greater than 1.5.

To draw the graph of $y = 3x - x^2$ for $x = ^-1$ to $x = 4$, first draw up a table of values.

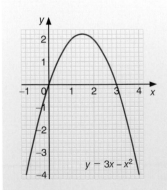

x	$^-1$	0	1	2	3	4
$y = 3x - x^2$	$^-4$	0	2	2	0	$^-4$
Coordinates	$(^-1, ^-4)$	$(0, 0)$	$(1, 2)$	$(2, 2)$	$(3, 0)$	$(4, ^-4)$

From the graph you can see that:

a) $3x - x^2$ is as large as possible at $x = 1.5$

b) $3x - x^2 = 1.5$ when $x = 0.6$ and when $x = 2.4$.

The values of x for which $3x - x^2$ is greater than 1.5 are $0.6 < x < 2.4$.

QUESTIONS

Q1 On the same set of axes, draw and label the following graphs.

   a) $y = x^2$

   b) $y = x^2 + 5$

   c) $y = x^2 - 2$

Q2 Draw the graph of $y = x^2 - 6x + 5$.
Use your graph to find:

   a) the coordinates of the minimum value of $x^2 - 6x + 5$

   b) the values of x when

   i) $x^2 - 6x + 5 = 0$
   ii) $x^2 - 6x + 5 = 5$.

Q3 The height reached by an object thrown into the air is given by the formula:
$h = 20t - 5t^2$

where h is the height in metres and t is the time in seconds.

Plot the graph of h against t for $0 \leqslant t \leqslant 4$ and use your graph to find the maximum height reached by the object.

More questions
on the CD ROM

Answers are on page 209.

29 GRADIENTS AND TANGENTS

You need to be able to **use a tangent to calculate the gradient of a curve**, and **interpret the gradient of a graph**.

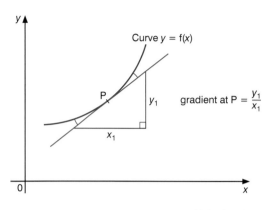

Gradient of a curve

Unlike the gradient of a straight line, **the gradient of a curve changes,** so it will be different depending upon where you want to calculate it. You can find the gradient at a point on a curve by drawing a tangent at that point and working out the gradient as before.

To draw a tangent to a curve you place your ruler on the curve at the required point so that the angles produced at either side are approximately equal.

Worked example

Find the gradient at the following points for the curve $y = 10x - x^2$.

a) $x = 3$

b) $x = 9$

c) Write down the coordinates of the point where the gradient $= 0$.

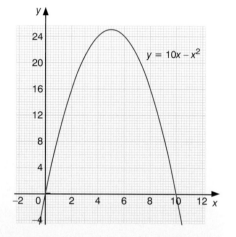

a) To find the gradient at $x = 3$ you need to draw a tangent at the point and work out the gradient.

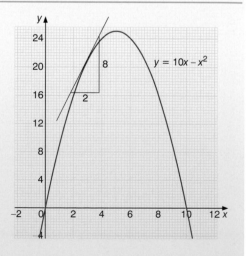

$$\text{Gradient} = \frac{\text{vertical distance}}{\text{horizontal distance}}$$

$$= \frac{8}{2} = 4$$

b) To find the gradient at $x = 9$ you need to draw a tangent at the point and work out the gradient.

$$\text{Gradient} = \frac{\text{vertical distance}}{\text{horizontal distance}}$$

$$= \frac{^-8}{1} = {^-8} \text{ As the gradient is negative.}$$

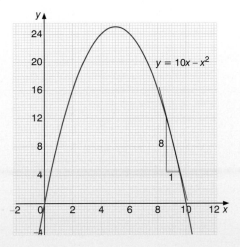

c) From the graph you can see that the gradient is 0 when $x = 5$. You can find the y-value at this point by substituting $x = 5$ in the equation $y = 10x - x^2$.

$y = 10x - x^2 = 10 \times 5 - 5^2 = 25$

So the coordinates when the gradient is 0 are $(5, 25)$.

HINT

- The point at which the gradient = 0 is sometimes called the turning point and represents the position of a maximum or minimum value for the function. In this case the maximum value of $y = 10x - x^2$ is 25.

QUESTIONS

Q1 Find the gradient of the curve $y = x^2$ at the following points.
   a) $x = 2$ **b)** $x = {^-2}$

   c) $x = 5$ **d)** $x = 0$

Q2 Find the gradient of the curve $y = x^3 + 2$ at the following points.
   a) $x = 2$ **b)** $x = 4$

   c) $x = {^-1}$ **d)** $x = {^-3}$

Answers are on page 209.

More questions on the CD ROM

30 FUNCTIONS

What is a function?

A function is a rule that maps each number of one set (the domain) to one (and only one) number of another set (the range).

For example $y = x^2$, maps the number -1 onto 1. 0 onto 0, 1 onto 1, 2 onto 4, 3 onto 9, ...

Each number in the domain is mapped onto a number in the range

This can be shown diagrammatically:

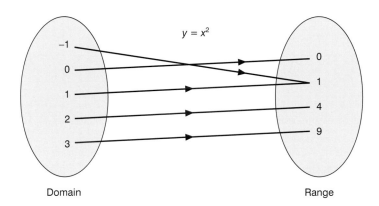

In this case $y = x^2$ is a function as it maps each number of one set (the domain) to one (and only one) number of another set (the range).

What is function notation?

Function notation is an alternative way of writing functions.

For example, instead of writing

$y = x^2 + 2x + 3$ we can write $f(x) = x^2 + 2x + 3$ (we say "f of $x = x^2 + 2x + 3$")

If we want to work out the function of $f(x)$ when $x = 3$ we can write $f(3)$

If $f(x) = x^2 + 2x + 3$ then $\qquad f(3) = 3^2 + 2 \times 3 + 3 = 18$
Similarly $\qquad\qquad\qquad f(-1) = (-1)^2 + 2 \times (-1) + 3 = 2$

$\qquad f(x) = x^2 + 2x + 3$ can also be written $f : x \mapsto x^2 + 2x + 3$
$\qquad\qquad$ (we say "f is such that x is mapped onto $x^2 + 2x + 3$")

Composite functions

If f(x) = x + 1 and g(x) = x^2, then we can combine functions as follows:

fg(x) means function g first **then** function f second
fg(x) = f (x^2) = x^2 + 1

Similarly   gf(x) means function f first **then** function g second
gf(x) = g (x +1) = $(x + 1)^2$

HINT

- Notice that fg(x) is NOT the same as gf(x).

Inverse functions

A function is a rule that maps each number of one set (the domain) to one (and only one) number of another set (the range). An inverse function is a rule that maps each number in the range back to the number in the domain. For the function f(x) we use $f^{-1}(x)$ to denote the inverse function

In general $f^{-1}(f(x)) = x$

Some examples of functions and their inverses

f(x) =	$f^{-1}(x)$ =
x + 3	x - 3
x - 7	x + 7
5x	x/5
x/2	2x
1/x	1/x
sin x	$\sin^{-1}$ x or arc sin x
cos x	$\cos^{-1}$ x or arc cos x
tan x	$\tan^{-1}$ x or arc tan x

You can always find the inverse by writing f(x) as y and changing the subject of the formula

e.g. Find the inverse of f(x) = 5x - 1

Let y = 5x − 1   replace f(x) with y and change the subject

5x − 1 = y

5x = y + 1

$x = \dfrac{y + 1}{5}$

So $f^{-1}(x) = \dfrac{x + 1}{5}$ replace y with x to complete the inverse

Worked example

Given that $f(x) = x + 1$ and $g(x) = x^3$ find

a) $f(1)$ **b)** $g(-2)$ **c)** $fg(x)$

d) $f^{-1}(x)$ **e)** $fg^{-1}(x)$

---

a) $f(1) = 1 + 1 = 2$ **b)** $g(-2) = (-2)^3 = -8$

c) $fg(x) = f(x^3) = x^3 + 1$ **d)** $f^{-1}(x) = x - 1$

e) $fg^{-1}(x) = f(x^{1/3}) = x^{1/3} + 1$

QUESTIONS

Q1 Given that $f(x) = 5 - 2x$ and $g(x) = 1/x$

    a) Find   **(i)** $f(-1)$

                     (ii) $g(-1)$

                     (iii) $g(2/3)$

    b)   **(i)** Given that $f(x) = -3$, find x

                     (ii) Given that $g(x) = \frac{1}{2}$, find x

                     (iii) Given that $g(x) = 5$, find x

Q2 State which values of x cannot be included in the domain of the following functions

    a) $f : x \longmapsto 1/x$

    b) $g : x \longmapsto \sqrt{(10 - x)}$

    c) $h : x \longmapsto 2/(x + 5)$

Q3 $f : x \longmapsto x^3$ and $g : x \longmapsto 1/(x - 2)$

    a) Find   **(i)** $fg(3)$ **(ii)** $gf(1)$

    b) Find   **(i)** $fg(x)$ **(ii)** $gf(x)$

                   (iii) $gg(x)$ giving your answer in its simplest terms

    c) For each composite function in part (b), state which values of x cannot be included in the domain

Q4 The functions p and q are defined as follows

    $p : x \longmapsto (x + 5)^2$ with domain $\{x : x$ is any number$\}$

    $q : x \longmapsto 5 - x$ with domain $\{x : x > 0\}$

    Find the range of each of these functions

Q5 The function $f(x)$ is defined as $f(x) = 5/(x + 2)$

    a) Given that $f(x) = 3$, find the value of x

    b) Find $f^{-1}(x)$

Q6 $f : x \longmapsto 2x - 1$

    $g : x \longmapsto \frac{3}{x}, x \neq 0$

    a) Find the value of   **(i)** $f(3)$ **(ii)** $fg(6)$

    b) Express the inverse function f^{-1} in the form $f^{-1} : x \longmapsto \ldots$

    c) i) Express the composite function gf in the form $gf : x \longmapsto \ldots$

        ii) Which value of x must be excluded from the domain of gf?

More questions on the CD ROM

Answers are on page 209.

31 CALCULUS

Finding the gradient of a curve

We have already seen that, unlike a straight line, the gradient of a curve changes so it will take different values at different places

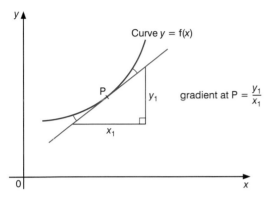

Curve $y = f(x)$

gradient at P $= \dfrac{y_1}{x_1}$

The gradient of a curve can be found by drawing a tangent to the curve at the required point. Alternatively, it is possible to work out the gradient by using differentiation so that if y is a function of x, i.e. $y = f(x)$, then $\dfrac{dy}{dx}$ is the gradient function of x.

> The notation $\dfrac{dy}{dx}$ is generally used to denote the gradient function of y with respect to x or the rate of change of y with respect to x.

> The gradient function of y with respect to x is also called the differential of y with respect to x

For example, if $y = x^n$ then the gradient function $\dfrac{dy}{dx} = nx^{n-1}$

Similarly if if $y = ax^n$ (where a is a constant) then the gradient function $\dfrac{dy}{dx} = anx^{n-1}$

Worked example

Differentiate **(a)** x^5 **(b)** $3x^5$ **(c)** $3x^5 + 2x^7$

(a) Differentiate x^5 is the same as finding the gradient function of x^5

In this case $\dfrac{dy}{dx} = 5x^{5-1}$ using the fact that if $y = x^n$ then the gradient function $\dfrac{dy}{dx} = nx^{n-1}$.

So the differential of x^5 is $5x^4$

(b) Differentiate $3x^5$ is the same as finding the gradient function of $3x^5$.

In this case $\dfrac{dy}{dx} = 3 \times 5x^{5-1}$ using the fact that if $y = ax^n$ then the gradient function $\dfrac{dy}{dx} = anx^{n-1}$

So the differential of x^5 is $15x^4$.

(c) Differentiate $3x^5 + 2x^7$ is the same as finding the gradient function of $3x^5$ and adding the gradient function of $2x^7$.

In this case $\dfrac{dy}{dx} = 3 \times 5x^{5-1} + 2 \times 7x^{7-1}$ using the fact that if $y = ax^n + bx^m$ then the gradient function $\dfrac{dy}{dx} = anx^{n-1} + bmx^{m-1}$

So the differential of $3x^5 + 2x^7$ is $15x^4 + 14x^6$

The gradient function works for all values of n including negative numbers, so that if $y = x^{-5}$ then the gradient function $\frac{dy}{dx} = -5x^{-5-1} = -5x^{-6}$ (or $-5/x^6$).

For constants the gradient function is equal to zero so that if $y = 2$ then the gradient function $\frac{dy}{dx} = 0$

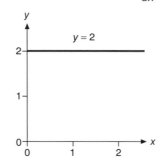

Turning points

The gradient function can be used to find the turning points of curves

From the graph you can see that the turning point has a gradient of zero. This fact can be used to find turning points and the maximum or minimum value of a curve

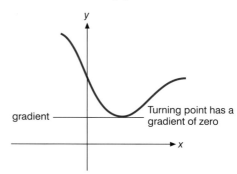

gradient —————— Turning point has a gradient of zero

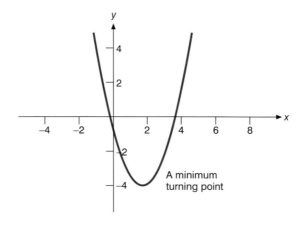

A minimum turning point

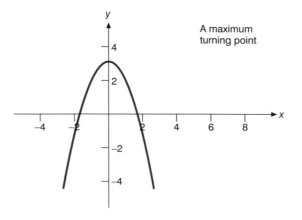

A maximum turning point

Worked example

A curve has the equation $y = x^2 - 8x + 15$.

a) Find $\frac{dy}{dx}$.

b) Find the gradient of the curve at the point with coordinates $(2, 3)$.

c) Find the coordinates of the turning point.

---

a) If $y = x^2 - 8x + 15$ then $\frac{dy}{dx} = 2x - 8$

The differential of x^2 is $2x^{2-1} = 2x^1 = 2x$
The differential of $-8x$ is $-8x^{1-1} = -8x^0 = -8$
The differential of $+15$ is 0

b) The gradient of the curve at the point $(2, 3)$ is the gradient when $x=2$
When $x=2$ $\frac{dy}{dx} = 2 \times 2 - 8$ *substituting $x=2$ into* $\frac{dy}{dx}$

$\frac{dy}{dx} = -4$

So the gradient of the curve at the point $(2, 3)$ is -4

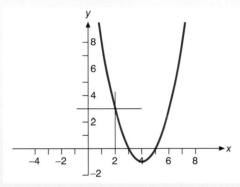

b) The coordinates of the turning point occur when $\frac{dy}{dx} = 0$
$2x - 8 = 0$ *as* $\frac{dy}{dx} = 2x - 8$
$2x = 8$
$x = 4$

The turning point occurs at $x = 4$
When $x = 4$, $y = x^2 - 8x + 15$
$y = 4^2 - 8 \times 4 + 15$
$y = 16 - 32 + 15$
$y = -1$ so $(4, -1)$

The coordinates of the turning point are $(4, -1)$.

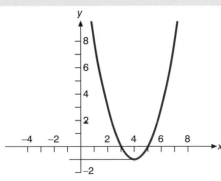

Rates of change

The gradient function is also a measure of the rate of change so that if s is the displacement of a body and s is a function of t then $s = f(t)$.

Then the velocity of the body, $\qquad\qquad v = \dfrac{ds}{dt}$

Similarly the acceleration of the body, $\qquad a = \dfrac{dv}{dt}$

Worked example

A body is moving in a straight line which passes through a fixed point O.

The displacement, s metres, of the body from O at time t seconds is given by the formula

$$s = 2t(t - 1)(t - 2)$$

a) Find an expression for the velocity, v m/s, at time t seconds.

b) Find the acceleration after 5 seconds.

HINT

- Expanding
  $s = 2t(t-1)(t-2)$ gives
  $s = 2t^3 - 6t^2 + 4t$

---

a) $s = f(t)$ and we can write $s = 2t^3 - 6t^2 + 4t$

The velocity of the body, $\qquad\qquad v = \dfrac{ds}{dt} = 6t^2 - 12t + 4\,\text{m/s}$

b) The acceleration of the body, $\qquad a = \dfrac{dv}{dt} = 12t - 12$

So the acceleration after 5 seconds $\quad = 12t - 12 = 12 \times 5 - 5 = 55\,\text{m/s}^2$

QUESTIONS

Q1 Differentiate

    a) $x^2 - 7x + 12$
    b) $5x^2 - 8x + 1$
    c) $x^3 - 8x^2 + 3x - 5$
    d) $x^3/5 - 3x^2/4$
    e) $(x+5)^2$
    f) $x^{-3} - 4x^{-2} + 3x^{-1}$

Q2 Find $\dfrac{dy}{dx}$ for the following

    a) $y = x^2 - 2x + 3$
    b) $y = (x-3)(x+2)$
    c) $y = 2/x + 3/x^2$

Q3 Find the gradient of the tangent at the given point on the following curves

    a) $y = 3x^2 - 5x + 1$ at the point where $x=3$.
    b) $y = 3x - 5 + 2x^{-1}$ at the point $(1, 0)$.
    c) $y = (3x - 5)(x + 1)$ at the point $(-2, 11)$.

Q4 A curve has the equation $y = x^2 - 12x + 35$

    a) Find $\dfrac{dy}{dx}$
    b) Find the gradient of the curve at the point with coordinates $(3, 8)$
    c) Find the coordinates of the turning point.

Q5 A curve has the equation $y = x^2 - 5x + 6$

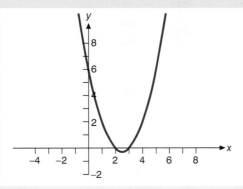

a) Find $\dfrac{dy}{dx}$

b) Find the coordinates of the turning point

c) State, with a reason, whether this turning point is a maximum or a minimum.

Q6 The temperature T of liquid after t seconds is given by the formula $T = t^2 - 12t + 35$

a) Find the rate of change of the temperature after 2 seconds

b) Find the time when the temperature is at its minimum.

Q7 A car is moving along a straight road. It passes a point O.
After t seconds its distance, s (in metres) from O is given by the formula $s = 8(t - t^2)$ where $0 \leq t \leq 10$.

a) Find the time when the car passes through the origin again

b) Find $\dfrac{ds}{dt}$

c) Find the time when the car is stationary

d) Find the speed of the car 3 seconds after passing O

Q8 An object has a velocity given by the equation $3t^2 + 8t - 5$.

What is the velocity and the acceleration when $t = 2$?

Q9 A curve has the equation $y = 2x^3 - 3x^2 - 72x$

a) Find $\dfrac{dy}{dx}$

b) Find the coordinates of the turning points.

Answers are on page 211.

More questions on the CD ROM

Hong Kong Harbour

Hong Kong

Earth

South-east Asia

Where do you think you are?

From space, Indonesia (for instance) looks like a few big islands, and measures a certain distance around the coast. But the closer you go, the more islands you see, and the more inlets and bays until, if you come close enough, you are staring at individual grains of sand. Do you measure round each grain? The closer you look, the longer and more irregular the coastline is. It's a problem for map-makers – and it's also an example of fractals – geometric objects with infinite complexity which mirror many patterns found in nature.

Maps tell you where you are, but what if there are few features to mark on the map – in a desert or jungle? If you can measure your direction from two known faraway points, where the lines cross is where you are. Using trigonometry in this way is the principle underlying satellite navigation systems.

SHAPE, SPACE AND MEASURES

32 GEOMETRIC TERMS

For your study of shape and space, you need to know and understand the following useful definitions.

Angles and lines

A **right angle** is equal to 90°.

right angle

An **obtuse angle** is more than 90° but less than 180°.

obtuse angle

A **reflex angle** is more than 180° but less than 360°.

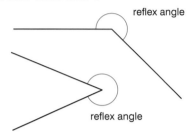

reflex angle

reflex angle

An **acute angle** is less than 90°.

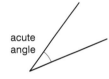

acute angle

Complementary angles add up to 90°.

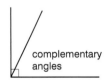

complementary angles

Supplementary angles add up to 180°.

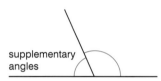

supplementary angles

Perpendicular lines meet at right angles.

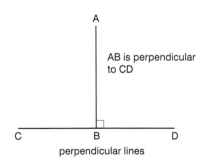

A

AB is perpendicular to CD

C   B   D

perpendicular lines

Parallel lines are the same perpendicular distance apart everywhere along their length.

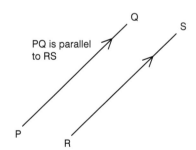

Q
S

PQ is parallel to RS

P
R

Triangles

PROPERTIES OF TRIANGLES

The sum of the **interior angles** of a triangle is 180°.

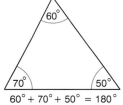

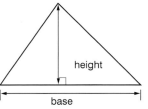

$$60° + 70° + 50° = 180°$$ $$40° + 130° + 10° = 180°$$

The smallest angle is always opposite the smallest side.

The largest angle is always opposite the largest side.

In general, the **area of a triangle** $= \frac{1}{2} \times$ base $\times$ perpendicular height.

TYPES OF TRIANGLE

You need to know about the following triangles and their properties.

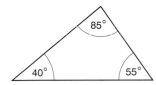

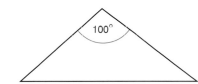

An **acute-angled triangle** has all of its angles less than 90°.

An **obtuse-angled triangle** has one of its angles greater than 90°.

A **scalene triangle** has all its sides different and all its angles different.

An **isosceles triangle** has two sides the same length and two angles the same size.

An **equilateral triangle** has all three sides the same length and all three angles the same size.

A **right-angled triangle** has one of its angles equal to 90°.

Worked example

Find the areas of the triangles.

a) Area of a triangle $= \frac{1}{2} \times$ base $\times$ perpendicular height

$\qquad\qquad\qquad = \frac{1}{2} \times 3 \times 5$ Perpendicular height is 5 cm.

$\qquad\qquad\qquad = 7.5$ cm^2 Remember to include the units of area.

(a)
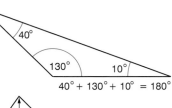

b) Area of a triangle $= \frac{1}{2} \times$ base $\times$ perpendicular height

$\qquad\qquad\qquad = \frac{1}{2} \times 7 \times 5$ Perpendicular height is 5 cm again.

$\qquad\qquad\qquad = 17.5$ cm^2

(b)
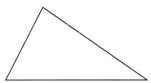

c) Area of a triangle $= \frac{1}{2} \times$ base $\times$ perpendicular height

$\qquad\qquad\qquad = \frac{1}{2} \times 4 \times 5$ Perpendicular height is still 5 cm.

$\qquad\qquad\qquad = 10$ cm^2

(c)
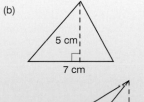

Quadrilaterals

PROPERTIES OF QUADRILATERALS

The sum of the interior angles of a quadrilateral is 360°.

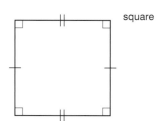

$100° + 120° + 60° + 80° = 360°$

TYPES OF QUADRILATERAL

You need to know about the following quadrilaterals and their properties.

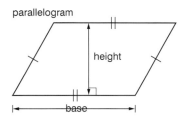
parallelogram

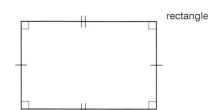
rectangle

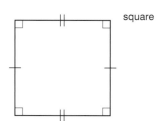
square

A **parallelogram** is a quadrilateral in which the two pairs of opposite sides are equal and parallel.

The area of a parallelogram = base × perpendicular height.

A **rectangle** is a parallelogram with four right angles.

The area of a rectangle = base × height.

A **square** is a rectangle with four equal sides.

The area of a square = base × height (where base = height).

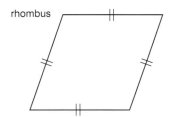
rhombus

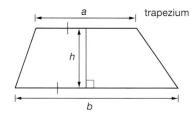
trapezium

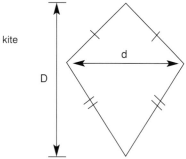
kite

A **rhombus** is a parallelogram with four equal sides.

The area of a rhombus = base × perpendicular height.

A **trapezium** is a quadrilateral with one pair of opposite sides parallel.

The area of a trapezium

$= \frac{1}{2} \times \left(\begin{array}{c}\text{sum of parallel} \\ \text{sides}\end{array}\right) \times \text{height}.$

This is usually written as

$\frac{1}{2}(a + b)h$

where a and b are the lengths of the parallel sides and h is the height.

A **kite** is a quadrilateral with two pairs of adjacent sides equal.

The area of a kite can be found by splitting the shape into two triangles.

Alternatively,

$\text{area} = \frac{1}{2} \times \text{width} \times \text{height}$

$= \frac{1}{2} \times d \times D$

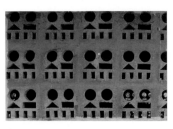

Shapes seen in architecture

Worked example

Find the areas of the quadrilaterals below.

a) Area of a parallelogram = base × perpendicular height

$\quad\quad$ = 8 × 4 $\quad$ Perpendicular height is 4 cm (not 5 cm).

$\quad\quad$ = 32 cm²

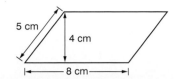
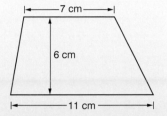

b) Area of trapezium = $\frac{1}{2}$ × (sum of parallel sides) × height

$\quad\quad$ = $\frac{1}{2}$ × (7 + 11) × 6 $\quad$ Perpendicular height is 6 cm.

$\quad\quad$ = $\frac{1}{2}$ × 18 × 6

$\quad\quad$ = 54 cm²

c) To find the area of a kite you can split the shape into two triangles and use:

area of a triangle = $\frac{1}{2}$ × base × perpendicular height

Area of kite = $\frac{1}{2}$ × 6 × 6.5 + $\frac{1}{2}$ × 6 × 8.5 $\quad$ Height of top triangle
$\quad\quad\quad\quad\quad\quad\quad\quad\quad\quad\quad\quad\quad\quad\quad$ = 15 − 8.5 = 6.5 cm.

$\quad\quad$ = 19.5 + 25.5

$\quad\quad$ = 45 cm²

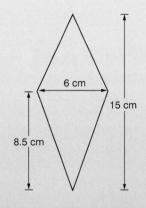

An easier way to find the area of a kite is to multiply the width by the height and divide by 2.

Area of kite = $\frac{1}{2}$ × width × height

Polygons

Any shape enclosed by straight lines is called a **polygon**. Polygons are named according to their number of sides.

A **regular polygon** has all sides equal and all angles the same.

A **convex polygon** has no interior angle greater than 180°.

A **concave** (or **re-entrant**) **polygon** has at least one interior angle greater than 180°.

Number of sides	Name of polygon
3	triangle
4	quadrilateral
5	pentagon
6	hexagon
7	heptagon
8	octagon
9	nonagon
10	decagon

Polygons seen in Islamic art

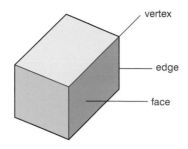

Solids

A **solid** is a three-dimensional shape such as cube, cuboid, prism, cylinder, sphere, pyramid or cone.

You need to understand the following definitions relating to solids.

A **face** is the surface of a solid which is enclosed by edges.

An **edge** is a straight line where two faces meet.

A **vertex** is the point where three or more edges meet.

TYPES OF SOLID

You should be aware of the following solids and their properties.

A **cube** is a three-dimensional shape with six square faces.

A **cuboid** is a three-dimensional shape with six rectangular faces. Opposite faces are equal in size.

A **prism** is a three-dimensional shape with uniform cross-section. The prism is usually named after the shape of the cross-sectional area.

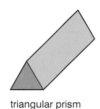 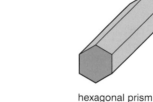 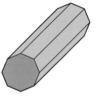

triangular prism   hexagonal prism   octagonal prism

Cubes and cuboids are also prisms as they have uniform cross-sections.

A **cylinder** is a prism with a uniform circular cross-section.

A **sphere** is a three-dimensional shape in which the surface is always the same distance from the centre.

sphere   hemisphere

A **hemisphere** is one half of a sphere.

A **pyramid** is a three-dimensional shape with a polygon-shaped base and the remaining triangular faces meeting at a vertex. The pyramid is usually named after the shape of the polygon forming the base.

 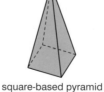 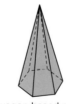

triangular pyramid   square-based pyramid   hexagon-based pyramid   cone

A **cone** is a pyramid with a circular base.

Angle properties

You need to learn the following angle properties, and use them when explaining work with lines and angles. You also need to remember that:

the **interior angles of a triangle add up to 180°** and the **interior angles of a quadrilateral add up to 360°**

the **exterior angle plus the adjacent interior angle add up to 180°** (angles on a straight line) and the **sum of all the exterior angles of a polygon is 360°**.

Properties of angles

Angles on a straight line add up to 180°.

$90° + 90° = 180°$

$a + b = 180°$

Angles at a point add up to 360°.

$90° + 90° + 90° + 90° = 360°$

$v + w + x + y + z = 360°$

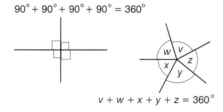

When two straight lines intersect the (vertically) opposite angles are equal.

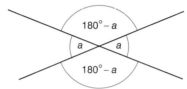

A **transversal** is a line which cuts two or more parallel lines.

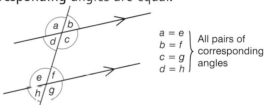

transversal

Corresponding angles are equal.

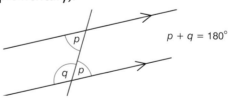

$a = e$
$b = f$
$c = g$
$d = h$ } All pairs of corresponding angles

Alternate angles are equal.

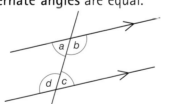

$a = c$
$b = d$ } Pairs of alternate angles

Interior angles add up to 180° (i.e. interior angles are **supplementary**).

$p + q = 180°$

Worked example

Find the values of a, b and c in this diagram. Give reasons for your answers.

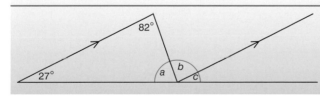

82°
27°

$a = 71°$ The angles of the triangle add up to 180°.
$b = 82°$ b is an alternate angle between the two given parallel lines.
$c = 27°$ The angles on a straight line add up to 180°.

Angle sum of a triangle

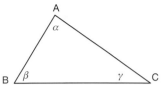

You can show that the angle sum of a triangle is 180°, as follows.

Let the angles of the triangle ABC be α, β and γ.

Draw a line segment CD, parallel to AB.

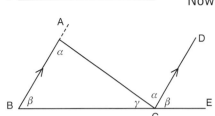

Now $\angle ACD = \angle BAC = \alpha$ Alternate angles between parallel lines.

$\angle ABC = \angle DCE = \beta$ Corresponding angles between parallel lines.

BC is a straight line, so $\alpha + \beta + \gamma = 180°$

As angles on a straight line add up to 180°.

So the angle sum of a triangle is 180°.

Angle sum of a polygon

You can find the sum of the angles of a polygon by dividing the polygon into a series of triangles where each triangle has an angle sum of 180°.

A four-sided polygon can be split into two triangles.

Angle sum = 2 × 180° = 360°

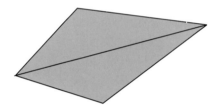

A six-sided polygon can be split into four triangles.

Angle sum = 4 × 180° = 720°

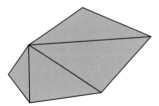

A seven-sided polygon can be split into five triangles.

Angle sum = 5 × 180° = 900°

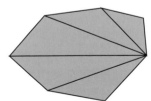

HINT

- The angle sum of an n-sided polygon is sometimes presented as $(2n - 4)$ right angles. This formula gives exactly the same results as $(n - 2) \times 180°$.

From the above, you can see that an n-sided polygon can be split into $(n - 2)$ triangles.

Angle sum of an n-sided polygon $= (n - 2) \times 180°$

Exterior angles

Another useful result involves the exterior angles. Since the sum of the exterior angles is 360°, each exterior angle of a regular polygon is 360° ÷ *n*.

You can use this fact to find the interior angle of a regular polygon.

Interior angle = 180° − exterior angle

The angle sum of an *n*-sided regular polygon can be found in the same way as the angle sum of a non-regular polygon.

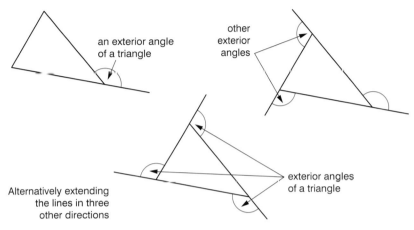

an exterior angle of a triangle

other exterior angles

Alternatively extending the lines in three other directions

exterior angles of a triangle

QUESTIONS

Q1 Find the value of each angle that is marked with a letter.

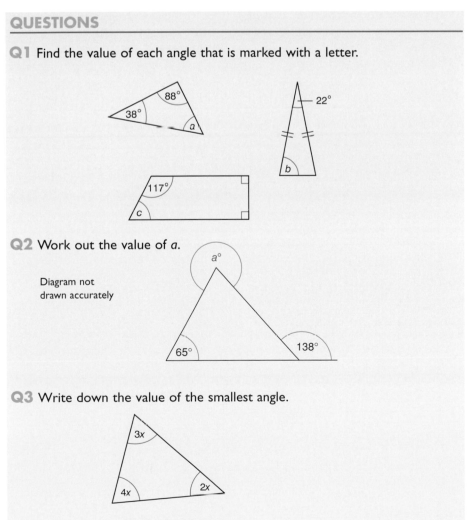

Q2 Work out the value of *a*.

Diagram not drawn accurately

a°

65°   138°

Q3 Write down the value of the smallest angle.

3*x*

4*x*   2*x*

Q4 Find the areas of the following polygons.

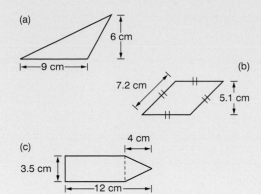

(a)

6 cm

|←—9 cm—→|

(b)

7.2 cm

5.1 cm

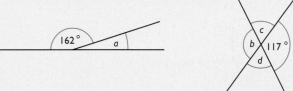

(c)

4 cm

3.5 cm

12 cm

Q5 Write down the value of the missing angles.

162°

a

c

b   117°

d

Q6 Prove that the exterior angle of a triangle is equal to the sum of the two opposite internal angles.

Q7 Write down the value of each of the missing angles.

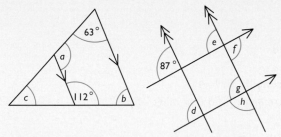

63°

a

c   112°   b

e   f

87°

d   g   h

Q8 Calculate the interior angle of a regular decagon.

Q9 Calculate the exterior angle of a regular hexagon.

Q10 This is part of the design of a pattern found at the theatre of Diana at Alexandria. It is made up of a regular hexagon, squares and equilateral triangles.

Diagram not drawn accurately.

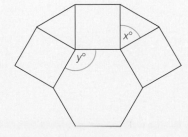

x°

y°

a) Write down the size of the angle marked x°.

b) Work out the size of the angle marked y°.

Answers are on page 212.

More questions
on the CD ROM

33 CONSTRUCTIONS

What will I need?

You will need the following equipment to construct diagrams, produce scale drawings and find the locus of points.

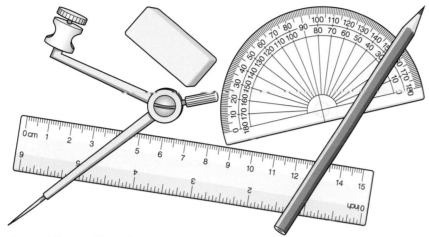

a sharp 2B pencil and an eraser

a ruler graduated in centimetres and millimetres

a pair of compasses

a protractor

You should always make your constructions as accurate as you possibly can – the examiner expects measurements of length to be accurate to the nearest millimetre and measurements of angles to be correct to the nearest degree.

Constructing triangles

When working with a triangle ABC, it is conventional to represent the side opposite angle A by the letter a, the side opposite angle B by the letter b and the side opposite angle C by the letter c, as shown here.

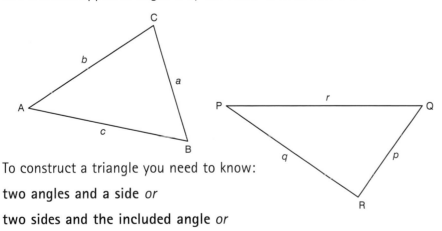

To construct a triangle you need to know:

two angles and a side *or*

two sides and the included angle *or*

three sides.

HINT

- Always leave your construction lines on your diagram.

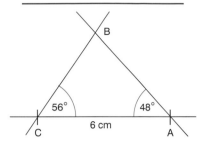

Given two angles and a side

Worked example

Construct triangle ABC in which $\angle A = 48°$, $\angle B = 76°$ and $b = 6$ cm.

1 Draw a rough sketch.

2 Draw the line segment AC = 6 cm.

3 Draw an angle of 56° at C.

4 Draw an angle of 48° at A.

5 Label the point of intersection as B.

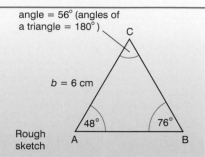

Given two sides and the included angle

Worked example

Construct triangle PQR in which $p = 8$ cm, $q = 6.5$ cm and $\angle QRP = 53°$.

1 Draw a rough sketch.

2 Draw the line segment QR = 8 cm.

3 Draw an angle of 53° at R.

4 Construct the point P which is 6.5 cm from R, using your compasses with centre R and radius 6.5 cm.

5 Join QP.

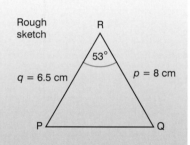

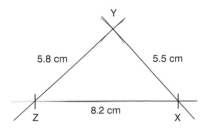

Given three sides

Worked example

Construct triangle XYZ in which $x = 5.8$ cm, $y = 8.2$ cm and $z = 5.5$ cm.

HINT

- Always start by drawing the longest side.

1 Draw a rough sketch.

2 Draw the line segment XZ = 8.2 cm (the longest side).

3 With centre Z and radius 5.8 cm, use your compasses to draw a circular arc giving points 5.8 cm from Z.

4 With centre X and radius 5.5 cm, use your compasses to draw a circular arc giving points 5.5 cm from X.

5 Label the point of intersection of the two arcs as Y.

6 Join ZY and XY.

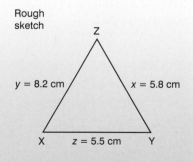

Worked example

Construct triangle ABC in which a = 7.6 cm, b = 5.6 cm and $\angle$ABC = 44°.

Before constructing the triangle, remind yourself what you need to know:

two angles and a side *or*

two sides and the included angle *or*

three sides.

In this particular case you *do not have sufficient information to draw the triangle*, since you are not given the included angle, so proceed as follows.

1   Draw a rough sketch.

2   Draw the line segment BC = 7.6 cm.

3   Draw an angle of 44° at B.

4   With compasses set to a radius of 5.6 cm, and centred on C, draw a circular arc giving points 5.6 cm from C.

5   You will find that there are two points where this arc cuts the line from B. Either of these points will give a point A which satisfies the conditions for the triangle.

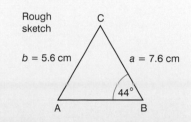

Rough sketch

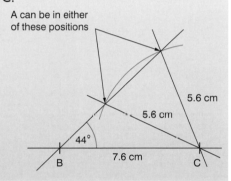

A can be in either of these positions

HINT

*   Because there are two possible solutions to the triangle, this is sometimes called the ambiguous case.

Geometrical constructions

You should be able to carry out the following constructions, using only a ruler and a pair of compasses:

the **perpendicular bisector of a line**
the **perpendicular from a point on a straight line**
the **angle bisector**.

Perpendicular bisector of a line

Worked example

Construct the perpendicular bisector of a line AB.

1   With the compasses set to a radius greater than half the length of AB, and centred on A, draw arcs above and below the line.

2   With the compasses still set to the same radius, and centred on B, draw arcs above and below the line, so that they cut the first arcs.

3   Join the points where these arcs cross (P and Q). This line is the perpendicular bisector of AB.

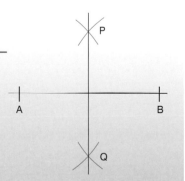

Perpendicular from a point to a straight line

Worked example

Construct the perpendicular at the point X on a line.

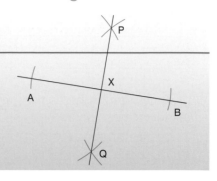

1 With the compasses set to a radius of about 5 cm, and centred on X, draw arcs to cut the line at A and B.

2 Now construct the perpendicular bisector of the line segment AB, as before.

The angle bisector

Worked example

Construct the bisector of an angle ABC.

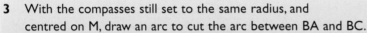

1 With the compasses set to a radius of about 5 cm, and centred on B, draw arcs to cut BA at L and BC at M.

2 With the compasses set to the same radius, and centred on L, draw an arc between BA and BC.

3 With the compasses still set to the same radius, and centred on M, draw an arc to cut the arc between BA and BC.

4 Label the point where the arcs cross as Q.

5 Join BQ. This is the bisector of the angle ABC.

What are bearings and scale drawings?

Bearings are a useful way of describing directions. They are usually given as three-figure numbers, so a bearing of 50° would usually be written as 050°.

Scale drawings are drawings or diagrams that are scaled according to some rule. The scale for the drawing or diagram must be clearly stated.

Using bearings

Worked example

The bearing of a ship from a lighthouse is 035°. What is the bearing of the lighthouse from the ship?

By drawing a sketch of the situation, you can see more clearly that the required bearing is 215°.

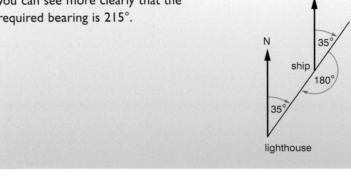

required bearing
= 180° + 35°
= 215°

Compass showing bearings

Worked example

A boat sails due east from a point A for 12 km to a position B, then for 6 km on a bearing of 160° to a point C. Using a scale of 1 cm to represent 2 km, show this on a scale drawing and use this to find the bearing and distance from A to C.

The bearing from A to C is measured as 112° and the distance from A to C is 7.6 cm which represents 15.2 km (remembering to use the given scale to convert back to kilometres).

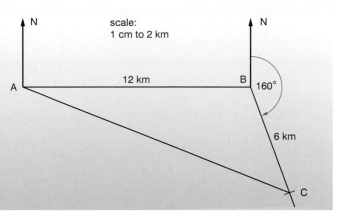

QUESTIONS

Q1 Draw any triangle ABC, then construct the perpendicular bisectors of the two longest sides. Label the point of intersection of these perpendicular bisectors O. Draw the circle centre O and radius OA.

Q2 Construct triangle PQR where p = 4.5 cm, q = 6 cm and r = 7.5 cm. What do you notice about your triangle?

Q3 Draw the line segment PQ so that PQ = 8 cm.
Construct the perpendicular bisector of PQ.
Construct the points R and S so that they lie on the perpendicular bisector a distance of 3 cm from the line PQ.
Join PR, RQ, QS and SP.
What is the special name given to this quadrilateral?

Q4 Find the bearing of B from A if the bearing of A from B is:
  a) 090°   **b)** 120°   **c)** 345°   **d)** 203°.

Q5 A plane takes off heading north-west and is told to take a left-hand turn at 5000 feet. What bearing is the plane now headed on?

Q6 On a map, the scale is given as 1 inch to 5 miles.
  a) What distance is represented by $4\frac{1}{2}$ inches on the map?
  b) A road is 36 miles long. How long is this on the map?

Q7 Two explorers set off from the same point one morning. One explorer travels at 4.5 mph on a bearing of 036° and the other explorer travels at 5.5 mph on a bearing of 063°. Using a scale of 0.5 cm to 1 mile, calculate how far they are apart after 2 hours.

Q8 Work out the bearing of:
  a) B from P
  b) P from A.

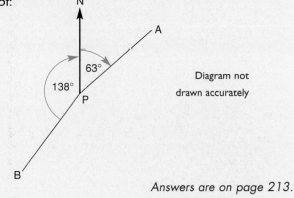

Diagram not drawn accurately

More questions on the CD ROM

Answers are on page 213.

34 ANGLE PROPERTIES OF CIRCLES

Parts of a circle

This diagram shows the main parts of a circle and the names given to them.

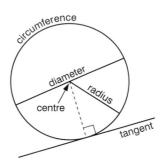

Angles in circles

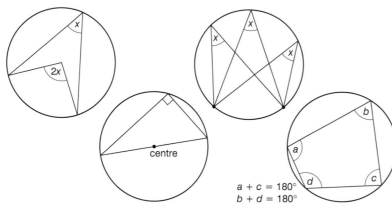

$a + c = 180°$
$b + d = 180°$

Make sure that you know the following angle properties.

The angle subtended by an arc (or chord) at the centre is twice that subtended at the circumference.

Angles subtended by the same arc (or chord) are equal.

The angle in a semicircle is always 90°.

The opposite angles of a cyclic quadrilateral are **supplementary** (they add up to 180°).

Worked example

PQRS is a quadrilateral inscribed in a circle centre O. Find, giving reasons for your answers, ∠QSR and ∠QPS.

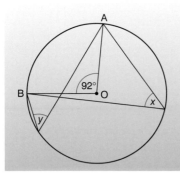

∠SQR = 90°   As RS is a diameter and the angle in a semicircle is 90°.

∠QSR = 180° − (67° + 90°) As the angles of a triangle add up to 180°.
    = 23°

∠QPS = 180° − 67°   As the opposite angles of a cyclic quadrilateral PQRS
                       add up to 180°.

    = 113°

Worked example

The angle subtended by the arc AB at the centre of the circle is 92°. Find the values of x and y.

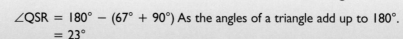

$x = 46°$ As the angle subtended by the arc AB at the centre is twice that subtended at the circumference.

$y = 46°$ As the angle subtended by the arc AB at the centre is twice that subtended at the circumference.

or else …   As the angles subtended by the arc AB at the circumference are equal and x = 46°, so y = 46°.

Chord properties

A **chord** is a straight line joining two points on the circumference of a circle.

You need to know the following chord properties.

A perpendicular from the centre of a circle to a chord bisects the chord. Conversely, a perpendicular bisector of a chord passes through the centre of the circle.

Chords that are equal in length are equidistant from the centre of the circle. Conversely, chords that are equidistant from the centre of a circle are equal in length.

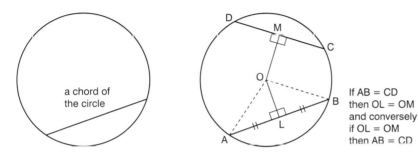

a chord of the circle

If AB = CD
then OL = OM
and conversely
if OL = OM
then AB = CD

Tangent properties

A **tangent** is a straight line which touches a circle at one point only.

You need to know the following tangent properties.

A tangent to a circle is perpendicular to the radius at the point of contact.

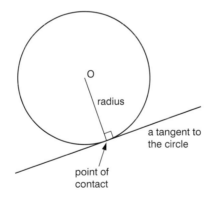

radius

a tangent to the circle

point of contact

Tangents to a circle from an external point are equal in length.

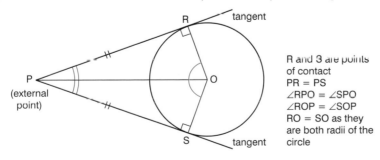

tangent

P
(external point)

tangent

R and S are points of contact
PR = PS
∠RPO = ∠SPO
∠ROP = ∠SOP
RO = SO as they are both radii of the circle

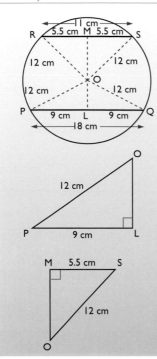

Worked example

Two chords PQ and RS are parallel to each other on opposite sides of a circle of radius 12 cm. If PQ = 18 cm and RS = 11 cm, find the distance between the chords.

Show this information on a diagram and use the chord properties to show the respective lengths.

For the right-angled triangle OPL:

$12^2 = 9^2 + OL^2$ Applying Pythagoras' theorem to the right-angled triangle.

$144 = 81 + OL^2$

$OL^2 = 63$

$OL = 7.937254$

For the right-angled triangle OMS:

$12^2 = 5.5^2 + OM^2$ Applying Pythagoras' theorem to the right-angled triangle.

$144 = 30.25 + OM^2$

$OM^2 = 113.75$

$OM = 10.665365$

Distance between the two chords = OL + OM

$= 7.937254 + 10.665365 = 18.602619$

$= 18.6$ cm (3 s.f.)

For Pythagoras' Theorem, see chapter 35.

The alternate segment theorem

The alternate segment theorem states that the angle between a tangent and a chord equals the angle subtended by the chord in the alternate segment.

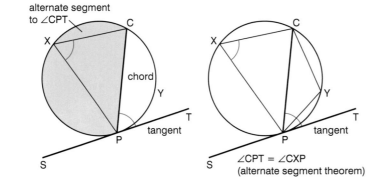

∠CPT = ∠CXP
(alternate segment theorem)

∠CPS = ∠CYP
(alternate segment theorem)

Worked example

The line ST is a tangent to the circle at P. Find the value of ∠XPC.

Using the alternate segment theorem:

∠CPT = ∠CXP = 51°   Alternate segment theorem.

∠XCP = ∠CPT = 51°   Alternate angles between parallel lines XC and PT.

∠XPC = 180° − (51° + 51°) Angles of triangle XCP add up to 180°.

∠XCP = 78°

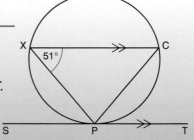

QUESTIONS

Q1 For each circle, where O marks the centre of the circle, find the missing angles.

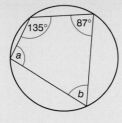 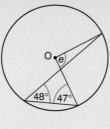 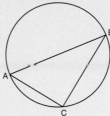 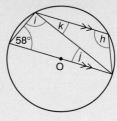 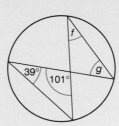

Q2 In the triangle ABC,
AB is a diameter of length 11 cm and AC measures 3.5 cm.
Find **a)** BC **b)** ∠BAC **c)** ∠ABC.

For Pythagoras' Theorem and sine, cosine and tangent in
right-angled triangles, see chapters 35 and 36.

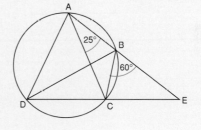

Q3 In the diagram, A, B and C are points on the circle,
centre O. Angle BCE = 63°.
FE is a tangent to the circle at point C.

a) Calculate the size of angle ACB.
Give reasons for your answer.

b) Calculate the size of angle BAC.
Give reasons for your answer.

Diagram not accurately drawn.

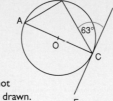

Q4 A chord AB is drawn on a circle of radius 6 cm. If the chord is 4.5 cm from the
centre of the circle, calculate the length of the chord.

For Pythagoras' Theorem see chapter 35.

Q5 A, B, C and D are four points on the circumference of a circle.
ABE and DCE are straight lines.
∠BAC = 25°.
∠EBC = 60°.
a) Find the size of ∠ADC. **b)** Find the size of ∠ADB.

∠CAD = 65°. Nelson says that BD is a diameter of the circle.

c) Is Nelson correct? You must explain your answer.

Q6 Given that angle CPT = 61° find:
a) ∠PXC **b)** ∠PYC.

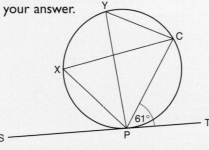

Q7 Given that angle CDP = 38° find:
a) ∠COP

b) ∠CPT

c) ∠OCP.

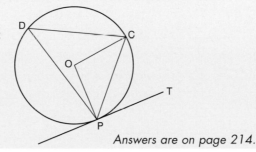

Answers are on page 214.

More questions on the CD ROM

35 PYTHAGORAS' THEOREM IN TWO DIMENSIONS

What is Pythagoras' theorem?

For any **right-angled triangle**, the square of the length of the hypotenuse is equal to the sum of the squares of the lengths of the other two sides.

$$a^2 + b^2 = c^2$$

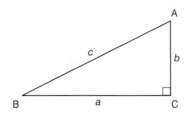

For a right-angled triangle, the side opposite the right angle is called the **hypotenuse** and this is always the longest side.

Using Pythagoras' theorem

Worked example

Find the length of the hypotenuse in this triangle.

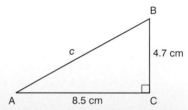

Using Pythagoras' theorem:

$$a^2 + b^2 = c^2$$

$$c^2 = a^2 + b^2$$

$c^2 = 4.7^2 + 8.5^2$ Substituting values for each of the given lengths.

$c^2 = 22.09 + 72.25$ Squaring individual lengths.

$c^2 = 94.34$

$c = 9.712\ 878$ Taking square roots of both sides to find c.

$c = 9.71$ cm (3 s.f.)   Rounding to an appropriate degree of accuracy.

Worked example

Calculate the height of this isosceles triangle.
Leave your answer in surd form.

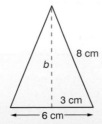

The isosceles triangle can be split into
two right-angled triangles to find the height.

Using Pythagoras' theorem:

$a^2 + b^2 = c^2$

$3^2 + b^2 = 8^2$ Substituting values for each of the given lengths
– in this case the length of the hypotenuse is known.

$9 + b^2 = 64$ Squaring individual lengths.

$b^2 = 64 - 9$ Making the height the subject.

$b^2 = 55$

$b = \sqrt{55}$ Taking square roots of both sides to find the height.

$b = \sqrt{55}$ cm   Leaving the answer in surd form.

QUESTIONS

Q1 Without using a calculator, find the length of a diagonal of a square of side 5 cm. Leave your answer in surd form.

Q2 Find the area of an equilateral triangle with side 6 cm. Use a calculator and give your answer correct to three significant figures.

Q3 A plane flies 24 km on a bearing of 020°, then a further 16.7 km on a bearing of 110°. How far is the plane away from its starting point? Use a calculator and given your answer correct to three significant figures.

Answers are on page 215.

More questions
on the CD ROM

36 SINE, COSINE AND TANGENT IN RIGHT-ANGLED TRIANGLES

The sides of a right-angled triangle are given special names. These names relate to the angles.

Sine of an angle

The sine of an angle (usually abbreviated as sin) = $\dfrac{\text{length of opposite side}}{\text{length of hypotenuse}}$

So $\sin A = \dfrac{\text{length of opposite side}}{\text{length of hypotenuse}} = \dfrac{BC}{AC}$

and $\sin C = \dfrac{\text{length of opposite side}}{\text{length of hypotenuse}} = \dfrac{AB}{AC}$ As AB is opposite angle C.

Worked example

Use the sine ratio to find p and q in these right-angled triangles.

a)
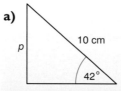

b)
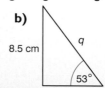

---

a) Using the formula $\sin A = \dfrac{\text{length of opposite side}}{\text{length of hypotenuse}}$:

$\sin 42° = \dfrac{p}{10}$

$p = 10 \times \sin 42°$ Rearranging the formula to make p the subject.

$p = 10 \times 0.669\,130\,6$ As $\sin 42° = 0.669\,130\,6$

$p = 6.691\,306$

$p = 6.69$ cm (3 s.f.)   Including the units and rounding to an appropriate degree of accuracy.

b) Using the formula $\sin A = \dfrac{\text{length of opposite side}}{\text{length of hypotenuse}}$:

$\sin 53° = \dfrac{8.5}{q}$

$q \times \sin 53° = 8.5$ Rearranging the formula to get q on the top line.

$q = \dfrac{8.5}{\sin 53°}$ Rearranging the formula to make q the subject.

$q = \dfrac{8.5}{0.798\,635\,5}$ As $\sin 53° = 0.798\,635\,5$

$q = 10.643\,153$

$q = 10.6$ cm (3 s.f.)   Including the units and rounding to an appropriate degree of accuracy.

Worked example

Use the sine ratio to find the angle θ.

Using the formula $\sin A = \dfrac{\text{length of opposite side}}{\text{length of hypotenuse}}$:

$\sin \theta = \dfrac{2.6}{5.2}$

$\sin \theta = 0.5$ As $\dfrac{2.6}{5.2} = 0.5$

$\theta = \sin^{-1} 0.5$ Use $\sin^{-1} 0.5$ (or arcsin 0.5) to show that you are working backwards to find the angle, given the sine of the angle (finding the inverse).

$\theta = 30°$ Use the inverse button ($\sin^{-1}$ or arcsin) on your calculator but make sure your calculator is in DEG (degree) mode.

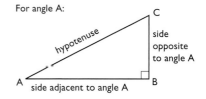

HINT

- Angles are frequently represented by letters of the Greek alphabet such as $\alpha, \beta, \gamma, \delta, \theta, \phi$.

For angle A:

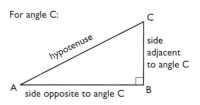

For angle C:

Cosine of an angle

The cosine of an angle (usually abbreviated as cos)

$= \dfrac{\text{length of adjacent side}}{\text{length of hypotenuse}}$

So $\cos A = \dfrac{\text{length of adjacent side}}{\text{length of hypotenuse}} = \dfrac{AB}{AC}$

and $\cos C = \dfrac{\text{length of adjacent side}}{\text{length of hypotenuse}} = \dfrac{BC}{AC}$

Worked example

Use the cosine ratio to find the angles α and β.

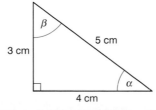

Using the formula $\cos A = \dfrac{\text{length of adjacent side}}{\text{length of hypotenuse}}$:

$\cos \alpha = \dfrac{4}{5}$

$\cos \alpha = 0.8$

$\alpha = \cos^{-1} 0.8$ Use $\cos^{-1} 0.8$ (or arccos 0.8) to show that you are working backwards to find the angle, given the cosine of the angle (finding the inverse).

$\alpha = 36.869\,898°$ Use the inverse button ($\cos^{-1}$ or arccos) on your calculator.

$\alpha = 36.9°$ (3 s.f.)

Similarly $\cos \beta = \dfrac{3}{5}$

$\cos \beta = 0.6$

$\beta = \cos^{-1} 0.6$ Use $\cos^{-1} 0.6$ (or arccos 0.6) to show that you are working backwards to find the angle, given the cosine of the angle.

$\beta = 53.130\,102°$ Use the inverse button ($\cos^{-1}$ or arccos) on your calculator.

$\beta = 53.1°$ (3 s.f.)

HINT

- Once the angle α had been found then it is possible to find β by using the fact that $\alpha + \beta + 90° = 180°$ (the angle sum of a triangle $= 180°$).

Worked example

Use the cosine ratio to find the lengths indicated on the right-angled triangles.

a)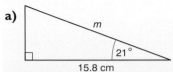

b)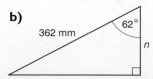

a) Using the formula $\cos A = \dfrac{\text{length of adjacent side}}{\text{length of hypotenuse}}$:

$$\cos 21° = \frac{15.8}{m}$$

$m \times \cos 21° = 15.8$ Rearranging the formula to get m on the top line.

$m = \dfrac{15.8}{\cos 21°}$ Rearranging the formula to make m the subject.

$m = \dfrac{15.8}{0.933\,580\,4}$ As $\cos 21° = 0.933\,580\,4$

$m = 16.924\,091$

$m = 16.9$ cm (3 s.f.)   Including the units and rounding to an appropriate degree of accuracy.

b) Using the formula $\cos A = \dfrac{\text{length of adjacent side}}{\text{length of hypotenuse}}$:

$\cos 62° = \dfrac{n}{362}$ As the side labelled n is adjacent to the angle 62°.

$n = 362 \times \cos 62°$ Rearranging the formula to make n the subject.

$n = 362 \times 0.469\,471\,6$ As $\cos 62° = 0.469\,471\,6$

$n = 169.948\,71$

$n = 170$ mm (3 s.f.)   Including the units and rounding to an appropriate degree of accuracy.

HINT

- The value of n might also be found by using $\sin 28° = \dfrac{n}{362}$ where 28° is the missing angle.

Tangent of an angle

The tangent of an angle (usually abbreviated as tan) $= \dfrac{\text{length of opposite side}}{\text{length of adjacent side}}$

So $\tan A = \dfrac{\text{length of opposite side}}{\text{length of adjacent side}} = \dfrac{BC}{AB}$

and $\tan C = \dfrac{\text{length of opposite side}}{\text{length of adjacent side}} = \dfrac{AB}{BC}$

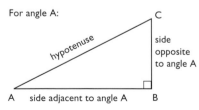

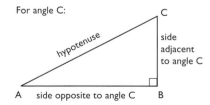

Worked example

Given that AD = 30 cm, BC = 10 cm and ∠DBC = 61°
find:

a) CD   **b)** ∠DAC.

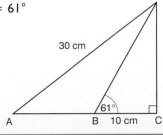

a) For the right-angled triangle DBC, using the formula

$$\tan DBC = \frac{\text{length of opposite side}}{\text{length of adjacent side}} :$$

$$\tan 61° = \frac{CD}{10}$$

CD = 10 × tan 61°   Rearranging the formula to make CD the subject.

CD = 10 × 1.804 047 8   As tan 61° = 1.804 047 8

CD = 18.040 478

CD = 18.0 cm (3 s.f.)   Including the units and rounding to an appropriate
                          degree of accuracy.

b) For the right-angled triangle DAC, using the formula

$$\sin A = \frac{\text{length of opposite side}}{\text{length of hypotenuse}} :$$

$$\sin DAC = \frac{18.040\,478}{30}$$ Using the original value of CD and not the
                                          rounded value.

sin DAC = 0.601 349 3

∠DAC = sin⁻¹ 0.601 349 3

∠DAC = 36.966 593°   Use the inverse button (sin⁻¹ or arcsin) on your
                       calculator.

∠DAC = 37.0° (3 s.f.)   Rounding to an appropriate degree of accuracy.

HINT

- Learn how to use the memory buttons on your calculator. You can use more exact values, and it makes you less likely to make a keying error.

Worked example

A rectangle measures 10 cm by 5 cm. What angle does the diagonal make
with the longer sides?

Start by drawing a sketch of the rectangle.
Let the required angle be A.

Using the formula $\tan A = \frac{\text{length of opposite side}}{\text{length of adjacent side}} :$

$$\tan A = \frac{5}{10}$$

tan A = 0.5

A = tan⁻¹ 0.5   Use tan⁻¹ 0.5 (or arctan 0.5) to show that you are working
                  backwards to find the angle, given the tangent of the angle
                  (finding the inverse).

A = 26.565 051°

The angle which the diagonal makes with the longest side is 26.6° (3 s.f.).

Angles of elevation and depression

The **angle of elevation** is the angle up from the horizontal.

The **angle of depression** is the angle down from the horizontal.

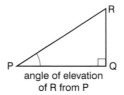

angle of elevation of R from P

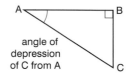

angle of depression of C from A

Worked example

An object is situated 25 metres from the foot of a mast of height 32 metres. What is the angle of depression of the object from the top of the mast?

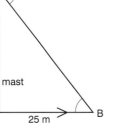

Start by drawing a diagram of the situation.

The angle of depression of the object from the top of the mast is ∠DCB.

∠DCB = ∠ABC   As these are alternate angles between parallel lines AB and CD.

$\tan ABC = \frac{32}{25}$ As the tangent of an angle $= \frac{\text{length of opposite side}}{\text{length of adjacent side}}$.

$\tan ABC = 1.28$

$\angle ABC = \tan^{-1} 1.28$ Use the inverse button ($\tan^{-1}$ or arctan) on your calculator.

$\angle ABC = 52.001\ 268°$

The angle of depression is 52.0° (3 s.f.).

QUESTIONS

Q1 Find the lengths of the sides in the following right-angled triangles.

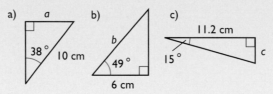

a)   *a*   b)   c)

38°   10 cm   *b*   49°   15°   11.2 cm   *c*

6 cm

Q2 Find the angles in the following triangles.

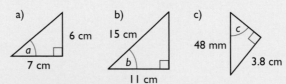

a)   6 cm   b)   15 cm   c)   *c*

a   7 cm   *b*   48 mm   3.8 cm

11 cm

Q3 A tree of height 30 feet casts a shadow which is 36 feet long. What is the angle of elevation of the sun?

Q4 The diagram shows a right-angled triangle ABC. AC = 12.6 m, angle CAB = 41° and angle ABC = 90°.

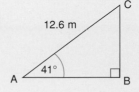

Find the length of the side AB. Give your answer correct to three significant figures.

Q5 Diagram not drawn accurately

DE = 6 m, EG = 10 m,
FG = 8 m, angle
DEG = 90°, angle
EFG = 90°.

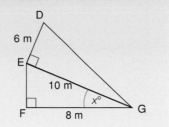

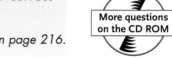

a) Calculate the length
of DG. Give your answer correct to
three significant figures.

b) Calculate the size of the angle marked $x°$. Give your answer correct
to one decimal place.

Answers are on page 216.

More questions
on the CD ROM

37 SINE AND COSINE RULES

Why use sine and cosine rules?

You can use the sine, cosine and tangent ratios to **solve** right-angled triangles but you need the sine and cosine rules to solve triangles that are not right-angled.

Use the **sine rule** when you are working with **two sides and two angles**.

Use the **cosine rule** when you are working with **three sides and one angle**.

Sine rule

The sine rule states that: $\dfrac{a}{\sin A} = \dfrac{b}{\sin B} = \dfrac{c}{\sin C}$

Sometimes it is useful to use the alternative form: $\dfrac{\sin A}{a} = \dfrac{\sin B}{b} = \dfrac{\sin C}{c}$

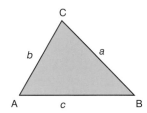

Cosine rule

The cosine rule states that:

$$a^2 = b^2 + c^2 - 2bc \cos A$$

or $\cos A = \dfrac{b^2 + c^2 - a^2}{2bc}$

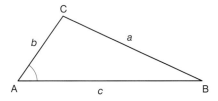

Area of a triangle

The sine and cosine rules can be extended to find the area of a triangle so that:

area of a triangle $= \frac{1}{2}ab\sin C$

where C is the 'included' angle between sides *a* and *b*.

Worked example

Find the angle *A* in the triangle ABC where AB is 11 cm, BC is 17.5 cm and angle *C* is 36°.

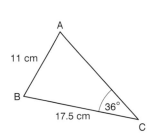

The information involves two sides and two angles, so use the sine rule.

$\dfrac{a}{\sin A} = \dfrac{b}{\sin B}$

$\dfrac{\sin A}{a} = \dfrac{\sin B}{b}$ Reciprocating both sides.

$\dfrac{\sin A}{17.5} = \dfrac{\sin 36°}{11}$

$\sin A = 17.5 \times \dfrac{\sin 36°}{11}$ Multiplying both sides by 17.5.

$\sin A = 0.935\,112\,9$

$A = 69.246\,393°$ Using the inverse button (sin^{-1} or arcsin) on your calculator.

HINT

- You will be given the formulae for:
  the sine rule:
  $$\dfrac{a}{\sin A} = \dfrac{b}{\sin B} = \dfrac{c}{\sin C}$$
  or $\dfrac{\sin A}{a} = \dfrac{\sin B}{b} = \dfrac{\sin C}{c}$
  the cosine rule:
  $$\cos A = \dfrac{b^2 + c^2 - a^2}{2bc}$$
  the area of a triangle:
  $$\triangle = \tfrac{1}{2}ab\sin C$$

Unfortunately the value of angle
$A = 69.246\,392°$ is not unique
since there is another possible
value that satisfies $\sin A = 0.935\,112\,9$.

From the graph you can calculate that
another possible value of A is $110.753\,61°$.

Angle $A = 69.2°$ or $110.8°$ (1 d.p.)

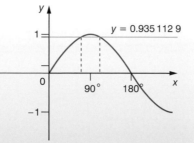

HINT

•Whenever you use the sine
rule you need to be aware of
the possibility that two
solutions exist. This problem
does not arise when using the
cosine rule and can be
avoided when using the sine
rule by finding the smallest
angle of a triangle first (if
possible).

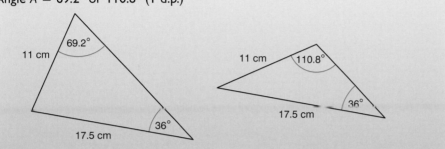

Worked example
Find the angle P and the area of the triangle.

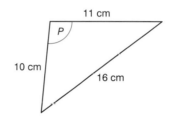

Since the information involves three sides and one angle, use the cosine rule.

$$\cos A = \frac{b^2 + c^2 - a^2}{2bc}$$

$$\cos P = \frac{10^2 + 11^2 - 16^2}{2 \times 10 \times 11} \quad \text{Substituting the given lengths.}$$

$$\cos P = \frac{100 + 121 - 256}{220}$$

$$\cos P = \frac{{}^-35}{220}$$

$\cos P = {}^-0.159\,090\,9$ The negative value shows that the angle P is obtuse.

$P = 99.154\,133°$ Using the inverse button ($\cos^{-1}$ or arccos) on the calculator.

$P = 99.2°$ (1 d.p.)

To find the area of the triangle use:

area of a triangle $= \frac{1}{2}ab\,\sin C$

$\qquad\qquad = \frac{1}{2} \times 10 \times 11 \times \sin 99.154\,133°$ Remembering to use the most accurate value of P.

$\qquad\qquad = 54.299\,517$

$\qquad\qquad = 54.3\ \text{cm}^2$ (3 s.f.)   Rounding to an appropriate degree of accuracy.

QUESTIONS

Q1 Calculate the angles and sides marked with letters in the following triangles.

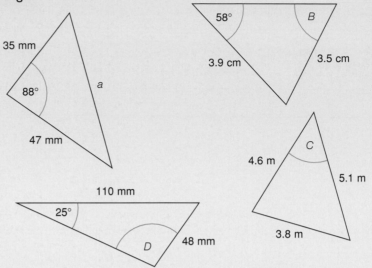

35 mm

88°

a

47 mm

58°

B

3.9 cm

3.5 cm

110 mm

25°

D

48 mm

4.6 m

C

5.1 m

3.8 m

Q2 Calculate the areas of the given shapes.

a)

4.7 m

3.6 m   31°

b)

16 cm

Q3 A ship leaves port and sails on a bearing of 035°. After 11 km the ship changes direction and sets sail on a bearing of 067°. The ship sails a distance of 16.5 km on this bearing. What is the distance and bearing of the ship from the port?

Q4 In triangle ABC, AB = 8.1 cm, AC = 7.5 cm and angle ACB = 30°.

A

8.1 cm   7.5 cm

30°

B   C

Diagram not accurately drawn.

a) Calculate the size of angle ABC. Give your answer correct to three significant figures.

b) Calculate the area of triangle ABC. Give your answer correct to three significant figures.

More questions on the CD ROM

Answers are on page 216.

38 THREE-DIMENSIONAL TRIGONOMETRY

Your course requires you to work with trigonometry in three dimensions. For this work, it is useful to identify right-angled triangles and show them diagrammatically to answer the questions.

Working in three dimensions

Worked example

The pyramid OABCD has a square base of length 15 cm and a vertical height of 26 cm. Calculate:

a) the length OA

b) the angle OAC.

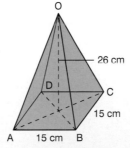

The pyramids of Egypt

---

a) Consider the base ABCD (where X is the centre of the square base).

$AC^2 = 15^2 + 15^2$ Using Pythagoras' theorem on the right-angled triangle ABC.

$AC^2 = 225 + 225$

$AC^2 = 450$

$AC = 21.213\ 203$ Taking square roots on both sides.

$AX = \frac{1}{2} \times AC$

$AX = 10.606\ 602$

Now consider triangle OAX.

$OA^2 = AX^2 + OX^2$ Using Pythagoras' theorem on the right-angled triangle AXO where OX is the vertical height.

$OA^2 = 10.606\ 602^2 + 26^2$

$OA^2 = 788.5$

$OA = 28.080\ 242$ Taking square roots on both sides.

$OA = 28.1$ cm (3 s.f.) Rounding to an appropriate degree of accuracy.

b) The angle OAC is the same as the angle OAX in the previous diagram.

$\tan OAC = \frac{OX}{AX}$ As $\tan \theta = \frac{\text{length of opposite side}}{\text{length of adjacent side}}$

$\tan OAC = \frac{26}{10.606\ 602}$

$\tan OAC = 2.451\ 303\ 4$

$\angle OAC = 67.807\ 182°$ Using $\tan^{-1}$ or arctan to find the angle.

$\angle OAC = 67.8°$ (3 s.f.) Rounding to an appropriate degree of accuracy.

QUESTIONS

Q1 Find the following lengths in the cuboid shown in the diagram. Give your answers in surd form, expressing them in their lowest terms where possible.

  a) AF   **b)** AC   **c)** AG

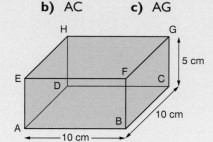

Q2 Find the area of the plane ADGF in this diagram.
Give your answer in surd form, expressing it in its lowest terms.

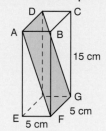

Q3 An electricity pylon XY is 30 m high. From a point S, due south of the pylon, the angle of elevation of the top of the pylon is 26° and from a point W, due west of the pylon, the angle of elevation is 32°. Find the distance WS.

Q4 The diagram represents a cuboid ABCDEFGH.
AB = 5 cm, BC = 7 cm,
AE = 3 cm.

Diagram not accurately drawn.

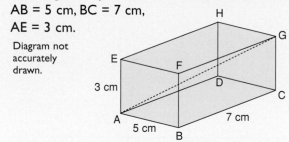

  a) Calculate the length of AG. Give your answer correct to three significant figures.

  b) Calculate the size of the angle between AG and the face ABCD. Give your answer correct to one decimal place.

Q5 The diagram represents a right pyramid. The base is a square of side 2x. The length of each of the slant edges is $8\sqrt{3}$ cm. The height of the pyramid is x cm. Calculate the value of x.

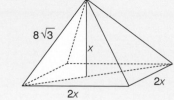

Diagram not drawn accurately

More questions on the CD ROM

Answers are on page 217.

39 MENSURATION

You will need to learn the formulas for the area of triangles and quadrilaterals, as well as the formulas for the circumference and area of a circle.

The following formulae will be given on the examination paper:

Volume of cone $= \frac{1}{3}\pi r^2 h$

Curved surface area of cone $= \pi r l$

Circumference of circle $= 2\pi r$

Area of circle $= \pi r^2$

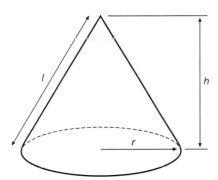

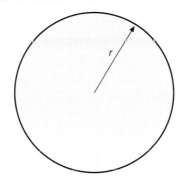

Volume of sphere $= \frac{4}{3}\pi r^3$

Surface area of sphere $= 4\pi r^2$

Volume of cylinder $= \pi r^2 h$

Curved surface area of cylinder $= 2\pi r h$

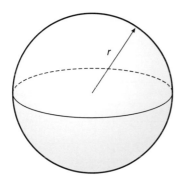

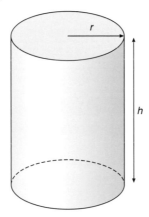

Volume of prism = area of cross section × length

Area of trapezium $= \frac{1}{2}(a + b)h$

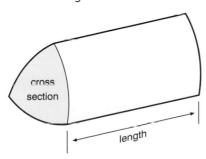

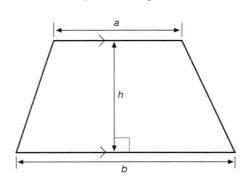

Worked example

Find the circumference and area of a circle of diameter 10 metres.

Circumference of a circle	$= \pi \times d$	Diameter of the circle $= d$
	$= \pi \times 10$	(without a calculator)
	$= 10\pi$ metres	Leaving the answer in terms of π.
	$= 31.4$ metres (3s.f.)	
Area of a circle	$= \pi \times r^2$	Area of a circle $= \pi r^2$
	$= \pi \times 5^2$	Radius $= \frac{1}{2} \times$ diameter
	$= 25\pi$ square metres (without a calculator)	
	$= 78.5$ square metres (3s.f.)	

Worked example

Find the volume of the prism with dimensions as shown.

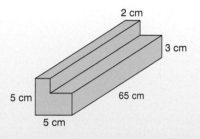

Volume of a prism = area of cross-section × length.

Area of cross-section $= 5 \times 3 + 2 \times 2$

$\qquad = 15 + 4$

$\qquad = 19$ cm^2

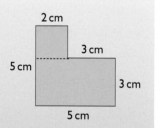

Volume of a prism = area of cross-section × length

$\qquad = 19 \times 65 \qquad$ Writing all lengths in the same units with 10 mm = 1 cm.

$\qquad = 1235$ cm^3

$\qquad = 1240$ cm^3 (3 s.f.)

Area and volume

Worked example

The dimensions of a cone are given in the diagram.

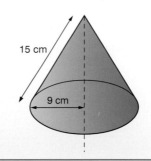

Calculate:

a) the area of the curved surface of the cone

b) the volume of the cone

giving your answers in terms of π.

a) Curved surface area of cone

$= \pi r l$

$= \pi \times 9 \times 15$ As radius = 9 cm and slant height = 15 cm.

$= \pi \times 135$

$= 135\pi$ cm^2

b) Volume of cone $= \frac{1}{3}\pi r^2 h$ Where h is the perpendicular height.

Using Pythagoras' theorem:

$l^2 = r^2 + h^2$

$15^2 = 9^2 + h^2$

$225 = 81 + h^2$

$h^2 = 225 - 81 = 144$

$h = 12$ Taking square roots on both sides.

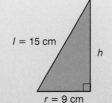

Volume of cone $= \frac{1}{3}\pi r^2 h$

$= \frac{1}{3} \times \pi \times 9^2 \times 12$

$= \pi \times 324$

$= 324\pi$ cm^3

Scale factors of length, area and volume

Two solids are **similar** if the ratios of their corresponding linear dimensions are equal.

In general:
the corresponding **areas of similar solids are proportional to the squares of their linear dimensions**

the corresponding **volumes of similar solids are proportional to the cubes of their linear dimensions.**

Buildings of different polygons

So if an object is enlarged by a scale factor of s:

lengths are multiplied by s

areas are multiplied by s^2

volumes are multiplied by s^3.

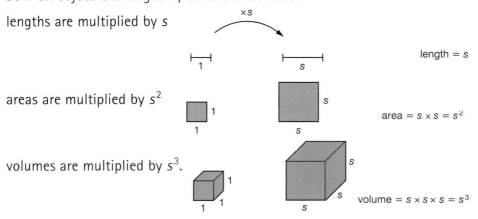

Worked example

The ratio of the surface areas of two similar cylinders is $16 : 25$. Calculate the ratio of their volumes and work out the volume of the larger cylinder given that the smaller cylinder has a volume of 540 mm^2.

If the ratio of the lengths is $\qquad x : y$

then the ratio of the areas is $\qquad x^2 : y^2$

and the ratio of the volumes is $\qquad x^3 : y^3$

Here $\qquad x^2 : y^2 \quad = \quad 16 : 25$

so $\qquad x : y \quad = \quad 4 : 5$

and $\qquad x^3 : y^3 \quad = \quad 4^3 : 5^3$

$\qquad\qquad\qquad\qquad = \quad 64 : 125$

So the ratio of the volumes is $64 : 125$.

$64 : 125 = 1 : \frac{125}{64}$ $\qquad$ Rewriting as an equivalent ratio.

$\qquad = 1 \times 540 : \frac{125}{64} \times 540$ $\qquad$ Rewriting as an equivalent ratio with 540 on the left-hand side.

$\qquad = 540 : 1054.6875$

The volume of larger cylinder is 1050 mm^3 (3 s.f.).

QUESTIONS

Q1 Calculate the areas of the shaded parts of the following shapes.

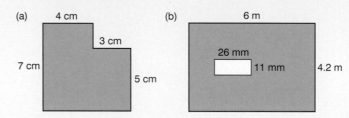

(a) 4 cm, 3 cm, 7 cm, 5 cm

(b) 6 m, 26 mm, 11 mm, 4.2 m

Q2 A circular disc is cut from a square of side 7 cm to leave a minimum amount of waste. What is the area of the waste and what is this as a percentage of the original area?

Q3 A circular pond has a surface area of 400 m^2. Calculate the diameter of the pond to an appropriate degree of accuracy.

Q4 A washer has an outside diameter of 12 mm and an inside diameter of 6 mm. Calculate the area of cross-section of the washer, leaving your answer in terms of π.

Q5 The diameter of a coin is 22 mm. The coin is 3 mm thick. Work out the volume of the coin, giving your answer in terms of π.

Q6 Calculate the volume of this triangular prism.

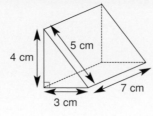

4 cm, 5 cm, 3 cm, 7 cm

Q7 The diagram shows a cylinder with a height of 10 cm and a radius of 4 cm.

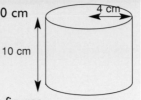

a) Calculate the volume of the cylinder.

Give your answer correct to three significant figures.

The length of a pencil is 13 cm. The pencil cannot be broken.

b) Show that the pencil cannot fit inside the cylinder.

Q8 The surface area of a sphere is 36π cm^2. Calculate the volume of the sphere, giving your answer in terms of π.

Q9 The corresponding lengths of two similar solids are in the ratio 3 : 5. What is the ratio of:
a) their surface areas
b) their volumes?

Q10 The curved surface area of a cone is 1165 mm^2. What is the curved surface area of a similar cone with height three times the height of the original cone?

Q11 X and Y are two geometrically similar shapes. The total surface area of shape X is 450 cm^2. The total surface area of shape Y is 800 cm^2. The volume of shape X is 1350 cm^3.

Calculate the volume of shape Y.

More questions on the CD ROM

Answers are on page 219.

40 ARC, SECTOR AND SEGMENT

Parts of a circle

Make sure you know the definitions of parts of the circle, given in the diagrams below. You will find the formulae and reminders in the rest of this session useful, too.

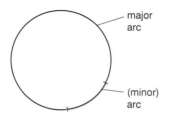

Arcs are parts of the circumference of the circle.

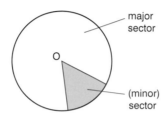

Sectors are parts of circles enclosed between two radii.

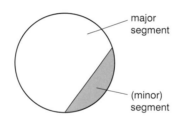

Segments are formed when chords divide the circle into different parts.

Arc

An arc is a part of the circumference of a circle.

$$\text{Arc length} = \frac{\text{angle subtended at centre}}{360} \times 2\pi r$$

$$\text{Arc length} = \frac{\theta}{360} \times 2\pi r$$

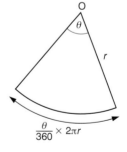

Worked example

Find the perimeter of this shape.

Perimeter = arc + radius + radius

$$= \frac{320}{360} \times 2\pi r + r + r$$

$$= \frac{320}{360} \times 2 \times \pi \times 4 + 4 + 4$$

$$= 30.340\,214$$

$$= 30.3 \text{ cm (3 s.f.)}$$

Sector

A sector is the area enclosed between an arc and two radii.

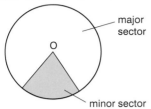

major sector

minor sector

$$\text{Sector area} = \frac{\text{angle subtended at centre}}{360} \times \pi r^2$$

$$\text{Sector area} = \frac{\theta}{360} \times \pi r^2$$

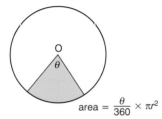

$\text{area} = \frac{\theta}{360} \times \pi r^2$

Segment

A segment is the area enclosed between an arc and a chord.

The following example illustrates how to find the area of a segment.

Worked example

Find the area of the segment shaded in this circle of radius 5 cm.

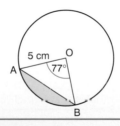

5 cm
A
77°
O
B

Area of segment = area of sector AOB − area of triangle AOB

Area of sector AOB $= \frac{77}{360} \times \pi r^2$

$\qquad = \frac{77}{360} \times \pi \times 5^2$

$\qquad = 16.798\ 794\ \text{cm}^2$

Area of triangle AOB $= \frac{1}{2}ab\sin\theta$

$\qquad = \frac{1}{2} \times 5 \times 5 \times \sin 77°$ Where a and b are equal to the radius of the circle.

$\qquad = 12.179\ 626\ \text{cm}^2$

Area of segment = area of sector AOB − area of triangle AOB

$\qquad = 16.798\ 794 - 12.179\ 626$

$\qquad = 4.619\ 168$

$\qquad = 4.62\ \text{cm}^2$ (3 s.f.)

QUESTIONS

Q1 Find the arc length and sector area for the circle below, giving your answers in terms of π.

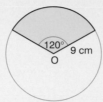

Q2 Calculate the segment area in this diagram.

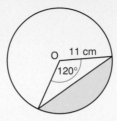

Q3 The arc length between two points A and B on the circumference of a circle is 8.6 cm. What is the angle subtended at the centre of the circle if the radius of the circle is 12 cm?

Q4 The sector of a circle is folded to make a cone of slant height 16 cm and base radius 12 cm. Calculate the arc length and the angle of the original sector.

Q5 The arc length of a sector of a circle is 15 cm. The radius of the circle is 12 cm. Work out the size of the angle, θ°, of the sector.

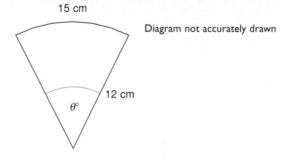

Diagram not accurately drawn

More questions on the CD ROM

Answers are on page 220.

41 SYMMETRY

What is symmetry?

There are two types of symmetry. A shape with **line symmetry** can be folded in half so that both sides match and a shape with **rotational symmetry** can be turned so that it looks the same in a different position.

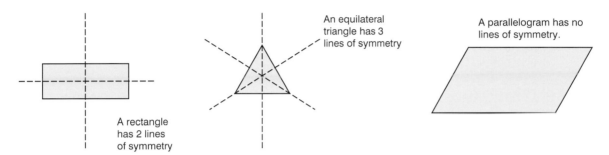

An equilateral triangle has 3 lines of symmetry

A parallelogram has no lines of symmetry.

A rectangle has 2 lines of symmetry

Line symmetry

When a shape can be folded so that one half fits exactly over the other half, the shape is **symmetrical** and the fold line is called a **line of symmetry**.

Tracing paper is useful when you need to identify lines of symmetry or to draw reflections. You can use tracing paper in the mathematics examination.

Plane of symmetry

A **plane of symmetry** divides a solid into two equal halves.

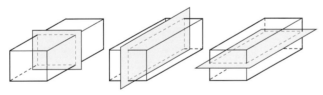

A cuboid has 3 planes of symmetry

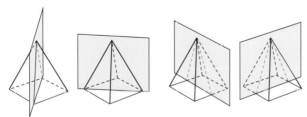

A square-based pyramid has 4 planes of symmetry

Symmetry seen in nature

Rotational symmetry

When a shape can be rotated about its centre to a new position, so that it fits exactly over its original position, then the shape has **rotational symmetry**.

The number of different positions tells you the **order** of rotational symmetry. An equilateral triangle has rotational symmetry of order 3.

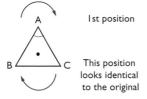

1st position

This position looks identical to the original

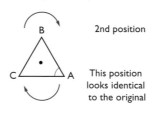

2nd position

This position looks identical to the original

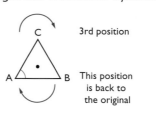

3rd position

This position is back to the original

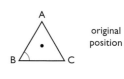

original position

Once again, tracing paper is useful when you need to identify rotational symmetry. You can use tracing paper in the mathematics examination.

QUESTIONS

Q1 Write down all of the letters below that have:
   a) a horizontal line of symmetry

   b) a vertical line of symmetry

   c) both horizontal and vertical lines of symmetry

   d) no line symmetry

   e) rotational symmetry of order 2.

A B C D E F G H I J K

Q2 How many planes of symmetry do the following solids have?
   a) regular triangular prism

   b) regular hexagonal prism

More questions on the CD ROM

Answers are on page 221.

42 TRANSFORMATIONS

What is a transformation?

If a point or a collection of points is moved from one position to another it undergoes a **transformation**. The **object** is the point or collection of points before the transformation and the **image** is the point or collection of points after the transformation.

The transformations you will need to know about include:

reflection   **enlargement**

rotation   **translation.**

Reflection

A reflection is a transformation in which any two corresponding points on the object and image are the same distance away from a fixed line (called the **line of symmetry** or **mirror line**).

You can define a reflection by giving the position of the line of symmetry.

The image of ABCDE is labelled A′B′C′D′E′ and corresponding pairs of points in the image and the object are **equidistant** from the line of symmetry.

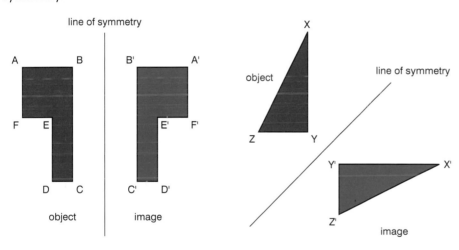

Rotation

A rotation is a transformation in which lines from any two corresponding points on the object and image make the same angle at a fixed point (called the **centre of rotation**).

You define a rotation by giving the position of the centre of rotation, along with the angle and direction of the rotation.

The diagram shows a rotation through 90° in an anticlockwise direction (called a rotation of $^{+}$90°) about the centre of rotation O.

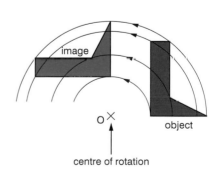

HINT

- An anticlockwise turn is described as positive and a clockwise turn is described as negative in mathematics.

+ ve   − ve

To find the centre of rotation you should join corresponding points on the object and image with straight lines and draw the **perpendicular bisectors** of these lines. The centre of rotation lies on the intersection of these bisectors.

To find the angle of rotation you should join corresponding points on the object and image to the centre of rotation. The angle between these lines is the angle of rotation.

Enlargement

An enlargement is a transformation in which the distance between a point on the image and a fixed point (called the **centre of enlargement**) is a factor of the distance between the corresponding point on the object and the fixed point.

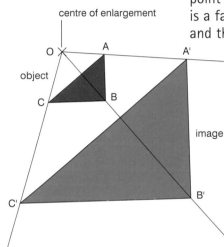

centre of enlargement

object

image

You can define an enlargement by giving the position of the centre of enlargement along with the factor (called the **scale factor**).

This diagram on the right shows an enlargement, scale factor 3, based on the centre of enlargement O.

OA = 1.1 cm   OA′ = 3 × 1.1 = 3.3 cm
OB = 1.7 cm   OB′ = 3 × 1.7 = 5.1 cm
OC = 1.35 cm OC′ = 3 × 1.35 = 4.15 cm

To find the centre of enlargement you join corresponding points – on the object and image – with straight lines. The centre of enlargement lies at the intersection of these straight lines.

You can find the scale factor (SF) of an enlargement as follows:

$$SF = \frac{\text{distance from the centre of a point on the image}}{\text{distance from the centre of the corresponding point on the object}}$$

$$\text{or } SF = \frac{\text{distance between two points on the image}}{\text{distance between two corresponding points on the object}}$$

A scale factor greater than 1 will enlarge the object.

A scale factor less than 1 will have the effect of reducing (or shrinking) the object.

Worked example

The points A(3, 8), B(7, 8), C(7, ⁻4) and D(3, ⁻2) are joined to form a trapezium which is enlarged, scale factor $\frac{1}{2}$, with (⁻5, ⁻6) as the centre of enlargement.
Draw ABCD on a graph and hence find A′B′C′D′.

The solution is shown on the right.

OA = 16.12 OA′ = $\frac{1}{2}$ × 16.12 = 8.06

OB = 18.44 OB′ = $\frac{1}{2}$ × 18.44 = 9.22

OC = 12.2   OC′ = $\frac{1}{2}$ × 12.2 = 6.1

OD = 8.94   OD′ = $\frac{1}{2}$ × 8.94 = 4.57

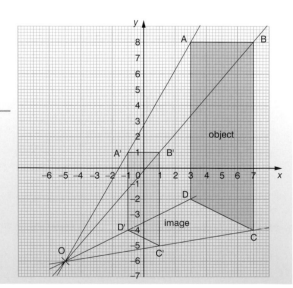

Translation

A translation is a transformation in which the distance and direction between any two corresponding points on the object and image are the same. You can define a translation by giving the distance and direction of the translation.

This translation can be described as a movement of five units to the left.

This translation can be described as a movement of seven units to the right and four units upwards.

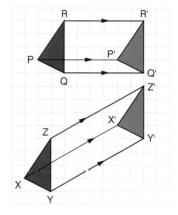

You can use **vector notation** to write a movement of seven units to the right and four units up as $\begin{pmatrix} 7 \\ 4 \end{pmatrix}$. In general, you can write:

$$\begin{pmatrix} a \\ b \end{pmatrix} \Rightarrow \quad \begin{array}{l} \text{number of units to the right in the positive } x\text{-direction} \\ \text{number of units upwards in the positive } y\text{-direction} \end{array}$$

Combinations of transformations

Combinations of the same type of transformation or combinations of different types of transformation can usually be described as a single transformation.

Worked example

If R is a reflection in the y-axis and T is a rotation about the origin of ⁻90°, show (on separate diagrams) the image of the triangle XYZ with vertices X(2, 1), Y(2, 5) and Z(4, 2), under the combined transformations:

a) R followed by T

b) T followed by R.

Which single transformation will return each of these combined transformations back to their original position?

a) The single transformation that will return A″B″C″ to ABC is a reflection in the line $y = {}^-x$.

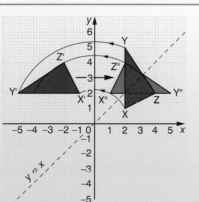

b) The single transformation that will return A″B″C″ to ABC is a reflection in the line $y = x$.

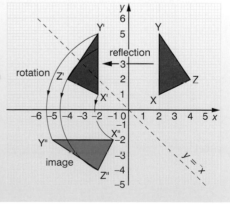

QUESTIONS

Q1 Find the images of the point (3, 4) reflected in the following lines.

a) $x = 0$ **b)** $y = 0$

c) $x = 2$ **d)** $y = x$

Q2 The triangle P has been drawn on the grid.

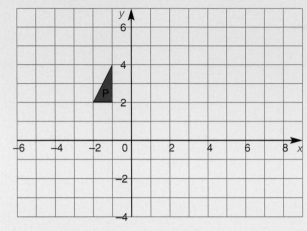

a) Reflect triangle P in the line $x = 2$. Label the image Q.

b) Rotate triangle Q through 180° about (2, 1). Label this image R.

Q3 Shape A is rotated 90° anticlockwise, centre (0, 1), to shape B.

Shape B is rotated 90° anticlockwise, centre (0, 1), to shape C.

Shape C is rotated 90° anticlockwise, centre (0, 1), to shape D.

a) Mark the position of shape D.

b) Describe the single transformation that takes shape C to shape A.

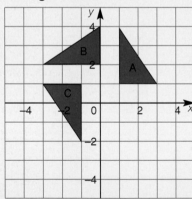

Q4 The triangle ABC with coordinates A(3, 1), B(4, 1) and C(4, 4) is reflected in the line
$y = x$ then the image undergoes a reflection in the line $x = 0$. The resulting triangle is then rotated through ⁻90° about (⁻1, 4) to A′B′C′. What single transformation would map ABC onto A′B′C′?

Q5 Draw the images of the following objects after an enlargement, scale factor $\frac{3}{2}$, with centre of enlargement O.

a)   **b)**

144

Q6 Draw the images of △ABC (triangle ABC) after the following translations.

a) $\begin{pmatrix} 3 \\ 2 \end{pmatrix}$ **b)** $\begin{pmatrix} ^-4 \\ 0 \end{pmatrix}$ **c)** $\begin{pmatrix} ^-2 \\ ^-5 \end{pmatrix}$

Write down the translation that will return the image to ABC in each case.

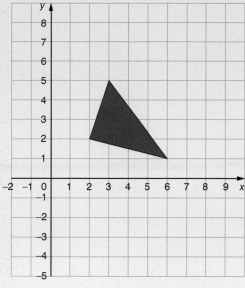

Q7 Find the centre of rotation and the angle of rotation for the following transformation.

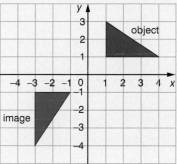

Answers are on page 221.

43 VECTORS AND VECTOR PROPERTIES

What is a vector?

A **vector** is a quantity which has magnitude (length) and direction (as indicated by the arrow).

Displacement, velocity, acceleration, force and **momentum** are all examples of vectors.

Representing a vector

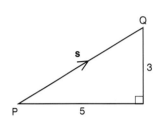

The vector on the left can be represented in a number of ways:

PQ or you can write $\overrightarrow{PQ}$

s or you can write s̲

as a column vector $\begin{pmatrix} 5 \\ 3 \end{pmatrix}$ as in Chapter 42, *Transformations*.

Equal vectors

Two vectors are equal if they have the same magnitude and direction, which means that they are the same length and they are parallel.

Components of a vector

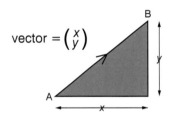

vector = $\begin{pmatrix} x \\ y \end{pmatrix}$

The components of a vector are usually described in terms of:

the number of units moved in the *x*-direction

the number of units moved in the *y*-direction.

These units are best expressed as a column vector, $\begin{pmatrix} \text{change in } x\text{-value} \\ \text{change in } y\text{-value} \end{pmatrix}$.

Adding and subtracting vectors

Vectors can be added or subtracted by placing them end to end, so that the arrows point in the same direction or lead on from one to the next.

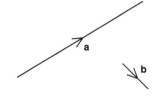
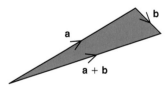
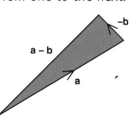

a − **b** is the same as **a** + (−**b**) where −**b** is the same as **b** but acts in the opposite direction.

An easier way to add vectors is to write them as column vectors so that if

$\mathbf{a} = \begin{pmatrix} 5 \\ 3 \end{pmatrix}$ and $\mathbf{b} = \begin{pmatrix} 1 \\ -1 \end{pmatrix}$ then:

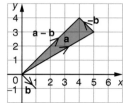 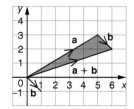

$\mathbf{a} + \mathbf{b} = \begin{pmatrix} 5 \\ 3 \end{pmatrix} + \begin{pmatrix} 1 \\ -1 \end{pmatrix} = \begin{pmatrix} 6 \\ 2 \end{pmatrix}$

$\mathbf{a} - \mathbf{b} = \begin{pmatrix} 5 \\ 3 \end{pmatrix} - \begin{pmatrix} 1 \\ -1 \end{pmatrix} = \begin{pmatrix} 4 \\ 4 \end{pmatrix}$

Magnitude of a vector

You can use Pythagoras' theorem to find the magnitude (length) of a vector.

Suppose that $\overrightarrow{AB} = \begin{pmatrix} x \\ y \end{pmatrix}$.

Then the length of the vector $\overrightarrow{AB} = \sqrt{x^2 + y^2}$ and you can write

$|\overrightarrow{AB}| = \sqrt{x^2 + y^2}$

where the two vertical lines stand for 'magnitude of' or 'length of'.

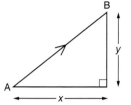

Worked example

Given that $\mathbf{p} = \begin{pmatrix} 3 \\ 4 \end{pmatrix}$ and $\mathbf{q} = \begin{pmatrix} 2 \\ -1 \end{pmatrix}$, find $\mathbf{p} + \mathbf{q}$ and $|\mathbf{p} + \mathbf{q}|$.

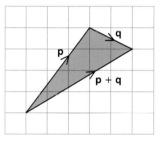

$\mathbf{p} + \mathbf{q} = \begin{pmatrix} 3 \\ 4 \end{pmatrix} + \begin{pmatrix} 2 \\ -1 \end{pmatrix}$

$\qquad = \begin{pmatrix} 5 \\ 3 \end{pmatrix}$

$|\mathbf{p} + \mathbf{q}| = \sqrt{5^2 + 3^2}$

$\qquad\quad = \sqrt{34}$ units

Multiplication of a vector

Vectors cannot be multiplied by other vectors but they can be multiplied by a constant (sometimes called **scalar multiplication**).

Worked example

Given that $\mathbf{p} = \begin{pmatrix} 3 \\ 4 \end{pmatrix}$ and $\mathbf{q} = \begin{pmatrix} 2 \\ -1 \end{pmatrix}$, find:

a) 2p   **b)** 2p − 3q.

a) $2\mathbf{p} = 2 \times \begin{pmatrix} 3 \\ 4 \end{pmatrix} = \begin{pmatrix} 6 \\ 8 \end{pmatrix}$

b) $2\mathbf{p} - 3\mathbf{q} = 2 \times \begin{pmatrix} 3 \\ 4 \end{pmatrix} - 3 \times \begin{pmatrix} 2 \\ -1 \end{pmatrix}$

$\qquad\qquad = \begin{pmatrix} 6 \\ 8 \end{pmatrix} - \begin{pmatrix} 6 \\ -3 \end{pmatrix}$

$\qquad\qquad = \begin{pmatrix} 0 \\ 11 \end{pmatrix}$

Vectors in geometry

Vectors are often used to prove geometrical theorems.

Worked example

In the triangle PQR, X and Y are the midpoints of PQ and PR respectively.

Given that $\overrightarrow{XP} = \mathbf{a}$ and $\overrightarrow{PY} = \mathbf{b}$ show that QR = 2XY and QR is parallel to XY.

From the diagram:

$\overrightarrow{XY} = \overrightarrow{XP} + \overrightarrow{PY}$ so $\overrightarrow{XP} = \mathbf{a} + \mathbf{b}$

As X is the midpoint of QP then $\overrightarrow{QX} = \overrightarrow{XP}$.

Similarly as Y is the midpoint of PR then $\overrightarrow{PY} = \overrightarrow{YR}$.

From the diagram:

$\overrightarrow{QR} = \overrightarrow{QP} + \overrightarrow{PR}$

$\overrightarrow{QR} = 2\mathbf{a} + 2\mathbf{b}$ As $\overrightarrow{QP} = \overrightarrow{QX} + \overrightarrow{XP} = 2\mathbf{a}$ and $\overrightarrow{PR} = \overrightarrow{PY} + \overrightarrow{YR} = 2\mathbf{b}$.

$\overrightarrow{QR} = 2(\mathbf{a} + \mathbf{b}) = 2\overrightarrow{XY}$ As $\overrightarrow{XY} = \mathbf{a} + \mathbf{b}$ above.

This tells you that the magnitude of $\overrightarrow{QR}$ is twice the magnitude of $\overrightarrow{XY}$ so that QR = 2XY. Since $\overrightarrow{QR}$ is a multiple of $\overrightarrow{XY}$ then QR and XY are in the same direction and must, therefore be parallel.

QUESTIONS

Q1 The diagram shows a series of parallel lines with $\overrightarrow{AB} = \mathbf{a}$ and $\overrightarrow{AE} = \mathbf{b}$.
Write down the following in terms of **a** and **b**.

a) $\overrightarrow{AC}$ b) $\overrightarrow{AM}$

c) $\overrightarrow{AF}$ d) $\overrightarrow{AK}$

e) $\overrightarrow{GA}$ f) $\overrightarrow{PE}$

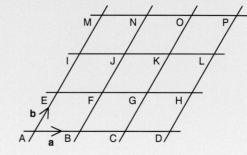

Q2 $\overrightarrow{AB} = \begin{pmatrix} 3 \\ 4 \end{pmatrix}$ and $\overrightarrow{BC} = \begin{pmatrix} 5 \\ -1 \end{pmatrix}$.
Find:

a) $|\overrightarrow{AB}|$ b) $|\overrightarrow{BC}|$

c) $|\overrightarrow{AC}|$.

Q3 ABCDEF is a regular hexagon with centre O,
$\overrightarrow{AB} = \mathbf{a}$ and $\overrightarrow{BC} = \mathbf{b}$.
Find:
a) $\overrightarrow{AC}$ b) $\overrightarrow{AO}$ c) $\overrightarrow{OB}$ d) $\overrightarrow{AD}$.

What can you say about the quadrilateral ACDF?
Give reasons for your answer.

Q4 OABC is a parallelogram.
P is the point on AC such that AP = $\frac{2}{3}$AC.
$\overrightarrow{OA}$ = 6**a**, $\overrightarrow{OC}$ = 6**c**.

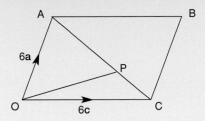

a) Find the vector $\overrightarrow{OP}$. Give your answer in terms of **a** and **c**.

The midpoint of CB is M.

b) Prove that OPM is a straight line.

More questions
on the CD ROM

Answers are on page 222.

Intra-regional trade

Extra-regional trade
... with Asia
... with other regions

Exports to Asia
Imports from Asia

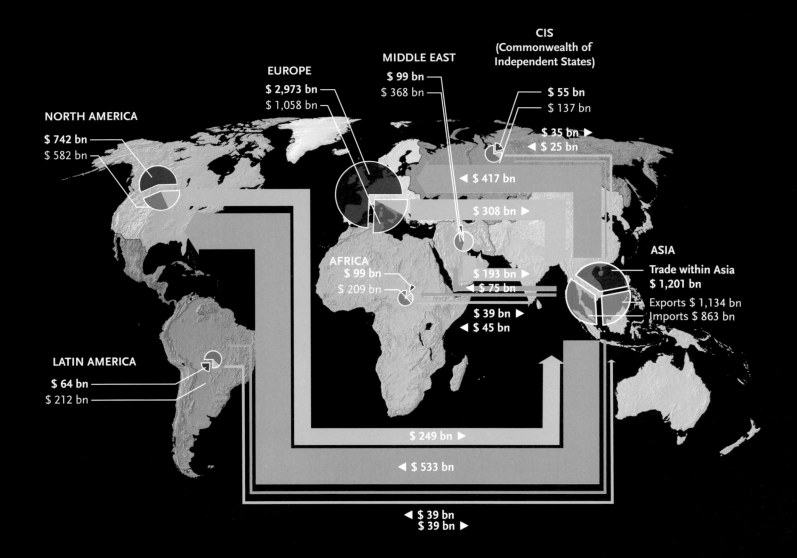

CIS
(Commonwealth of
Independent States)
$ 55 bn
$ 137 bn
$ 35 bn ▶
◀ $ 25 bn

MIDDLE EAST
$ 99 bn
$ 368 bn

EUROPE
$ 2,973 bn
$ 1,058 bn

NORTH AMERICA
$ 742 bn
$ 582 bn

◀ $ 417 bn

$ 308 bn ▶

ASIA
Trade within Asia
$ 1,201 bn

Exports $ 1,134 bn
Imports $ 863 bn

AFRICA
$ 99 bn
$ 209 bn

$ 193 bn ▶
◀ $ 75 bn

$ 39 bn ▶
◀ $ 45 bn

LATIN AMERICA
$ 64 bn
$ 212 bn

$ 249 bn ▶

◀ $ 533 bn

◀ $ 39 bn
$ 39 bn ▶

Numbers telling tales

Numbers on their own are just numbers. But put numbers in context and they start to mean something.
A company's annual accounts may seem lacklustre, but set in the context of a poorly performing industry
sector, an ailing national economy or a global recession, they might tell a different story. It pays to see the
bigger picture, to know the background story.

STATISTICS

44 COLLECTING AND REPRESENTING DATA

How should I represent data?

Representing data is an important aspect of statistics and data handling. You must always make sure that the way you choose to represent the data is appropriate to the data you need to present. This session describes a variety of different representations with which you will need to be familiar.

Classifying data

A group of children shows continuous variation

Data that can take any values within a given range is called **continuous** data. This includes heights, temperatures, lengths and mass.

Data that can only take particular values (such as whole or half numbers) is called **discrete** data. This includes numbers of children, separate colours and shoe sizes.

Quantitative data can only take numerical values such as length, mass, capacity or temperature.

Qualitative (or **categorical**) data includes qualities such as colour, taste, shade or touch.

Raw data and tally charts

Raw data is information that has been collected but has not yet been organised in any way. A **tally chart** is often used to collect data. A tally chart consists of a series of tallies grouped into fives, as shown below.

Tallies	Frequency	
IIII	= 4	
IIII	= 5	
IIII I	= 6	
IIII II	= 7	
IIII IIII	= 10	etc.

Notice that to construct a tally chart, you make one stroke for every item of data counted, and draw every fifth stroke through the preceding four.

This makes it easy to count how many times each data item occurs. The **frequency** of an item of data is the number or times it occurs.

Frequency distributions

You can easily draw a **frequency distribution** from a tally chart by totalling the tallies to find the frequencies. In some circumstances, it may be helpful to group the data and produce a grouped frequency distribution.

Worked example

The raw data gives the times (in minutes) for 20 pupils to complete a test.
Construct a grouped frequency distribution using class intervals 15–17, 18–20, 21–23 and 24–26.

| 23 | 23 | 26 | 22 | 19 | 23 | 22 | 24 | 20 | 21 |
| 25 | 15 | 22 | 24 | 20 | 17 | 21 | 22 | 24 | 18 |

The grouped frequency distribution, with the given class intervals, is shown below.

Times	Tallies	Frequency
15–17	||	2
18–20	||||	4
21–23	卌 ||||	9
24–26	卌	5

Pictograms

A **pictogram** (or **pictograph** or **ideograph**) is a simple way of representing data. The frequency is indicated by a number of identical pictures. When using a pictogram, remember to include a key to explain what the individual pictures represent, as well as giving the diagram an overall title. You may also need to use a symbol that can easily be divided into halves, quarters, tenths and so on.

Drink	Frequency
Cola	10
Sparkling water	13
Lemonade	4
Iced tea	8
Other	3

Worked example

The frequency distribution on the left shows the number of different drinks purchased from a vending machine. Show this information as a pictogram.

The pictogram looks like this.

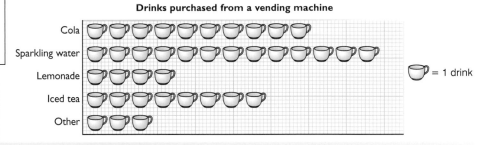

Drinks purchased from a vending machine

Alternatively, you could allow one cup to stand for two drinks.

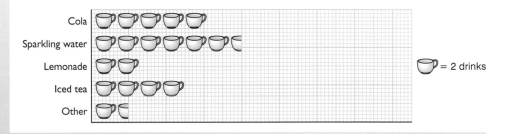

Bar charts

A **bar chart** is a common way of representing data. The frequencies of the data items are indicated by vertical or horizontal bars, all with the same width. When using a bar chart, you must remember to label the axes clearly and give the diagram a title to explain what it represents.

Worked example

The bar chart shows the average price for cars in a number of trade magazines.

a) What was the average price for a car in the *What Car?* magazine?

b) Which magazine had the lowest average price for a car?

c) In which two magazines were the average prices the closest?

d) What is the biggest difference between average prices in the trade magazines?

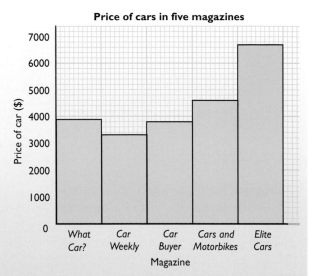

From the graph:

a) The average price for a car in the *What Car?* magazine is $3900.

b) The *Car Weekly* had the lowest average price for a car.

c) The two magazines where the average prices were the closest are *What Car?* and *Car Buyer*.

d) The biggest difference between average prices is $3400 ($6700 − $3300).

Line graphs

A **line graph** is another way of representing data. The frequencies are plotted at suitable points and joined by a series of straight lines. Once again, you must remember to label the axes clearly and give the diagram a title to explain what it represents.

Worked example

The information in the table shows the temperatures of a patient over a period of seven hours.

a) Draw a line graph to show this data.

b) What was the maximum recorded temperature?

c) Use your graph to find an estimate of the patient's temperature at 0930.

d) Explain why your answers in parts (b) and (c) are only approximate.

Time	Temperature (°F)
0600	102.5
0700	102.8
0800	101.5
0900	100.2
1000	99.0
1100	98.8
1200	98.6

a) This line graph shows the data.

b) The maximum temperature recorded was 102.8 °F at 0700.

c) To find the patient's temperature at 0930 you read off the value at 0930.

The patient's temperature at 0930 was 99.6 °F.

d) The answers in parts (b) and (c) are only approximate as the temperature might not necessarily increase or decrease uniformly between the times at which the temperatures were taken.

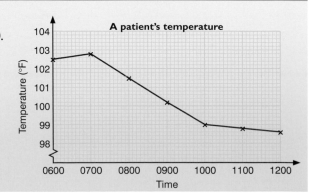

Frequency polygons

A **frequency polygon** can be drawn from a bar chart (or histogram), by joining the midpoints of the tops of consecutive bars, with straight lines, to form a polygon. The lines should be extended to the horizontal axis on both sides, so that the area under the frequency polygon is the same as the area under the bar chart (or histogram).

HINT

• The frequency polygon can be drawn without the bar chart, by plotting the frequencies at the midpoints of each interval.

Worked example

The frequency distribution shows the heights of 50 plants, measured to the nearest centimetre.

Draw a frequency polygon to show this information.

Height (cm)	Frequency
6–10	1
11–15	3
16–20	7
21–25	9
26–30	7
31–35	10
36–40	7
41–45	5
46–50	1

The length is continuous and you can draw a bar chart (or histogram) of the information as usual. You can obtain the frequency polygon by joining up the midpoints of the tops of the bars, in order, with straight lines.

The lines should be extended to the horizontal axis on each side, as shown.

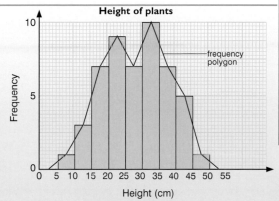

Pie charts

A **pie chart** is another common way of representing data where the frequency is represented by the angles (or areas) of the sectors of a circle. When using a pie chart, you must remember to label each of the sectors clearly and give the diagram a title to explain what it represents.

The following worked examples are given to illustrate the construction of a pie chart.

Worked example

In a survey, 180 people were asked which TV channel they watched the most the previous evening. The answers to the survey are given in the table.

Construct a pie chart to show this information.

Channel	Frequency
CNN	58
MTV	20
BBC World	42
Fox	21
Al-Jazeera	11
Other	18
Not watching	10

The pie chart needs to be drawn to represent 180 people. There are 360° in a full circle so each person will be represented by $\frac{360°}{180} = 2°$ of the pie chart.

Channel	Frequency	Angle
CNN	58	$58 \times 2° = 116°$
MTV	20	$20 \times 2° = 40°$
BBC World	42	$42 \times 2° = 84°$
Fox	21	$21 \times 2° = 42°$
Al-Jazeera	11	$11 \times 2° = 22°$
Other	18	$18 \times 2° = 36°$
Not watching	10	$10 \times 2° = 20°$
		$\overline{\qquad 360°}$

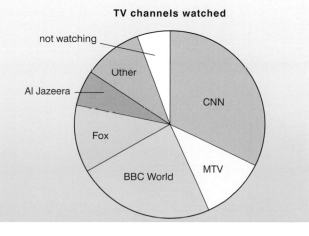

QUESTIONS

Q1 The table shows the sales of different coloured socks in a department store.

Show this information as:

a) a pictogram

b) a bar chart.

Colour	Frequency
White	18
Black	13
Blue	10
Brown	6
Other	7

Q2 The weight of a child is recorded at birth and at the end of each month as shown in the table.

Age (months)	0	1	2	3	4	5
Weight (pounds)	8	9.5	10.8	12.4	13.8	15.2

Draw a line graph to represent this information.

Q3 The lengths of 35 bolts are measured and recorded in this table.

Length (mm)	20–25	25–30	30–35	35–40	40–45
Frequency	3	8	15	7	2

Draw a frequency polygon to show this information.

Q4 250 students at a college were asked about the courses they are following.
Their responses were as follows.

Business studies 106
Hotel managements 42
Computer skills 86
Others 16

Construct the pie chart to show the different courses.

Q5 This pie chart shows how 100 city workers travelled to work one day.

a) Which method of transport was the most popular?

b) Which method of transport was the least popular?

c) What angle is represented by the 'cycle' sector?

Twice as many travelled to work by bus as by car.

d) How many city workers travelled to work by bus?

e) How many city workers travelled to work by car?

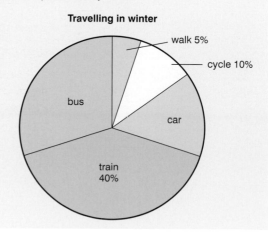

Travelling in winter

walk 5%
cycle 10%
bus
car
train 40%

More questions on the CD ROM

Answers are on page 223.

45 Histograms – unequal class intervals

What are histograms?

Histograms are like bar charts except that it is the *area* of each bar that represents the frequency, rather than the *length* or *height*.

Using histograms

You should draw the bars on the horizontal axis at the class boundaries and the area of the bars should be proportional to the frequency, i.e.

class width × height = frequency

so height = $\dfrac{\text{frequency}}{\text{class width}}$

and the height is referred to as the **frequency density**. This means that the vertical axis of a histogram should be labelled frequency density where:

frequency density = $\dfrac{\text{frequency}}{\text{class width}}$

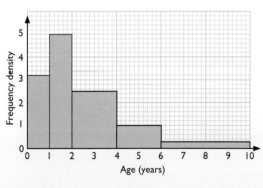

Worked example

The histogram shows the ages of cars in an office car park.

a) How many cars in the sample were from two to four years old?

b) How many cars were there in the sample altogether?

Remember that the frequency is represented by the area and is found by multiplying the frequency density (on the vertical axis) by the class width (on the horizontal axis).

a) The number of cars that are from two to four years old
= frequency density × class width
= 2.5 × 2
= 5

b) The total number of cars can be calculated using the above method for each class width.

Age (years)	0–1	1–2	2–4	4–6	6–10
Frequency density	3	5	2.5	1	0.25
Frequency	3 × 1 = 3	5 × 1 = 5	2.5 × 2 = 5	1 × 2 = 2	0.25 × 4 = 1

Frequency = frequency density × class width

The number of cars in the sample = total frequency
= 3 + 5 + 5 + 2 + 1
= 16

Worked example

The frequency distribution below shows the height of 50 bushes, measured to the nearest centimetre.

Height (cm)	Frequency
10–14	3
15–19	6
20–24	7
25–29	9
30–39	12
40–49	8
50–74	4
75–99	1

Draw a histogram to represent this information.

First draw up a table to calculate the respective frequency densities, and then draw the histogram.

Since the height is measured to the nearest centimetre, the 10–14 interval extends from 9.5 to 14.5, giving it a width of 5 cm, and so on.

Height (cm)	Frequency	Class width	Frequency density
10–14	3	5	3 ÷ 5 = 0.6
15–19	6	5	6 ÷ 5 = 1.2
20–24	7	5	7 ÷ 5 = 1.4
25–29	9	5	9 ÷ 5 = 1.8
30–39	12	10	12 ÷ 10 = 1.2
40–49	8	10	8 ÷ 10 = 0.8
50–74	4	25	4 ÷ 25 = 0.16
75–99	1	25	1 ÷ 25 = 0.04

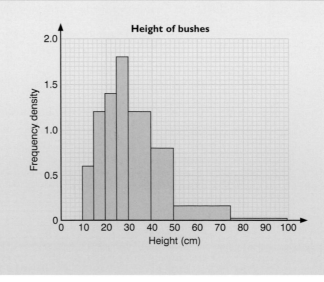

Frequency polygons

Frequency polygons were first discussed in Chapter 44 *Collecting and presenting data.* A frequency polygon can be drawn from a histogram by joining the midpoints of the tops of the bars and extending the lines to the horizontal axis on either side. The area under the frequency polygon should be the same as the area under the histogram.

Worked example

The heights of people queuing for a fairground ride were as shown in the table.

Height (inches)	Frequency
35 up to 45	8
45 up to 55	13
55 up to 60	20
60 up to 65	29
65 up to 70	23
70 up to 90	11

Draw a frequency polygon to represent this information.

First draw up a table to calculate the respective frequency densities.

Height (inches)	Frequency	Class width	Frequency density
35 up to 45	8	10	0.8
45 up to 55	13	10	1.3
55 up to 60	20	5	4
60 up to 65	29	5	5.8
65 up to 70	23	5	4.6
70 up to 90	11	20	0.55

Then draw the histogram and frequency polygon.

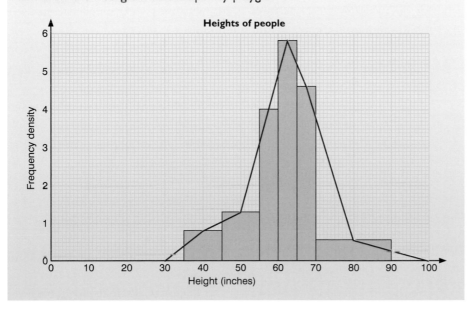

QUESTIONS

Q1 The following table shows the lengths of time taken by 120 workers to travel home one evening.

Time (t minutes)	Frequency
$0 \leqslant t < 10$	8
$10 \leqslant t < 20$	17
$20 \leqslant t < 30$	23
$30 \leqslant t < 60$	42
$60 \leqslant t < 90$	18
$90 \leqslant t < 120$	9
$120 \leqslant t < 240$	3

Draw a histogram to represent these data.

Q2 The following information shows the distance travelled by 100 salespeople one week.

The distance is measured in miles to the nearest mile.

Distance (miles)	Frequency
0–500	3
501–1000	19
1001–2000	27
2001–4000	36
4001–6000	15

Use this information to construct:

a) a histogram

b) a frequency polygon.

Q3 The distance travelled by 50 lecturers to work is shown in the histogram below.

Use the information in the histogram to complete the following table.

Distance (miles)	0–	5–	10–	15–	20–	30–50
Number of lecturers						

Q4 The histogram gives information about the times, in minutes, 135 students spent on the Internet last night.

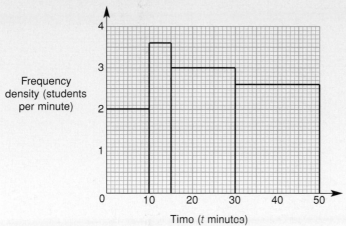

Frequency density (students per minute)

Timo (*t* minutos)

Use the histogram to complete the table.

Time (*t* minutes)	Frequency
$0 < t \leqslant 10$ $10 < t \leqslant 15$ $15 < t \leqslant 30$ $30 < t \leqslant 50$	
Total	135

Answers are on page 224.

More questions on the CD ROM

46 MEASURES OF CENTRAL TENDENCY

What does it mean?

Measures of central tendency are more often referred to as **measures of average**. You will need to understand the differences between the **mode**, **median** and **mean**, and be able to find them, for the examination.

Mode of a distribution

The **mode** of a distribution is the value that occurs most frequently. If there are two modes then the distribution is called **bimodal**. If there are more than two modes then the distribution is called **multimodal**.

Worked example
Find the mode of the following distribution.

8, 6, 7, 4, 9, 8, 8, 6, 7, 6, 8

The number 4 occurs 1 time.

The number 5 occurs 0 times.

The number 6 occurs 3 times.

The number 7 occurs 2 times.

The number 8 occurs 4 times.

The number 9 occurs 1 time.

The number 8 occurs the most frequently so the mode is 8.

MODE OF A FREQUENCY DISTRIBUTION

The mode of frequency distribution is the value that has the highest frequency.

Worked example
Find the mode of this frequency distribution.

Value	Frequency
4	1
5	0
6	3
7	2
8	4
9	1

Mode of frequency distribution. ——→ 8

The mode of the frequency distribution is 8.

MODE OF A GROUPED FREQUENCY DISTRIBUTION

The mode of a grouped frequency distribution has little meaning, although it is possible to identify a **modal group**.

Worked example

Find the modal group of this grouped frequency distribution.

Weight (grams)	Frequency
15–25	11
25–35	17
35–45	23
45–55	16
55–65	10

Modal group. ⟶ 35–45

The modal group of the grouped frequency distribution is 35–45.

Median of a distribution

The **median** of a distribution is the middle value when the values are arranged in order. Where there are two middle values (i.e. for an even number of values) then you add the two numbers and divide by 2.

Worked example

Find the median of each of the following distributions.

a) 8, 6, 7, 4, 9, 8, 8, 6, 7, 6, 8

b) 8, 6, 7, 4, 9, 8, 8, 6, 7, 6, 8, 10

> **HINT**
>
> - If there are n values in the distribution then the median position is given by $\frac{1}{2}(n + 1)$.

a) For the distribution: 8, 6, 7, 4, 9, 8, 8, 6, 7, 6, 8

Rearrange in order: 4, 6, 6, 6, 7, 7, 8, 8, 8, 8, 9

The median position is given by $\frac{1}{2}(n + 1) = \frac{1}{2}(11 + 1) = $ 6th value.

4, 6, 6, 6, 7, ⑦, 8, 8, 8, 8, 9

So the median is 7.

b) For the distribution: 8, 6, 7, 4, 9, 8, 8, 6, 7, 6, 8, 10

Rearrange in order: 4, 6, 6, 6, 7, 7, 8, 8, 8, 8, 9, 10

The median position is given by $\frac{1}{2}(n + 1) = \frac{1}{2}(12 + 1)$

$$= 6\frac{1}{2}\text{th value}$$

(i.e. between the 6th and 7th values).

4, 6, 6, 6, 7, ⑦, 8, 8, 8, 8, 9, 10

So the median is $\frac{1}{2}(7 + 8) = 7\frac{1}{2}$.

MEDIAN OF A FREQUENCY DISTRIBUTION

To find the median of a frequency distribution you need to work out the **cumulative frequency distribution**, as shown in the next example.

Worked example

Find the median of the frequency distribution in this table on the right.

Value	Frequency
4	1
5	0
6	3
7	2
8	4
9	1

To find the median of a frequency distribution you can work out the cumulative frequency like this.

From the cumulative frequency you can see that the middle value (i.e. the 6th value) occurs at 7.

Value	Frequency	Cumulative frequency
4	1	1
5	0	1
6	3	4
7	2	6
8	4	10
9	1	11

To find the median of a group frequency distribution you need to draw up a cumulative frequency diagram. Cumulative frequency diagrams are considered fully in Chapter 47, *Measures of spread and cumulative frequency diagrams*.

Mean of a distribution

The **mean** (or **arithmetic mean**) of a distribution is found by summing the values of the distribution and dividing by the number of values.

Worked example

Find the mean of the following distribution.

8, 6, 7, 4, 9, 8, 8, 6, 7, 6, 8

Add the values of the distribution and dividing by the number of values.

$$\text{Mean} = \frac{8 + 6 + 7 + 4 + 9 + 8 + 8 + 6 + 7 + 6 + 8}{11} = \frac{77}{11} = 7$$

The definition for the mean is often written as:

$$\text{mean} = \frac{\text{sum of the values}}{\text{number of values}} \quad \text{or} \quad \text{mean} = \frac{\Sigma \text{ values}}{\text{number of values}}$$

MEAN OF A FREQUENCY DISTRIBUTION

You can find the mean of a frequency distribution by summing the values of the distribution and dividing by the number of values.

$$\text{Mean} = \frac{\text{sum of the values}}{\text{number of values}}$$

For a frequency distribution the sum of the values is equal to the sum of the products (frequency × value) or Σfx.

The number of values is the sum of the frequencies Σf. So the mean is $\frac{\Sigma fx}{\Sigma f}$

Worked example

Find the mean of this frequency distribution.

Value x	Frequency f	Frequency × value fx
4	1	1 × 4 = 4
5	0	0 × 5 = 0
6	3	3 × 6 = 18
7	2	2 × 7 = 14
8	4	4 × 8 = 32
9	1	1 × 9 = 9
	$\Sigma f = 11$	$\Sigma fx = 77$

Mean for the frequency distribution $= \dfrac{\Sigma fx}{\Sigma f} = \dfrac{77}{11} = 7$ (as before)

Mean of a grouped frequency distribution

You can find the mean of a grouped frequency distribution in the same way as for a frequency distribution, using the **mid-interval values** (or midpoints) as representative of the interval.

Worked example

The following table shows the heights of trees growing in a nursery. Calculate an estimate of the mean height of the trees.

Height (cm)	15–20	20–30	30–40	40–50	50–60	60–70	70–80
Frequency	8	4	5	11	17	2	1

Height	Mid-interval value x	Frequency f	Frequency × mid-interval value fx
15–20	17.5	8	8 × 17.5 = 140
20–30	25	4	4 × 25 = 100
30–40	35	5	5 × 35 = 175
40–50	45	11	11 × 45 = 495
50–60	55	17	17 × 55 = 935
60–70	65	2	2 × 65 = 130
70–80	75	1	1 × 75 = 75
		$\Sigma f = 48$	$\Sigma fx = 2050$

For the grouped frequency distribution:

mean $= \dfrac{\Sigma fx}{\Sigma f} = \dfrac{2050}{48} = 42.708\,333\,3 = 43$ cm to an appropriate degree of accuracy.

HINT

- The mid-interval values are used as an estimate of the particular interval so that the final answer will not be exact but will be an 'estimate of the mean'.
- The mid-interval value is found by taking the mean of the upper and lower class boundaries – See Chapter 47, *Measures of spread*, for definitions.

An answer of 43 cm is appropriate, bearing in mind the accuracy of the original data and the inaccuracies resulting from the use of the mid-interval values as an estimate of the particular interval.

QUESTIONS

Q1 Find the mode of the following pictorial representations.

a)

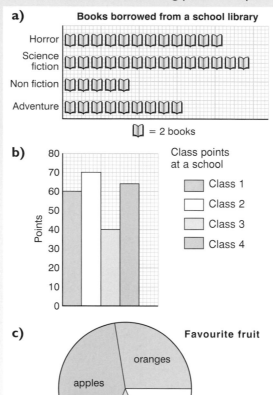

Books borrowed from a school library

Horror · Science fiction · Non fiction · Adventure

📖 = 2 books

b)

Points / Class points at a school

Class 1 · Class 2 · Class 3 · Class 4

c)

Favourite fruit

oranges · apples · pears · grapes

Q2 Find the median of the following frequency distribution which shows the number of goals scored in 34 football matches.

Number of goals	Frequency
0	4
1	8
2	11
3	7
4	3
5	0
6	1

Q3 Find the mean of the following data.

Age (years)	17	18	19	20	21
Frequency	23	13	4	0	1

Q4 Kemal records the time intervals, in minutes, between successive aircraft passing over his house. The table shows the results.

Time (t minutes)	Frequency
$0 < t \leqslant 4$	2
$4 < t \leqslant 8$	1
$8 < t \leqslant 12$	3
$12 < t \leqslant 16$	10
$16 < t \leqslant 20$	15

a) Calculate the class interval in which the median lies.

Kemal claims that his results show that the mean time is 10 minutes.

b) Is Kemal correct? Explain briefly your answer.

Q5 Calculate an estimate of the mean for this distribution.

Weight (kg)	0–10	10–20	20–30	30–40	40–50	50–60
Frequency	11	18	16	11	5	2

Q6 The amount of money spent by customers in a restaurant is shown in this table.

Amount ($)	Frequency
0 and less than 5	12
5 and less than 10	15
10 and less than 15	8
15 and less than 20	7
20 and less than 25	3

Use the information to calculate an estimate of the mean.

More questions on the CD ROM

Answers are on page 225.

47 MEASURES OF SPREAD AND CUMULATIVE FREQUENCY DIAGRAMS

What are measures of spread?

The measure of spread gives a measure of how spread out the data values are. For the examination you need to be familiar with the **range** and **interquartile range**.

The range

You can find the **range** of a distribution by working out the difference between the greatest value and least value. You should always give the range as a single value.

Worked example

The insurance premiums paid by eleven households are listed below.

$340 $355 $400 $320 $380 $320 $632 $365 $340 $380 $370

Calculate the mean and the range.

$$\text{Mean} = \frac{\$340 + \$355 + \$400 + \$320 + \$380 + \$320 + \$632 + \$365 + \$340 + \$380 + \$370}{11}$$

$$\text{Mean} = \frac{4202}{11}$$

$$= \$382$$

The mean of **$382** is deceptive as a measure of central tendency because it is affected by the value of $632 – this type of value is sometimes called an **extreme value**.

Greatest value = $632

Least value = $320

Range = greatest value − least value

$$= \$632 - \$320$$

$$= \$312$$

Similarly, the range of $312 is deceptive as a measure of spread because again, it is also affected by the value of $632.

Interquartile range

Although the range is affected by extreme values, the **interquartile range** considers only the middle 50% of the distribution.

You can find the interquartile range by dividing the data into four parts or **quartiles** and working out the difference between the upper quartile and the lower quartile, as shown in the following worked example.

Worked example

The insurance premiums paid by eleven households are listed below.

$340 $355 $400 $320 $380 $320 $632 $365 $340 $380 $370

Calculate the interquartile range.

Arranging the data in order and considering the middle 50%:

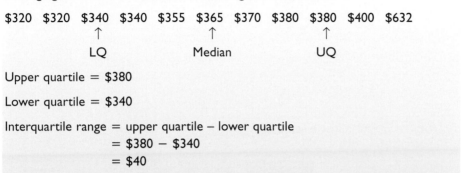

Upper quartile = $380

Lower quartile = $340

Interquartile range = upper quartile − lower quartile
$$= \$380 - \$340$$
$$= \$40$$

You have already seen that if there are n values in the distribution then the median position is given by $\frac{1}{2}(n + 1)$.

The lower quartile position is given by $\frac{1}{4}n$ and the upper quartile position is given by $\frac{3}{4}n$. Once these are calculated, if the answers are decimal, then always round up to the nearest whole number.

Cumulative frequency diagrams

Cumulative frequency diagrams can be used to find the median and the quartiles of a variety of distributions, including grouped frequency distributions. To find the cumulative frequency you find the accumulated totals and plot them on the cumulative frequency diagram (or **ogive**), then join them with a smooth curve.

CLASS LIMITS

Class limits are the values given in each of the individual groups (or **class intervals**). For the class interval 1–3, in the example below, the class limits are 1 and 3 (where the **lower class limit** is 1 and the **upper class limit** is 3).

CLASS BOUNDARIES

As the times are given to the nearest minute then the interval 1–3 will actually include times from 0.5 minutes to 3.5 minutes. The **class boundaries** are 0.5 and 3.5 (where the **lower class boundary** is 0.5 and the **upper class boundary** is 3.5).

CLASS WIDTH

The **class width**, **class length** or **class size** is the difference between the upper and lower class boundaries.

For the class interval 1–3 with lower class boundary 0.5 and upper class boundary 3.5, then the class width equals 3.5 − 0.5 = 3 minutes.

Worked example

The table shows the times (given to the nearest minute) that customers have to wait in a checkout queue.

Waiting time (minutes)	Frequency
1–3	8
4–6	19
7–9	11
10–12	6
13–15	2
16–18	1

Draw the cumulative frequency diagram for the information. Use your diagram to find:

a) how many customers waited less than 5 minutes

b) how many waited more than 10 minutes

c) the median and the interquartile range.

First complete the table to include the cumulative frequencies.
Then draw the cumulative frequency diagram.

Waiting time (minutes)	Frequency	Cumulative frequency
1–3	8	8
4–6	19	27
7–9	11	38
10–12	6	44
13–15	2	46
16–18	1	47

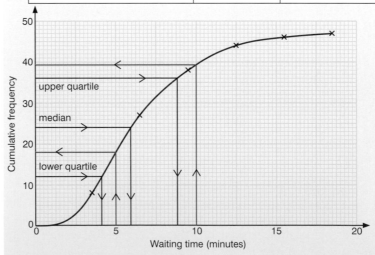

HINT

- The final cumulative frequency should equal the sum of the frequencies.
- The cumulative frequencies must be plotted at the upper class boundaries (i.e. 3.5, 6.5, 9.5, 12.5, 15.5 and 18.5).

a) To find out how many customers waited less than 5 minutes, read the information against a waiting time of 5 minutes.

From the graph, the number of customers who waited less than 5 minutes is 18.

b) To find out how many customers waited more than 10 minutes, read the information against a waiting time of 10 minutes.

From the graph, the number of customers who waited less than 10 minutes is 39 so that the number of customers who waited more than 10 minutes is 47 – 39 = 8.

c) To find the median waiting time you need to read off the median value on the cumulative frequency.

The median position is given by $\frac{1}{2}(n + 1) = \frac{1}{2}(47 + 1) = $ 24th value.

To find the interquartile range you need to find the lower quartile and the upper quartile.

The lower quartile position is given by $\frac{1}{4}n = \frac{1}{4} \times 47 = 11.75 = $ 12th value.

The upper quartile position is given by $\frac{3}{4}n = \frac{3}{4} \times 47 = 35.25 = $ 36th value.

From the graph, the median = 6.

Similarly, from the graph, the upper quartile = 8.8 and
the lower quartile = 4.1

so the interquartile range = upper quartile − lower quartile
$$= 8.8 - 4.1$$
$$= 4.7$$

QUESTIONS

Q1 The times, in seconds, taken by 11 teachers to solve a puzzle are listed, in order.

4 12 13 17 18 20 22 24 25 30 34

Find:
a) the lower quartile
b) the interquartile range.

Q2 The frequency distribution for the time taken to obtain clearance through customs is given in the following table.

Draw a cumulative frequency curve and use it to find an estimate of the median and the interquartile range.

Time (t minutes)	Frequency
$20 \leqslant t < 25$	3
$25 \leqslant t < 30$	7
$30 \leqslant t < 35$	15
$35 \leqslant t < 40$	18
$40 \leqslant t < 45$	22
$45 \leqslant t < 50$	17
$50 \leqslant t < 55$	8
$55 \leqslant t < 60$	2

Q3 The following table shows the number of words per paragraph in a children's book.

Draw a cumulative frequency curve to Illustrate this information and use your graph to estimate:

Number of words per paragraph	Number of paragraphs
1−10	17
11−20	33
21−30	51
31−40	21
41−50	18

a) the median and interquartile range
b) the percentage of paragraphs over 35 words in length.

Q4 The cumulative frequency graph gives information about the examination marks of a group of students.

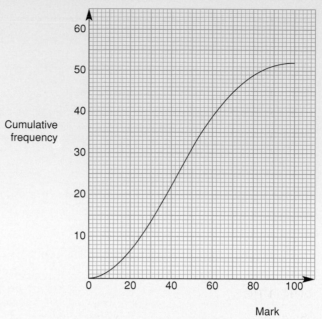

Cumulative frequency

Mark

a) How many students were in the group?

b) Use the graph to estimate the median mark.

The pass mark for the examination was 56.

c) Use the graph to estimate the number of students who passed the examination.

More questions on the CD ROM

Answers are on page 226.

48 PROBABILITY

What is probability?

Probability is the branch of mathematics that allows you to work out how likely or unlikely an **outcome** or result of an **event** might be.

In probability, an outcome that is certain to happen has a probability of 1 and an event that is impossible has a probability of 0. Probabilities greater than 1 or less than 0 have no meaning.

Theoretical probability is based on equally likely outcomes. You can use it to tell how an event should perform in theory, whereas **experimental probability** (or **relative frequency**) tells you how an event performs in an experiment.

Events and outcomes

An **event** is something that happens, such as throwing a die, or tossing a coin, or picking a card from a pack.

An **outcome** is the result of an event, such as scoring a 3 or a 6 when you throw a dic.

If the outcome is the required result, such as throwing a 6 to start a game, then the outcome is a **success**.

The **probability** is a measure of how likely an outcome is to happen.

In general:

$$\text{probability of success} = \frac{\text{number of 'successful' outcomes}}{\text{number of 'possible' outcomes}}$$

and you can use p(success) as shorthand for the probability of success.

$$p(\text{success}) = \frac{\text{number of 'successful' outcomes}}{\text{number of 'possible' outcomes}}$$

Using a die

Worked example

A box contains 25 coloured balls, where seven balls are red, ten balls are blue and eight balls are yellow. A ball is selected from the box at random. Calculate the probability of selecting:

a) a red ball **b)** a blue ball **c)** a red or a yellow ball

d) a red or a blue or a yellow ball **e)** a green ball.

Use:

$$p(\text{success}) = \frac{\text{number of 'successful' outcomes}}{\text{number of 'possible' outcomes}}$$

a) $p(\text{red ball}) = \frac{\text{number of red balls}}{\text{number of balls}} = \frac{7}{25}$

b) $p(\text{blue ball}) = \frac{\text{number of blue balls}}{\text{number of balls}} = \frac{10}{25} = \frac{2}{5}$ Cancelling to lowest terms.

HINT

- You could also give the answer as a decimal or a percentage.
  So p(red ball) = 0.28
  or p(red ball) = 28%

c) p(red or yellow ball) = $\dfrac{\text{number of red or yellow balls}}{\text{number of balls}}$

$= \dfrac{15}{25} = \dfrac{3}{5}$ Cancelling to lowest terms.

d) p(red or yellow or blue ball) = $\dfrac{\text{number of red or yellow or blue balls}}{\text{number of balls}}$

$= \dfrac{25}{25}$

$= 1$ Meaning that this outcome is certain to happen.

e) p(green ball) = $\dfrac{\text{number of green balls}}{\text{number of balls}} = \dfrac{0}{25}$

$= 0$ Meaning that this outcome is impossible, it cannot happen.

TOTAL PROBABILITY

The probability of an outcome happening is equal to 1 minus the probability of the outcome not happening.

p(outcome occurs) = 1 − p(outcome does not occur)

HINT

- You may see the word 'dice' used instead of 'die' in these questions.
Die is the singular form, dice is the plural.

Worked example

The probability that it will rain tomorrow is $\frac{1}{5}$. What is the probability that it will not rain tomorrow?

p(rain) = $\frac{1}{5}$

p(not rain) = $1 - \frac{1}{5} = \frac{4}{5}$ p(not rain) = 1 − p(rain)

Possibility spaces

A **possibility space** is a diagram which can be used to show the outcomes of various events.

Worked example

Two fair dice are thrown and the sum of the scores on the faces is noted. What is the probability that the sum is 8?

Draw a diagram to illustrate the possible outcomes.

The diagram to illustrate the possible outcomes is shown below. There are 36 possible outcomes. There are 5 outcomes that give a total of 8.

Probability that the sum is 8 = $\dfrac{5}{36}$.

		Second die					
		1	2	3	4	5	6
	1	2	3	4	5	6	7
	2	3	4	5	6	7	8
First	3	4	5	6	7	8	9
die	4	5	6	7	8	9	10
	5	6	7	8	9	10	11
	6	7	8	9	10	11	12

Theoretical and experimental probability

Worked example

A die is thrown 100 times.

a) How many times would you expect to throw a six?

This frequency distribution is obtained.

b) What is the relative frequency of a score of 6?

Score	1	2	3	4	5	6
Frequency	18	15	19	17	16	15

c) What is the relative frequency of getting an even number?

d) For which score are the theoretical probability and relative frequency the closest?

a) When throwing a die 100 times:

expected number of sixes $= 100 \times \frac{1}{6} = 16.666\ 66\ldots$

$= 17$ (to the nearest whole number)

b) The relative frequency of a score of 6 is $\frac{15}{100} = \frac{3}{20}$.

c) The frequency of getting an even number is $15 + 17 + 15 = 47$.

The relative frequency of getting an even number is $\frac{47}{100}$.

d) The theoretical and experimental probabilities are closest for a score of 4.

HINT

- The term relative frequency is used to describe the experimental probability.

QUESTIONS

Q1 A box contains 50 balls coloured blue, red and green. The probability of getting a blue ball is 32% and the probability of getting a red ball is 0.46.

   a) How many blue balls are there in the box?

   b) How many red balls are there in the box?

   c) How many green balls are there in the box?

Q2 The probability that a train arrives early is 0.2 and the probability that the train arrives on time is 0.45. What is the probability that the train arrives late?

Q3 An experiment consists of throwing a die and tossing a coin. Draw a possibility space for the two events and use this to calculate the probability of scoring:

   a) a head and a 1

   b) a tail and an odd number.

Q4 Two tetrahedral dice, each numbered 1 to 4, are thrown simultaneously. Draw a possibility space for the total of the two dice and use this information to calculate the probability of scoring a total of:

   a) 2   **b)** 6   **c)** 9.

   What is the most likely outcome?

Q5 A die is thrown 120 times. What is the expected frequency of a number greater than 4?

More questions on the CD ROM

Q6 The probability that a new car will develop a fault in the first month after delivery is 0.062%. A garage sells 1037 new cars in one year. How many of these cars will be expected to develop a fault in the first month after delivery?

Answers are on page 227.

49 The addition and multiplication rules

Two or more events are **mutually exclusive** if they cannot happen at the same time. Two events are **independent** if the outcome of one does not affect the outcome of the other.

Mutually exclusive events

THE ADDITION RULE

When you are working with **mutually exclusive** events you can apply the **addition rule** (also called the **or rule**) which states that:

$$p(A \text{ or } B) = p(A) + p(B)$$

and for more than two mutually exclusive events:

$$p(A \text{ or } B \text{ or } C \text{ or } ...) = p(A) + p(B) + p(C) + ...$$

Worked example

A spinner with ten sides, numbered 1 to 10, is spun. What is the probability of getting:

a) a five

b) a five or a six

c) a multiple of 3 or a multiple of 4

d) a multiple of 2 or a multiple of 3?

a) $p(5) = \frac{1}{10}$

b) $p(5 \text{ or } 6) = p(5) + p(6)$ As the events are mutually exclusive.

$$= \frac{1}{10} + \frac{1}{10}$$
$$= \frac{2}{10}$$
$$= \frac{1}{5} \qquad \text{Cancelling down to the lowest terms.}$$

c) p(multiple of 3 or multiple of 4)
$= p(3) + p(6) + p(9) + p(4) + p(8)$ As the events are mutually exclusive.
$$= \frac{1}{10} + \frac{1}{10} + \frac{1}{10} + \frac{1}{10} + \frac{1}{10} = \frac{5}{10}$$
$$= \frac{1}{2} \qquad \text{Cancelling down to the lowest terms.}$$

d) p(multiple of 2 or multiple of 3)
$= p(2 \text{ or } 3 \text{ or } 4 \text{ or } 6 \text{ or } 8 \text{ or } 9 \text{ or } 10)$

As the events are not mutually exclusive, because the number 6 is common to both events and if the probabilities are added then this probability will be added twice.

$= p(2) + p(3) + p(4) + p(6) + p(8) + p(9) + p(10)$
As these events are now mutually exclusive.

$$= \frac{1}{10} + \frac{1}{10} + \frac{1}{10} + \frac{1}{10} + \frac{1}{10} + \frac{1}{10} + \frac{1}{10}$$
$$= \frac{7}{10}$$

Independent events

TREE DIAGRAMS

In a **tree diagram**, you write the probabilities of the outcomes of different events on different branches of the 'tree'.

Worked example

A bag contains four red and three blue counters. A counter is drawn from the bag, replaced and then a second counter is drawn from the bag. Draw a tree diagram to show the various possibilities that can occur.

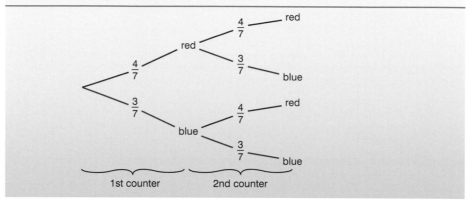

THE MULTIPLICATION RULE

For **independent events** you can use the **multiplication rule** (also called the **and rule**) which states that:

$$p(A \text{ and } B) = p(A) \times p(B)$$

Similarly for more than two independent events:

$$p(A \text{ and } B \text{ and } C \text{ and } ...) = p(A) \times p(B) \times p(C) \times ...$$

Worked example

A bag contains four red and three blue counters. A counter is drawn from the bag, replaced and then a second counter is drawn from the bag. Draw a tree diagram and use it to calculate the probability that:

a) both counters will be red

b) both counters will be blue

c) the first counter will be red and the second counter blue

d) one counter will be red and one counter will be blue.

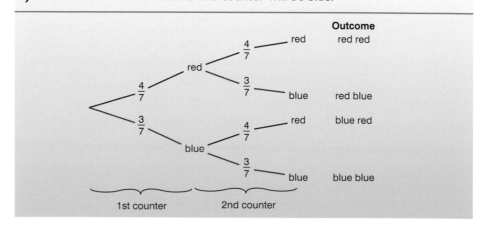

a) p(red and red) = p(red) × p(red)   As the events are independent.

$$= \frac{4}{7} \times \frac{4}{7} = \frac{16}{49}$$

b) p(blue and blue) = p(blue) × p(blue)   As the events are independent.

$$= \frac{3}{7} \times \frac{3}{7} = \frac{9}{49}$$

c) p(red and blue) = p(red) × p(blue)   As the events are independent.

$$= \frac{4}{7} \times \frac{3}{7} = \frac{12}{49}$$

d) p(one counter will be red and one counter will be blue) is the same as p(red and blue or blue and red).

= p (red and blue) + p(blue and red). As the events are mutually
exclusive.

= p(red) × p(blue) + p(blue) × p(red) As the events are independent.

$$= \frac{4}{7} \times \frac{3}{7} + \frac{3}{7} \times \frac{4}{7} = \frac{12}{49} + \frac{12}{49} = \frac{24}{49}$$

Both of these outcomes give one red and one blue.

QUESTIONS

Q1 A die with faces numbered 1 to 6 is rolled and the value on the face uppermost is noted. Find the probability that the result will be:

a) a 5 or a 6   b) an even number

c) a factor of 8.

Q2 Letters are chosen from the word:

PROBABILITY

Find the probability that the chosen letter is:

a) the letter P   b) the letter B

c) the letter B or the letter I.

Q3 A counter is selected from a box containing three red, four green and five blue counters and a second counter is selected from a different box containing five red and four green counters. Draw a tree diagram to show the various possibilities when a counter is drawn from each bag.

Q4 The probability that a car will fail its safety test because of the lights is 0.32 and the probability that a car will fail the safety test because of the brakes is 0.55. Calculate the probability that the car fails because of:

a) its lights and its brakes

b) its lights only.

Q5 The probability that a particular component will fail is 0.015. Draw and label a tree diagram to show the possible outcomes when two such components are chosen at random. Calculate the probability that:

a) both components will fail

b) exactly one component will fail.

More questions
on the CD ROM

Answers are on page 228.

50 MULTIPLICATION RULE FOR DEPENDENT EVENTS

What are dependent events?

Two or more events are **dependent** if one event affects the probability of the other event.

The multiplication rule

Worked example

A bag contains four red and three blue counters. A counter is drawn from the bag and then a second counter is drawn from the bag. Draw a tree diagram to show the various possibilities that can occur and use the diagram to find the probability that both counters are blue.

The question does not make it clear whether the first counter is replaced before the second counter is drawn. This gives rise to two possibilities as shown in the following tree diagrams.

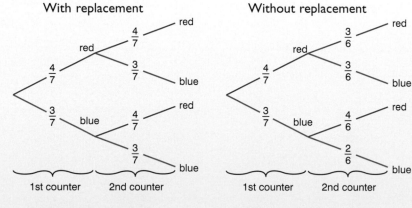

With replacement	Without replacement
Independent events	**Dependent events**

With replacement (independent events)

If the first counter is replaced before the second counter is drawn, then the two events are independent and the probabilities for each event are the same.

From the diagram, the probability that both counters are blue

= p(blue counter drawn first and blue counter drawn second)

= p(blue counter drawn first) × p(blue counter drawn second)

$= \frac{3}{7} \times \frac{3}{7} = \frac{9}{49}$

Without replacement (dependent events)

If the first counter is not replaced before the second counter is drawn, then the two events are not independent (i.e. they are dependent) and the probabilities on the second event will be affected by the outcomes on the first event.

For the second counter:

if the first counter was blue, there are now two blue counters and six counters altogether

if the first counter was not blue, there are still three blue counters and six counters altogether.

From the diagram you can see that:

the probability that both counters are blue

= p(blue counter drawn first and blue counter drawn second)

= p(blue counter drawn first) × p(blue counter drawn second)

$$= \frac{3}{7} \times \frac{2}{6} = \frac{6}{42} = \frac{1}{7}$$

QUESTIONS

Q1 Mohammed has ten black and six brown socks in his drawer. If he removes two socks from the drawer, one after the other, calculate the probability that:

    a) both socks are black

    b) both socks are brown

    c) the socks are different colours.

Q2 The probability that Sara passes the driving theory test on her first attempt is $\frac{6}{7}$. If she fails then the probability that she passes on any future attempt is $\frac{7}{8}$.

Draw a tree diagram to represent this situation and use it to calculate the probability that Sara passes the driving test on her third attempt.

Q3 A bag contains three black beads, five red beads and two green beads. Grace takes a bead at random from the bag, records its colour and replaces it. She does this two more times.

Work out the probability that, of the three beads Grace takes, exactly two are the same colour.

More questions
on the CD ROM

Answers are on page 229.

EXAM PRACTICE

Paper 3H Higher Tier

Time: 2 hours

Answer all questions

1 Work out $5\frac{1}{5} - 1\frac{2}{3}$. [3]

2 The population of the Earth is approximately 5×10^9 and the Earth's surface area is approximately $4 \times 10^{11} km^2$. Calculate the approximate area, in km^2, per head of population. Give your answer in standard form. [3]

3 Draw accurately the net of this prism. Give your answer on a clean sheet of paper. [3]

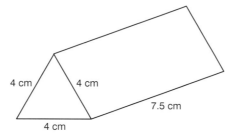

4 cm   4 cm

7.5 cm

4 cm

4 Give an approximate answer to: $\dfrac{28.65 \times 0.0852}{14.6 \times 3.22}$

by rounding the numbers to a sensible degree of accuracy. [3]

5 The equation of the straight line $y = mx + c$ is satisfied at the points $(2, 3)$ and $(1, {}^{-}2)$. What is the equation of the straight line?

6 A sequence of numbers is shown here.

Term number	1	2	3	4	5
Term	2	5	10	17	26

a) Write down the next term of the sequence.

b) Write down the nth term of the sequence in terms of n.

c) Work out the 100th term of the sequence. [3]

7 Factorise fully the expression $2\pi rh + 2\pi r^2$. [3]

8 XYZ is an equilateral triangle of side 4.5 cm. Show all of the points outside of the triangle which are less than 2.5 cm from the edges of the triangle. Give your answer on a clean sheet of paper. [2]

9 a) Express 200 as the product of its prime factors.
b) Work out the Lowest Common Multiple of 75 and 200. [4]

Higher 3H May 2004

10 Two points A and B, are plotted on a centimetre grid.
A has coordinates (2, 1) and B has coordinates (8, 5).

a) Work out the coordinates at the midpoint of the line joining A and B.
b) Use Pythagoras' Theorem to work out the length of AB.
   Give your answers correct to 3 significant figures. [5]

Higher 3H May 2004

11 A = {1, 2, 3, 4}
B = {1, 3, 5}

a) List the members of the set
   (i) $A \cap B$,
   (ii) $A \cup B$.

b) Explain clearly the meaning of $3 \in A$. [4]

12 Explain why the expression $\frac{4}{3}\pi r^2$ cannot represent the volume of a sphere. [3]

13 This table shows the cumulative frequency for the test results of 72 students.

Marks	$\leqslant 10$	$\leqslant 20$	$\leqslant 30$	$\leqslant 40$	$\leqslant 50$
Cumulative frequency	6	19	36	56	72

From the table calculate:
a) how many students got marks less than or equal to 20

b) how many students got marks between 30 and 40.

Draw the cumulative frequency curve for the data on a clean sheet of graph paper and use it to calculate:
c) the median and the interquartile range.

In the next test, also marked out of 50, the interquartile range was 30.
d) Comment on the two tests, using the interquartile ranges. [8]

14 Solve these simultaneous equations.

$4x - y = 13$
$3x + y = 15$ [2]

15 Vijay and Baljit are playing a game with two fair five-sided spinners, one red and one blue. The blue spinner is numbered 5, 6, 7, 8, 9 and the red spinner is numbered 1, 2, 3, 4, 5. The final score is calculated by multiplying the two spinner scores together.

   a) Complete a grid to show all the possible final scores.

   b) Find the probability that the final score is a square number.

   c) Find the probability that the final score is less than 20. [3]

16 The diagram represents a garden in the shape of a rectangle. All measurements are given in metres. The garden has a flowerbed in one corner. The flowerbed is a square of side x.

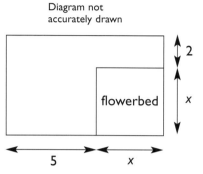

Diagram not accurately drawn

   a) Write down an expression, in terms of x, for the short side of the garden.

   b) Find an expression, in terms of x, for the perimeter of the garden. Give your answer in its simplest form.

The perimeter of the garden is 20 metres.

   c) Find the value of x. [6]

17 In the diagram, RT and PT are tangents to the circle. Calculate:

   a) $\angle$ROP

   b) $\angle$RSP

   c) $\angle$RQP. [6]

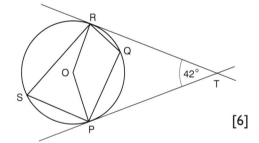

18 Show that $0.2\dot{3}\dot{4}$ is a rational number. [3]

19 a) Find the value of $16^{\frac{1}{2}}$.

   b) Given that $\sqrt{40} = k\sqrt{10}$, find the value of k.

   A large rectangular piece of card is $(\sqrt{5} + \sqrt{20})$ cm long and $\sqrt{8}$ cm wide.

   A small rectangle $\sqrt{2}$ cm long and $\sqrt{5}$ cm wide is cut out of the piece of card.

   c) Express the area of the card that is left as a percentage of the large rectangle.

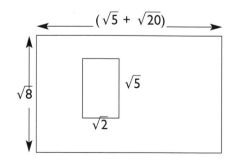

[6]

20 Oil is stored in either small drums or large drums. The shapes of the drums are mathematically similar.

A **small** drum has a volume of 0.006 m³ and a surface area of 0.2 m².

The height of a **large** drum is 3 times the height of a small drum.

a) Calculate the volume of a large drum.

b) The cost of making a drum is $1.20 for each m² of surface area.

A company wants to store 3240 m³ of oil in large drums.

Calculate the cost of making enough large drums to store this oil. [8]

Higher 3H Nov 2004

21 This histogram gives information about the books sold in a bookshop one Saturday.

Use the histogram to complete the table.

Price (*P*) in dollars ($)	Frequency
$0 < P \leqslant 5$	
$5 < P \leqslant 10$	
$10 < P \leqslant 20$	
$20 < P \leqslant 40$	

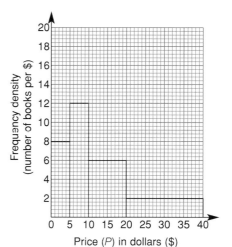

[6]

22 A formula was given as $s = \dfrac{p + q}{p}$.

Rearrange the formula to make *p* the subject. [4]

23 Write as a single fraction $\dfrac{1}{x + 3} + \dfrac{1}{x - 4}$. [3]

24 A curve has equation $y = x^2 - 4x + 1$

a) For this curve find

(i) $\dfrac{dy}{dx}$

(ii) the coordinates of the turning point.

b) State, with a reason, whether the minimum turning point is a maximum or a minimum.

c) Find the equation of the line of symmetry of the curve $y = x^2 - 4x + 1$ [6]

Higher 3H Nov 2004

More questions on the CD ROM

Time: 2 hours

Answer all questions

1 The speed of traffic on a three-lane stretch of road is in the ratio 2 : 3 : 5.
If the speed of the traffic in the fastest lane is 60 miles per hour calculate
the speed of traffic in the other two lanes. [3]

2 Find the reciprocal of 0.25. [2]

3 The frequency distribution shows the different types of books borrowed from
a library one weekend.
Show this information as a pie chart.

Type of book	Frequency
Sport	12
Crime	31
Horror	29
Romance	34
Other	14

[4]

4 The travel graph shows a train journey between
two towns A and C stopping at B.

Use the graph to find:
a) the average speed between towns A and B

b) the average speed between towns A and C.

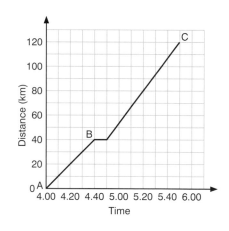

5 Solve the inequality $2(3 + 2x) > 4$ and show the solutions on a number line. [3]

6 Calculate the value of:

$$\frac{5.06 \times (10.32)^2}{281 + 217}$$

Write down all the figures on your calculator display. [3]

7 A flat is valued at $576 720 which represents an 8% increase on the original value. What was
the original value? [3]

8 The lengths, in cm, of the sides of a triangle are
$(a + 5)$, $(3a - 7)$ and $(2a - 1)$.

The perimeter of the triangle is 24 cm.

Work out the value of a.

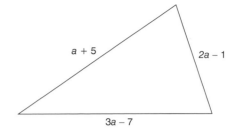

[3]

Higher 4H Nov 2004

9 The formula for the surface area of a sphere, with area A cm^2 and radius r cm, is given as
$A = 4\pi r^2$.

a) Find A when $r = 20$ cm.

b) Rearrange the formula to make r the subject.

c) Use this formula to find r when $A = 100$ cm^2. [6]

10 Simplify the expression $(x + 5)^2 - (x - 5)^2$. [3]

11 Two sides AB and DC of a regular pentagon ABCDE when produced meet at a point P.
Calculate $\angle$BPC. [3]

12 A nanosecond is 0.000 000 001 of a second.

a) Write the number 0.000 000 001 in standard form.

A computer does a calculation in 5 nanoseconds.

b) How many of these calculations can the computer do in 1 second? Give your answer in
standard form. [4]

13 Given that PR and PS are tangents to a circle and
the points of contact are R and S respectively, find:

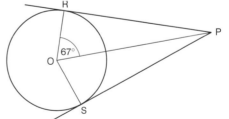

a) $\angle$POS

b) $\angle$OPR

c) $\angle$OPS. [6]

14 A vertical cliff is 485 metres high. The angle of depression of a boat at sea is 20°.
What is the distance of the boat from the foot of the cliff? [3]

15 ABC and ADE are straight lines. CE is a diameter.
Angle DCE = $x°$ and angle BCD = $2x°$.
Find, in terms of x, the sizes of the angles:

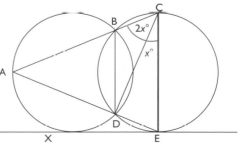

a) ABD

b) DBE

c) BAD. [6]

16 The outer diameter of a hollow spherical ball is 10 cm.

The ball is made from rubber which is 0.4 cm thick.

Calculate the volume of rubber needed to make the ball.

Give your answer correct to 3 significant figures.

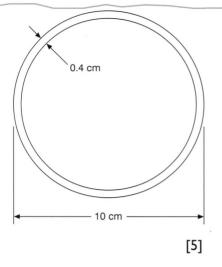

0.4 cm

10 cm

[5]

Higher 4H Nov 2003

17 The frequency diagram gives information about the marks gained by a group of 59 students in a test.

a) Which is the modal class?

A student is chosen at random from the whole group.

b) Find the probability that this student's mark is less than 30.

c) Calculate an estimate of the total number of marks scored by all the students in the group.

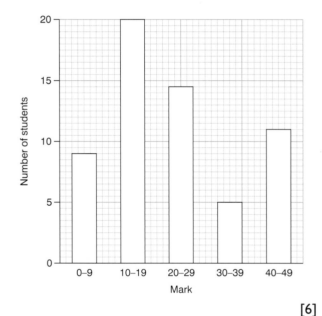

[6]

Higher 4H May 2005

18 f and g are functions.

f: $x \longmapsto 2x - 3$

g: $x \longmapsto 1 + \sqrt{x}$

a) Calculate f(−4)

b) Given that f(a) = 5, find the value of a.

c) Calculate gf(6)

d) Which values of x cannot be included in the domain of g?

e) Find the inverse function of g^{-1} in the form $g^{-1}: x \longmapsto \ldots$

[7]

Higher 4H May 2005

19 The value of a car, $v, is inversely proportional to its age, a years. After 1 year a car has a value of $7000. Find: [4]

a) the value of the car after $3\frac{1}{2}$ years

b) the age of the car when it is worth $2500.

20 A bag contains four red and six blue balls. One ball is chosen and its colour noted. It is not put back into the bag. A second ball is chosen and its colour noted.

a) Draw a tree diagram to represent this situation.

b) i) Find the probability of obtaining two red balls.

    ii) Find the probability of obtaining one ball of each colour. [6]

21 A windscreen wiper of length 25cm sweeps out an angle of 110° as illustrated in the diagram.
What is the area of the screen covered?

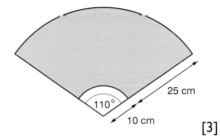

[3]

22 A is the point with coordinates (3, 4)

$$\overrightarrow{AB} = \begin{pmatrix} 5 \\ -3 \end{pmatrix}$$

Find the coordinates of B [3]

23 The diagram represents a prism.

AEFD is a rectangle.
ABCD is a square.
EB and FC are perpendicular to plane ABCD.
AB = 60 cm
AD = 60 cm
Angle ABE = 90°
Angle BAE = 30°

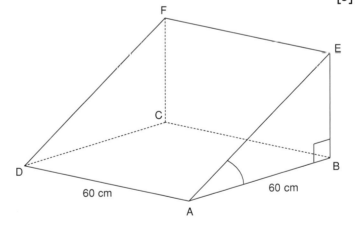

Diagram not drawn accurately.

Calculate the size of the angle that the line DE makes with the plane ABCD.

Give your answer correct to 1 decimal place. [6]

24 A train travels 42 miles (to the nearest mile) in a time of 35 minutes (to the nearest minute).
Find the maximum and minimum speed of the train in miles per hour, correct to 3 significant figures. [4]

More questions on the CD ROM

ANSWERS AND SOLUTIONS

NUMBER

1 Integers and the number system (page 15)

Q1 a 7, 14 or 21   b 1, 2, 5 or 10
   c 1, 3 or 17   d 16 or 25
   e 17, 19 or 23   f 2
   g 21

Comments

a) The numbers 7, 14 and 21 are all multiples of 7 and appear in the table.

b) The numbers 1, 2, 5 and 10 all divide exactly into 10 without a remainder.

c) The numbers 1, 3 and 17 all divide exactly into 51 and appear in the table.

d) The square numbers are 1, 4, 9, 16, 25, 36, 49, ... and the numbers 16 and 25 are both bigger than 10 and appear in the table.

e) The numbers 2, 3, 5, 7, 11, 13, 17, 19, 23, 29, 31, 37, ... are all prime numbers (i.e. they each only have two factors) although only 17, 19 and 23 are bigger than 16 and appear in the table.

f) The number 2 is the only prime number which is even. All other even numbers will have at least three factors i.e. 1, 2 and the number itself.

g) The numbers 3, 6, 9, 12, 15, 18, 21, 24, 27, ... are multiples of 3 and the numbers 7, 14, 21, 28, 35, 42, ... are multiples of 7. Of the numbers that appear in the table, only 21 is a multiple of 3 and also a multiple of 7.

Q2 $264 = 2 \times 2 \times 2 \times 3 \times 11$
     or $264 = 2^3 \times 3 \times 11$

Comments

Use the factor tree method.

$$264$$

$=$ 2×132 Writing 264 as the product 2×132

$=$ $2 \times 2 \times 66$ Writing 132 as the product 2×66

$=$ $2 \times 2 \times 6 \times 11$ Writing 66 as the product 2×33

$= 2 \times 2 \times 2 \times 3 \times 11$

                     Writing 6 as the product 2×3

Q3 a (i) $2^3 \times 7$
      (ii) $2^2 \times 3 \times 7$
   b $2^2 \times 7 = 28$

Comments

a) (i) factor tree for 56: $56 = 2 \times 28$, $28 = 2 \times 14$, $14 = 2 \times 7$
   (ii) factor tree for 84: $84 = 2 \times 42$, $42 = 2 \times 21$, $21 = 3 \times 7$

b) Use the results from part a).
Alternatively:
factors of 56:   1, 2, 4, 7, 8, 14, 28, 56
factors of 84:   1, 2, 3, 4, 6, 7, 12, 14, 21, 28, 42, 84
common factors: 1, 2, 4, 7, 14, 28
highest common factor of 56 and 84 is 28.

2 Directed numbers (page 16)

Q1 a $^+6$ or 6   b $^-6$ c $^-7$
   d $^+5$ or 5   e $^+1$ or 1   f $^-13$
   g $^-6$

Comments

a) $^-2 + 8 = 6$ Start at $^-2$ and go up 8.

b) $^-9 + 3 = ^-6$ Start at $^-9$ and go up 3.

c) $^-2 - 5 = ^-7$ Start at $^-2$ and go down 5.

d) $^+7 - ^+2 = ^+7 - 2 = 5$ Remember, $- + = -$ so rewrite as $^+7 - 2$.

e) $^-3 - ^-4 = ^-3 + 4 = 1$ Remember, $- - = +$ so rewrite as $^-3 + 4$.

f) $^-11 + ^-2 = ^-11 - 2 = ^-13$ $+ - = -$

g) $^-10 - ^-4 = ^-10 + 4 = ^-6$ $- - = +$

Q2 a $^-6$
   b $^-21$
   c $^+30$ or 30
   d $^+4$ or 4   e $^-8$ f $^-2.5$ or $^-2\frac{1}{2}$
   g $^+12$ or 12

Comments

a) $^-3 \times ^+2 = ^-6$ $- \times + = -$

b) $^+7 \times ^-3 = ^-21$ $+ \times - = -$

c) $^-6 \times ^-5 = ^+30$ or 30 $- \times - = +$

d) $^+12 \div ^+3 = ^+4$ or 4 $+ \div + = +$

e) $^+16 \div ^-2 = ^-8$ $+ \div - = -$

f) $^-10 \div ^+4 = ^-2.5$ $10 \div 4 = 2.5$ and the sign is $- \div + = -$

g) $^-4 \times ^+3 \times ^-1 = 12$ $^-4 \times ^+3 = ^-12$ and $^-12 \times ^-1 = ^+12$ or 12

3 Fractions and decimals (page 21)

Q1 $2\frac{1}{20}$

> **Comments**
> $3\frac{1}{4} - 1\frac{1}{5}$
> $= \frac{13}{4} - \frac{6}{5}$ Converting to top-heavy fractions.
> $= \frac{65}{20} - \frac{24}{20}$ Writing both fractions with a
>   denominator of 20.
> $= \frac{41}{20} = 2\frac{1}{20}$ Rewriting as a mixed number..

Q2 $\frac{3}{10}$

> **Comments**
> $\frac{3}{\overset{}{{}_2}4} \times \frac{\overset{1}{\cancel{2}}}{5} = \frac{3 \times 1}{2 \times 5}$ Cancelling fractions.
> $\quad = \frac{3}{10}$

Q3 $4\frac{1}{2}$

> **Comments**
> $4\frac{4}{5} \div 1\frac{1}{15} = \frac{24}{5} \div \frac{16}{15}$ Converting to top-heavy
>   fractions.
> $= \frac{\overset{3}{\cancel{24}}}{{}_1\cancel{5}} \times \frac{\overset{3}{\cancel{15}}}{\cancel{16}_2}$ Multiplying by reciprocal
>   and cancelling fractions.
> $= \frac{9}{2}$
> $= 4\frac{1}{2}$ Rewriting as a mixed number.

Q4 $\frac{81}{500}$

> **Comments**
> $0.162 = \frac{1}{10} + \frac{6}{100} + \frac{2}{1000}$
> $= \frac{100}{1000} + \frac{60}{1000} + \frac{2}{1000}$
> $= \frac{162}{1000}$
> $= \frac{81}{500}$ Cancelling down.

Q5 Raj has more paint. He has $\frac{9}{12}$ of a tin
of paint and Mei has $\frac{8}{12}$ of a tin of paint.

> **Comments**
> Raj has $\frac{3}{4}$ of a tin $= \frac{9}{12}$
> $\frac{3}{4} \overset{\times 3}{=} \frac{9}{12}$
>   ($\times 3$)
> Mei has $\frac{4}{6}$ of a tin $= \frac{8}{12}$
> $\frac{4}{6} \overset{\times 2}{=} \frac{8}{12}$
>   ($\times 2$)

Q6 $\frac{253}{999}$

> **Comments**
> Notice that $1000 \times 0.\dot{2}5\dot{3} = 253.253\,253\ldots$
>   Multiplying both sides by
>   1000.
> and $1 \times 0.\dot{2}5\dot{3} = 0.253\,253\ldots$
> Subtracting: $999 \times 0.\dot{2}5\dot{3} = 253$
> and $0.\dot{2}5\dot{3} = \frac{253}{999}$ Dividing both sides by 999.

Q7 $\frac{827}{990}$

> **Comments**
> Notice that $100 \times 0.8\dot{3}\dot{5} = 83.5353535\ldots$
>   Multiplying both sides by 100.
> and $1 \times 0.8\dot{3}\dot{5} = 0.8353535\ldots$
> Subtracting: $99 \times 0.8\dot{3}\dot{5} = 82.7$
> and $0.8\dot{3}\dot{5} = \frac{82.7}{99}$ Dividing both sides by 99.
> $= \frac{827}{990}$ Writing as a proper fraction.

Q8 $\frac{8}{15}$

> **Comments**
> $10 \times 0.5\dot{3} = 5.33333$
> $\quad 0.5\dot{3} = 0.53333$
> $9 \times 0.5\dot{3} = 4.8$
> $\quad 0.5\dot{3} = \frac{4.8}{9} = \frac{48}{90} = \frac{24}{45} = \frac{8}{15}$

4 Powers, roots and reciprocals (page 23)

Q1 $\sqrt{36} = \pm 6$, $\sqrt{10} = \pm 3.162\,277\,7$

> **Comments**
> The square root of a number is the number which,
> when squared, gives that number.
> $\sqrt{36} = \pm 6$ as $6 \times 6 = 36$, and $^-6 \times {}^-6 = 36$
> (You should be able to do this without a calculator.)
> $\sqrt{10}$ is not an exact number but lies between 3 and 4
> (as $3 \times 3 = 9$ and $4 \times 4 = 16$). Using the $\boxed{\sqrt{}}$
> key on your calculator gives $\sqrt{10} = 3.162\,277\,7$.
> You must remember the negative square root
> as well.

Q2 $\sqrt[3]{4096} = 16$, $\sqrt[3]{-10} = {}^-2.1544347$

Comments

The cube root of a number is the number which, when cubed, gives that number.
$\sqrt[3]{4096} = 16$ as $16 \times 16 \times 16 = 4096$.

$\sqrt[3]{{}^-10}$ is not an exact number but lies between $^-2$ and $^-3$ (as $^-2 \times {}^-2 \times -2 = {}^-8$ and $^-3 \times {}^-3 \times {}^-3 = {}^-27$).
Using the $\boxed{\sqrt[3]{}}$ key on your calculator gives $\sqrt[3]{{}^-10} = {}^-2.154\,434\,7$.

Q3 $\frac{4}{3}, \frac{1}{15}, \frac{5}{6}$

Comments

The reciprocal of $\frac{3}{4}$ is found by turning the fraction upside-down to give $\frac{4}{3}$. The number 15 can be written as $\frac{15}{1}$ and the reciprocal of $\frac{15}{1}$ is $\frac{1}{15}$.

Similarly the mixed number $1\frac{1}{5}$ can be written as $\frac{6}{5}$ (as a top-heavy or an improper fraction) and the reciprocal of $\frac{6}{5}$ is $\frac{5}{6}$.

5 Indices (page 26)

Q1 a 729   b $\frac{1}{16}$ c 6

Comments

a) An answer of 27 is a common mistake, caused by multiplying 9×3.
9^3 tells you that three lots of 9 (the base number) are to be multiplied together (3 is the power or index).
So $9^3 = 9 \times 9 \times 9 = 729$
b) 4^{-2} has a negative power.
So $4^{-2} = \frac{1}{4^2} = \frac{1}{16}$ as $4^2 = 4 \times 4 = 16$
c) $6^1 = 6$ as any number raised to the power 1 is always equal to that number.

Q2 a 3^{23} b 8^2 c 1   d 1600

Comments

a) $3^{11} \times 3^{12} = 3^{11+12} = 3^{23}$
b) $8^6 \div 8^4 = 8^{6-4} = 8^2$
c) $13^4 \div 13^4 = 13^{4-4} = 13^0 = 1$
d) As the base numbers are not the same you cannot use the rules of indices on this question and must work out the answer by working out 4^3 and 5^2.
$4^3 = 4 \times 4 \times 4 = 64$
$5^2 = 5 \times 5 = 25$
So $4^3 \times 5^2 = 64 \times 25 = 1600$

Q3 a 64   b 3   c 12

Comments

a) $(2^2)^3 = 4^3 = 64$
b) $(\sqrt{3})^2 = \sqrt{3} \times \sqrt{3} = 3$
c) $\sqrt{2^4 \times 9} = \sqrt{2^4} \times \sqrt{9} = 2^2 \times 3 = 4 \times 3 = 12$

Q4 a ± 6 b 4   c 10

Comments

a) $36^{\frac{1}{2}} = \sqrt{36} = \pm 6$
b) $64^{\frac{1}{3}} = \sqrt[3]{64} = 4$
c) $10\,000^{\frac{1}{4}} = \sqrt[4]{10\,000} = 10$

Q5 a 25   b $\frac{1}{25}$

Comments

a) $125^{\frac{2}{3}} = (125^{\frac{1}{3}})^2 = (5)^2 = 25$
b) $125^{-\frac{2}{3}} = \dfrac{1}{125^{\frac{2}{3}}}$

$\qquad = \dfrac{1}{\left(125^{\frac{1}{3}}\right)^2}$

$\qquad = \dfrac{1}{5^2}$

$\qquad = \dfrac{1}{25}$

Q6 $n = -\frac{1}{2}$

Comments

$4^{\frac{1}{2}} = 2$ and $4^{-\frac{1}{2}} = \frac{1}{2}$ so $n = -\frac{1}{2}$

Q7 a 1   b $\frac{1}{9}$ c 64

Comments

a) Any number to the power 0 is 1.
b) $3^{-2} = \frac{1}{3^2} = \frac{1}{9}$
c) $16^{\frac{3}{2}} = (16^{\frac{1}{2}})^3 = 4^3 = 64$

Q8 a (i) xy (ii) y^2 (iii) $\frac{x}{2}$
    b $p = 6, q = -1$

Comments

a) (i) $2^{p+q} = 2^p \times 2^q = xy$
   (ii) $2^{2q} = (2^q)^2 = y^2$
   (iii) $2^{p-1} = 2^p \times 2^{-1} = x \times \frac{1}{2} = \frac{x}{2}$

b) $xy = 32$ ①
   $2xy^2 = 32$ ②
   ② $= 2y(xy) = 32$ As $xy^2 = y(xy)$
      $2y \times 32 = 32$ Substituting $xy = 32$ from 1.
      $2y = 1$ Dividing both sides by 32.
      $y = \frac{1}{2}$
   $xy = 32$
   $x \times \frac{1}{2} = 32$
   $x = 64$

   $x = 2^p$ $y = 2^q$
   $64 = 2^6 = 2^p =$ so $p = 6$ $\frac{1}{2} = 2^{-1} = 2^q$ so $q = -1$

6 Rational and irrational numbers (page 27)

Q1 $(\sqrt{3})^2$ and $\sqrt{6\frac{1}{4}}$ are rational numbers.

$(\sqrt{3})^2 = \frac{3}{1}$ and $\sqrt{6\frac{1}{4}} = \frac{5}{2}$

Comments
$(\sqrt{3})^2 = 3$ Since $(\sqrt{3})^2 = 3 = \frac{3}{1}$ in the form $\frac{p}{q}$.

$\sqrt{6\frac{1}{4}} = \frac{5}{2}$ Since $\sqrt{6\frac{1}{4}} = \sqrt{\frac{25}{4}} = \frac{\sqrt{25}}{\sqrt{4}} = \frac{5}{2}$.

Q2 a $5\sqrt{3}$ b $3\sqrt{5}$ c $\frac{\sqrt{7}}{7}$

Comments
a) $\sqrt{5} \times \sqrt{15} = \sqrt{75} = \sqrt{25 \times 3} = \sqrt{25} \times \sqrt{3} = 5\sqrt{3}$
b) $\sqrt{5} + \sqrt{20} = \sqrt{5} + \sqrt{4 \times 5} = \sqrt{5} + 2\sqrt{5} = 3\sqrt{5}$
c) $\frac{1}{\sqrt{7}} = \frac{1}{\sqrt{7}} \times \frac{\sqrt{7}}{\sqrt{7}} = \frac{\sqrt{7}}{7}$

Q3 $(4 + \sqrt{3})(4 - \sqrt{3}) = 13$

Comments
$(4 + \sqrt{3})(4 - \sqrt{3}) = 4 \times 4 - 4\sqrt{3} + 4\sqrt{3} - \sqrt{3}\sqrt{3}$
$= 16 - 3$
$= 13$

Q4 $\sqrt{22}$

Comments
$\dfrac{(5 + \sqrt{3})(5 - \sqrt{3})}{\sqrt{22}}$

$= \dfrac{5 \times 5 - 5 \times \sqrt{3} + 5 \times \sqrt{3} - \sqrt{3} \times \sqrt{3}}{\sqrt{22}}$

Using FOIL to expand the numerator.

$= \dfrac{25 - 3}{\sqrt{22}}$ Simplifying the numerator.

$= \dfrac{22}{\sqrt{22}}$

$= \dfrac{22 \times \sqrt{22}}{\sqrt{22} \times \sqrt{22}}$ Multiplying numerator and denominator by $\sqrt{22}$.

$= \dfrac{22 \times \sqrt{22}}{22}$

$= \sqrt{22}$ Cancelling.

Q5 a $2\sqrt{5}$

Comments
$\frac{10}{\sqrt{5}} = \frac{10\sqrt{5}}{\sqrt{5}\sqrt{5}} = \frac{10\sqrt{5}}{5} = 2\sqrt{5}$

b $28 + 10\sqrt{3}$

Comments
$(5 + \sqrt{3})^2 = (5 + \sqrt{3})(5 + \sqrt{3})$
$= 25 + 10\sqrt{3} + 3$
$= 28 + 10\sqrt{3}$

7 Sets and set notation (page 33)

Q1 a (i) $B \cap C = \{3, 15\}$
(ii) $A \cap B = \emptyset$ or $\{\ \}$
(iii) $A' \cap B = \{1, 3, 5, 7, 9, 11, 13, 15, 16, 17, 18, \ldots\} \cap \{1, 3, 5, 15\} = \{1, 3, 5, 15\}$
(iv) $A \cup B = \{2, 4, 6, 8, 10, 12, 14\} \cup \{1, 3, 5, 15\} = \{1, 2, 3, 4, 5, 6, 8, 10, 12, 14, 15\}$

Comments
$\mathscr{E} = \{\text{Positive integers}\} = \{1, 2, 3, 4, 5, \ldots\}$
$A = \{\text{Even numbers less than 16}\} = \{2, 4, 6, 8, 10, 12, 14\}$
$B = \{\text{Factors of 15}\} = \{1, 3, 5, 15\}$
$C = \{\text{Multiples of 3}\} = \{3, 6, 9, 12, 15, \ldots\}$

b (i) $16 \in A$ FALSE
(ii) $n(C) = 4$ FALSE
(iii) $A \cap B \cap C = \emptyset'$ TRUE
(iv) $B \subset A'$ TRUE

Q2 a

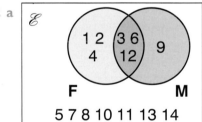

b $n(F \cap M') = 3$

Comments
$F = \{\text{Factors of 12}\} = \{1, 2, 3, 4, 6, 12\}$
$M = \{\text{Multiples of 3}\} = \{3, 6, 9, 12\}$

Q3

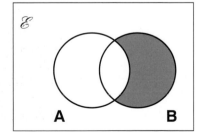

Q4

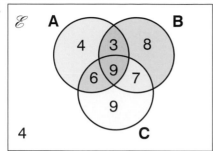

a $n(A \cap B \cap C) = 9$

b (i) $n(C) = 31$
   (ii) $n(A \cap B) = 12$
   (iii) $n((A \cup B)') = 13$

Q5 Completing the Venn diagram

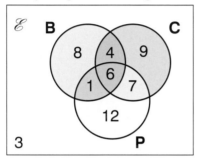

a 26 students study chemistry altogether.

b 12 students study physics only.

Q6 (i) If $n(A') = 20$ and $n(\mathcal{E}) = 32$
       then $(A) = 32 - 20 = 12$
     (ii) $n(A \cap B') = 8$
       so $= n(A \cap B) = 4$

Q7 a (i)

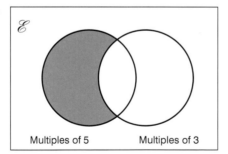

Multiples of 5   Multiples of 3

(ii) Any three out of 5, 10, 20, 25, 35, …
     (These are multiples of 5 but not 15.)

b (i)

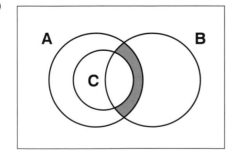

(ii) 15, 45, 75. Other answers are possible.

8 Percentages (page 39)

Q1 a 360   b 22%

> **Comments**
> **a)** To calculate 45% of 800:
> 1% of 800 = $\frac{800}{100}$ = 8
> 45% of 800 = 45 × 8 = 360
>
> **b)** To write 176 out of 800 as a percentage:
> 176 as a fraction of 800 = $\frac{176}{800}$
> 176 as a percentage of 800 = $\frac{176}{800}$ × 100 = 22%

Q2 $2646

> **Comments**
> Percentage cost after discount is 94.5%.
>
> 100% − 5.5% = 94.5%
> $2800 × 94.5% = $2800 × 0.945
>   = $2646

Q3 0.08%

> **Comments**
> Percentage error = $\frac{error}{actual\ amount}$ × 100%
> Error = 6.005 − 6 = 0.005kg
>
> Percentage error = $\frac{0.005}{6.005}$ × 100% = 0.08%
> to an appropriate degree of accuracy.

Q4 70.38 million

> **Comments**
> 1% of 69 million.
> 1% of 69 000 000
> = 690000
> so 2% = 2 × 690000
> = 138 0000
> = 1.38 million
> Population in 2003 = 69 million + 1.38 million
> = 70.38 million

Q5

182 units at $0.0821 per unit	$ 14.94
429 units at $0.0704 per unit	$ 30.20
Total amount	$ 45.14
Tax at 5% of the total amount	$ 2.26
Amount to pay	$ 47.40

9 Reverse percentages (page 40)

Q1 $380

Comments
After a reduction of 5%, the price represents 95%
(100% − 5%) of the original cost of the holiday.
95% of the original cost of the holiday = $361
1% of the original cost of the holiday = $$\frac{361}{95}$$ = $3.80
100% of the original cost = 100 × $3.80 = $380

Q2 £9500

Comments
After a depreciation of 45%, the price represents
55% (100% − 45%) of the original purchase price.
55% of original purchase price = $5225
1% of original purchase price = $$\frac{5225}{55}$$ = $95
100% of original price = 100 × $95 = $9500

10 Ratios and proportional division (page 42)

Q1 25 : 3

Comments
To find the ratio of 5 km to 600 m, you need to
express both parts in the same units. 5 km = 5000 m
so the ratio is 5000 : 600 = 25 : 3 in its simplest form.

Q2 1 : 2.5 or 1 : $2\frac{1}{2}$

Comments
2 : 5 = 1 : 2.5   Dividing both sides by 2 to make an
equivalent ratio in the form 1 : n.

Q3 4 : 3

Comments
$\frac{1}{3} : \frac{1}{4}$ = 4 : 3   This is found by multiplying both
sides by 12 to make an equivalent
ratio.

Q4 $12, $18 and $42

Comments
For the ratio 2 : 3 : 7, the number of parts
= 2 + 3 + 7 = 12.
The value of each part = $72 ÷ 12 = $6.
The children raise $12 (2 parts at £6), $18
(3 parts at $6) and $42 (7 parts at $6 each).
Check $12 + $18 + $42 = $72 as required.

11 Degrees of accuracy (page 44)

Q1 174.9 = 175 (3 s.f.)
174.9 = 170 (2 s.f.)
174.9 = 200 (1 s.f.)

Comments
174.9 = 175 (3 s.f.)
174 are the first 3 s.f. and the next most
significant figure is 9. As 9 is bigger than 5, add 1
to the previous digit, giving 5.
The number 175 = 180 (2 s.f.) but you must round
the original 174.9.

174.9 = 170 (2 s.f.)
17 are the first 2 s.f. and the next most significant
figure is 4. As 4 is less than 5, leave the previous
digit alone. Fill with 0s to keep the number at its
correct size.

174.9 = 200 (1 s.f.)
1 is the first s.f. and the next most significant
figure is 7. As 7 is bigger than 5, add 1 to the
previous digit, giving 2. Fill with 0s to keep the
number at its correct size.

Q2 699.06 = 699 (3 s.f.)
699.06 = 700 (2 s.f.)
699.06 = 700 (1 s.f.)

Comments
699.06 = 699 (3 s.f.)
699 are the first 3 s.f. and the next most
significant figure is 0.
As 0 is less than 5, leave the previous digit alone.

699.06 = 700 (2 s.f.)
Here the second 0 is being included as a
significant figure.
69 are the first 2 s.f. and the next most significant
figure is 9.
As 9 is bigger than 5, add 1 to the previous digit,
giving 70.
Fill with 0s to keep the number at its correct size.

699.06 = 700 (1 s.f.)
6 is the first s.f. and the next most significant
figure is 9.
As 9 is bigger than 5, add 1 to the previous digit,
giving 7
Fill with 0s to keep the number at its correct size.

Q3 5

> **Comments**
>
> $$\frac{3.87 \times 5.07^3}{5.16 \times 19.87} \approx \frac{4 \times 125}{5 \times 20} = \frac{500}{100} = 5$$
>
> Take 5.07^3 as approximately $5^3 = 125$.

Q4 1

> **Comments**
>
> $$\frac{2.78 + \pi}{\sqrt{5.95 \times 6.32}} \approx \frac{3 + 3}{\sqrt{6 \times 6}} = \frac{6}{6} = 1 \quad \text{Take } \pi \approx 3.}$$

Q5 10

> **Comments**
>
> $$\frac{59.96}{40.21 + 19.86} + \sqrt{80.652} \approx \frac{60}{40 + 20} + \sqrt{81} = 1 + 9 = 10$$

12 Upper and lower bounds (page 45)

Q1 26.5225 cm² minimum
27.5625 cm² maximum

> **Comments**
>
> Area of square = length × length
> minimum length = 5.15 cm
> area = 5.15 × 5.15 = 26.5225 cm²
> maximum length = 5.25 cm
> area = 5.25 × 5.25 = 27.5625 cm²

Q2 $1300.01

> **Comments**
>
> As each price is given to the nearest $100 then:
> For the sports car at $18 700:
> maximum = $18 749.99
> Note that $18 750 would be rounded up to $18 800.
> minimum = $18 650.00
> You must always take care when working with
> money or ages to identify lower and upper bounds.
> For the family car at $17 300:
> maximum = $17 349.99
> Note that $17 350 would be rounded up to $17 400.
> minimum = $17 250.00
> Least possible difference in price
> $= S_{min} - C_{max} = \$18\,650 - \$17\,349.99 - \$1300.01$

Q3 a 3966.25 mm²   b 1.017 964 1

> **Comments**
>
> **a)** Area $\triangle ABC = \frac{1}{2} \times$ base × height
> $= \frac{1}{2} \times 83.5 \times 95$ Using the upper bound for each.
>   = 3966.25 mm²
> **b)** $\tan x° = \frac{BC}{AB} = \frac{85}{83.5}$ Using the lower bound for the numerator and the upper bound for the denominator.
>   = 1.017 964 1

13 Standard form involving positive and negative indices (page 47)

Q1 a 2.5×10^5 miles   b 1.67×10^{-21} milligrams

> **Comments**
>
> **a)** $A = 2.5$ and $n = 5$.
> **b)** $A = 1.67$ and $n = {}^-21$. The negative value of n tells you that the number is very small.

Q2 a (i) 4×10^7 (ii) 0.000 03
    b 1.2×10^3

> **Comments**
>
> **a)** (i) $A = 4$ and $n = 7$. (ii) $A = 3$ and $n = {}^-5$.
> **b)** $4 \times 10^7 \times 3 \times 10^{-5} = 4 \times 3 \times 10^7 \times 10^{-5}$
>   Working in standard form
> $= 12 \times 10^{7-5}$ Laws of indices
> $= 1.2 \times 10^1 \times 10^2$
> $= 1.2 \times 10^{1+2}$
> $= 1.2 \times 10^3$

Q3 a 1.19×10^5 b 7.81×10^{-4}
    c 2.4×10^2 d 5×10^6

> **Comments**
>
> **a)** $2.69 \times 10^5 - 1.5 \times 10^5 = (2.69 - 1.5) \times 10^5$
> $= 1.19 \times 10^5$
> **b)** $4.31 \times 10^{-4} + 3.5 \times 10^{-4} = 7.81 \times 10^{-4}$
> **c)** $(6 \times 10^3) \times (4 \times 10^{-2})$
> $= (6 \times 4) \times 10^3 \times 10^{-2}$
> $= 24 \times 10^{3-2} = 24 \times 10^1$
> $= 2.4 \times 10^2$
>   Rewriting in standard form where $24 = 2.4 \times 10^1$.
> **d)** $(3 \times 10^{11}) \div (6 \times 10^4)$
> $= (3 \div 6) \times (10^{11} \div 10^4)$
> $= 0.5 \times 10^{11-4} = 0.5 \times 10^7$
> $= 5 \times 10^6$
>   Rewriting in standard form where $0.5 = 5 \times 10^{-1}$.

Q4 9.46×10^{12} km

Comment

If light travels at 3×10^5 km per second

then it travels 3×10^5 km in one second

$3 \times 10^5 \times 60$ km in one minute

$3 \times 10^5 \times 60 \times 60$ km in one hour

$3 \times 10^5 \times 60 \times 60 \times 24$ km in one day

$3 \times 10^5 \times 60 \times 60 \times 24 \times 365$ km in one year

$= 9\ 460\ 800\ 000\ 000$ km

$= 9.4608 \times 10^{12}$ km

$= 9.46 \times 10^{12}$ km (to an appropriate degree of accuracy)

14 Using a calculator (page 49)

Q1 26.01

Q2 3.456 607 1

Q3 0.031 25

Q4 500

Q5 0.0483

Q6 $\frac{9}{14}$ or 0.642 857 1

Q7 $1\frac{2}{9}$ or 1.222 22

Comments

Refer to your user manual if you have any difficulties with this work.

Q8 a 0.611 835 415

b 0.61 (2 d.p.)

Comments

The numbers in the question are given to two places of decimals, so this is an appropriate degree of accuracy for the answer.

Q9 a 4.232

b (i) $(14.5 - 2.6) \times 4.5 - 3.6 = 49.95$

(ii) $(14.5 - 2.6) \times (4.5 - 3.6) = 10.71$

Comment

These are the only combinations that give the required results.

ALGEBRA

15 Use of symbols (page 53)

Q1 a $a + 6b - 5c$ b $7x + 7y - xy$

c $x^3 - 6x^2 + 3x - 2$ d $24xyz$

e $10a^3$ f $16a^4b^3c^2$ g $2mn^2$

Comments

a) $3a + 6b - 2a - 5c = 3a - 2a + 6b - 5c$

Collecting like terms together along with their signs.

$$= a + 6b - 5c$$

b) $5x + 7y - 3xy + 2x + 2yx$

$= 5x + 2x + 7y - 3xy + 2xy$ Collecting

like terms and rewriting $2yx$ as $2xy$.

$= 7x + 7y - xy$

c) $x^3 + 3x^2 - 9x^2 - 4x + 7x - 2$

$= x^3 - 6x^2 + 3x - 2$ Collecting like terms.

d) $3x \times 4y \times 2z = 3 \times 4 \times 2 \times x \times y \times z$

$= 24xyz$

e) $5a \times 2a^2 = 5 \times 2 \times a \times a^2$

$= 10 \times a \times a \times a$ As $a^2 = a \times a$.

$= 10a^3$

f) $(4abc)^2 \times a^2b = 4abc \times 4abc \times a^2b$

$= 16a^2b^2c^2 \times a^2b$

Multiplying $4abc \times 4abc$.

$= 16a^4b^3c^2$

g) $8mn^3 \div 4n = \dfrac{8 \times m \times n \times n \times n}{4 \times n}$

$= \dfrac{{}^2 8 \times m \times n \times n \times n^1}{{}_1 4 \times n_1} = 2mn^2$

16 Algebraic indices (page 54)

Q1 a x^5 b y^6

c $8a^{12}$ d d^3

e $2x^3$ f $\frac{1}{3}x^{-2}$ or $\dfrac{1}{3x^2}$

g $8x$ h $x^{\frac{11}{12}}$

Comments

a) $x^4 \times x = x^{4+1} = x^5$ As $x = x^1$.

b) $(y^3)^2 = y^3 \times y^3 = y^{3+3} = y^6$

c) $(2a^4)^3 = (2a^4) \times (2a^4) \times (2a^4)$

$= 2 \times a^4 \times 2 \times a^4 \times 2 \times a^4$ Removing the brackets.

$= 8 \times a^4 \times a^4 \times a^4$ As $2 \times 2 \times 2 = 8$.

$= 8 \times a^{4+4+4} = 8a^{12}$

d) $d^{12} \div d^9 = d^{12-9} = d^3$

e) $6x^7 \div 3x^4 = 2x^{7-4} = 2x^3$

f) $3x^6 \div 9x^8 = \frac{1}{3}x^{6-8} = \frac{1}{3}x^{-2}$ As $\frac{3}{9} = \frac{1}{3}$.

$x^{-2} = \dfrac{1}{x^2}$ so $\frac{1}{3}x^{-2}$ can be written as $\dfrac{1}{3x^2}$.

g) $(2x^{\frac{1}{3}})^3 = 2^3 \times (x^{\frac{1}{3}})^3$

$\qquad = 8 \times x^1$

$\qquad = 8x$

h) $\dfrac{x^{\frac{1}{2}} \times x^{\frac{3}{4}}}{x^{\frac{1}{3}}} = x^{\frac{1}{2} + \frac{3}{4} - \frac{1}{3}}$

$\qquad = x^{\frac{6}{12} + \frac{9}{12} - \frac{4}{12}}$ Converting to fraction with common denominator

$\qquad = x^{\frac{11}{12}}$

Q2 a $x = 4$ **b** $y = 2$ **c** $x = 1$

Comments

a) $3^x = 81$ $3^4 = 81$ so $x = 4$

b) $2^{3y} = 64$ $2^6 = 64$ so $3y = 6$ or $y = 2$

c) $5^{2x+1} = 125$ $5^3 = 125$ so $2x + 1 = 3$

$\qquad 2x = 2$ or $x = 1$

17 Expanding and factorising (page 59)

Q1 a $x - 3y$ **b** $3a + 9b - 16c$

     c $2a^2 - ab + 2b^3$

Comments

a) $5x - (3y + 4x)$

$\qquad = 5x - 1 \times 3y - 1 \times 4x$

$\qquad$ The $-$ outside the bracket is taken as $^-1$.

$\qquad = 5x - 3y - 4x$ Multiplying out.

$\qquad = x - 3y$ Collecting like terms together.

b) $5(a + b - 2c) - 2(a - 2b + 3c)$

$\qquad = 5 \times a + 5 \times b + 5 \times {}^-2c$

$\qquad \quad - 2 \times a - 2 \times {}^-2b - 2 \times 3c$

$\qquad = 5a + 5b - 10c - 2a + 4b - 6c$

$\qquad = 3a + 9b - 16c$ Collecting like terms together.

c) $a(2a + b) - 2b(a - b^2)$

$\qquad = a \times 2a + a \times b - 2b \times a - 2b \times {}^-b^2$

$\qquad = 2a^2 + ab - 2ab + 2b^3$ $a \times a = a^2$

$\qquad\qquad\qquad\qquad\qquad\qquad$ ba is the same as ab

$\qquad\qquad\qquad\qquad\qquad\qquad$ ${}^-2b \times {}^-b^2 = 2b^3$

$\qquad = 2a^2 - ab + 2b^3$ Collecting like terms together.

Q2 a $2x(2x - 3)$ **b** $2(lw + wh + hl)$

     c $5xy(x - 2y)$

Comments

a) $4x^2 - 6x = 2x(2x - 3)$

$\qquad 2x$ is a common factor, $4x^2 = 2x \times 2x$ and $6x = 2x \times 3$.

b) $2lw + 2wh + 2hl = 2(lw + wh + hl)$

$\qquad 2$ is the only factor common to all three terms.

c) $5x^2y - 10xy^2 = 5xy(x - 2y)$

$\qquad 5xy$ is a common factor, $5x^2y = 5xy \times x$ and $10xy^2 = 5xy \times 2y$.

Q3 a (i) $a + 3b$ (ii) $2x^2 + x$

    b (i) $8x - 12$ (ii) $pq - p^3$

    c $5p + 16$

Comments

b) (ii) Remember that $p \times p^2 = p^3$

c) $5(3p - 2) - 2(5p - 3) = 15p + 10 - 10p + 6 = 5p + 16$

Q4 a $x^2 + 5x + 4$ **b** $6y^2 - 31y + 35$

    c $9x^2 + 6x + 1$

Comments

a) $(x + 1)(x + 4)$

$\qquad = x \times x + x \times 4 + 1 \times x + 1 \times 4$

$\qquad = x^2 + 4x + 1x + 4$

$\qquad = x^2 + 5x + 4$ Collecting like terms.

b) $(3y - 5)(2y - 7)$

$\qquad = 3y \times 2y + 3y \times {}^-7 + {}^-5 \times 2y + {}^-5 \times {}^-7$

$\qquad = 6y^2 - 21y - 10y + 35$ As ${}^-5 \times {}^-7 = {}^+35$.

$\qquad = 6y^2 - 31y + 35$ Collecting like terms.

c) $(3x + 1)^2 = (3x + 1)(3x + 1)$

$\qquad = 3x \times 3x + 3x \times 1 + 1 \times 3x + 1 \times 1$

$\qquad = 9x^2 + 3x + 3x + 1$

$\qquad = 9x^2 + 6x + 1$ Collecting like terms.

Q5 a $(x + 2)(x + 4)$ **b** $(x + 1)(x - 2)$

    c $(x + 2)(x - 9)$

Comments

a) $x^2 + 6x + 8$

$\qquad = (x \quad)(x \quad)$ Look for numbers that multiply together to give a product of ${}^+8$.

$\qquad\qquad\qquad\qquad\qquad$ Try ${}^+1 \times {}^+8$ ${}^-1 \times {}^-8$

$\qquad\qquad\qquad\qquad\qquad\qquad\quad$ ${}^+2 \times {}^+4$ ${}^-2 \times {}^-4$

$\qquad = (x + 2)(x + 4)$ Check by multiplying out.

b) $x^2 - x - 2$

$\qquad = (x \quad)(x \quad)$ Look for numbers that multiply together to give a product of ${}^-2$.

$\qquad\qquad\qquad\qquad\qquad$ Try ${}^-1 \times {}^+2$ ${}^+1 \times {}^-2$

$\qquad = (x + 1)(x - 2)$ Check by multiplying out.

c) $x^2 - 7x - 18$

$\qquad = (x \quad)(x \quad)$ Look for numbers that multiply together to give a product of ${}^-18$.

$\qquad\qquad\qquad\qquad\qquad$ Try ${}^-1 \times {}^+18$ ${}^+1 \times {}^-18$

$\qquad\qquad\qquad\qquad\qquad\qquad\quad$ ${}^-2 \times {}^+9$ ${}^+2 \times {}^-9$

$\qquad\qquad\qquad\qquad\qquad\qquad\quad$ ${}^-3 \times {}^+6$ ${}^+3 \times {}^-6$

$\qquad = (x + 2)(x - 9)$ Check by multiplying out.

Q6 a $x^2 + 2xy + y^2$ **b** 25

Comments

a) $(x + y)^2 = (x + y)(x + y) = x^2 + xy + xy + y^2$
$= x^2 + 2xy + y^2$

b) $3.47^2 + 2 \times 3.47 \times 1.53 + 1.53^2 = (3.47 + 1.53)^2 = 5^2 = 25$

Q7 $x = \frac{1}{4}$

Comments

$1 + \dfrac{3x^2}{x - 1} = 3x$ Multiply throughout by x.

$1(x - 1) + 3x^2 = 3x(x - 1)$ Multiply throughout by $(x - 1)$.

$x - 1 + 3x^2 = 3x^2 - 3x$ Expanding.

$4x - 1 = 0$ Simplifying.

$x = \frac{1}{4}$

Q8 $x = \frac{4}{5}$ or 0.8

Comments

Using the fact that $x^2 - 1 = (x + 1)(x - 1)$:

$\dfrac{2}{x + 1} + \dfrac{3}{x - 1} = \dfrac{5}{(x + 1)(x - 1)}$

Now multiply each term by $(x + 1)(x - 1)$:

$\dfrac{2\cancel{(x + 1)}(x - 1)}{\cancel{x + 1}} + \dfrac{3(x + 1)\cancel{(x - 1)}}{\cancel{x - 1}} = \dfrac{5\cancel{(x + 1)}\cancel{(x - 1)}}{\cancel{(x + 1)}\cancel{(x - 1)}}$

$2(x - 1) + 3(x + 1) = 5$

$2x - 2 + 3x + 3 = 5$

$5x = 4$

$x = \frac{4}{5}$ or 0.8

18 Changing the subject (page 61)

Q1 a $r = \dfrac{C}{2\pi}$ **b** $u = v - at$

   c $a = \dfrac{v - u}{t}$ **d** $r = \pm\sqrt{\dfrac{A}{\pi}}$

   e $h = \dfrac{V}{\pi r^2}$ **f** $r = \pm\sqrt{\dfrac{V}{\pi h}}$

   g $T = \dfrac{100 I}{PR}$

Comments

a) $r = \dfrac{C}{2\pi}$ Dividing both sides by 2π.

b) $u = v - at$ Subtracting at from both sides.

c) $at = v - u$ Subtracting u from both sides.

$a = \dfrac{v - u}{t}$ Dividing both sides by t.

d) $r^2 = \dfrac{A}{\pi}$ Dividing both sides by π.

$r = \pm\sqrt{\dfrac{A}{\pi}}$ Taking the square root of both sides.

e) $h = \dfrac{V}{\pi r^2}$ Dividing both sides by πr^2.

f) $r^2 = \dfrac{V}{\pi h}$ Dividing both sides by πh.

$r = \pm\sqrt{\dfrac{V}{\pi h}}$ Taking the square root of both sides.

g) $100 I = PRT$ Multiplying both sides by 100.

$T = \dfrac{100 I}{PR}$ Dividing both sides by PR.

Q2 $b = \pm\sqrt{\dfrac{m}{a}}$

Comments

$a = \dfrac{m}{b^2}$

$ab^2 = m$ Multiplying both sides by b^2.

$b^2 = \dfrac{m}{a}$ Dividing both sides by a.

$b = \pm\sqrt{\dfrac{m}{a}}$ Taking the square root of both sides.

Q3 $s = \dfrac{r^2 t}{1 - r^2}$

Comments

$r^2 = \dfrac{s}{s + t}$ Squaring both sides.

$r^2(s + t) = s$ Multiplying both sides by $(s + t)$.

$r^2 s + r^2 t = s$ Expanding the brackets.

$s - r^2 s = r^2 t$ Collecting together terms in s on one side.

$s(1 - r^2) = r^2 t$ Factorising the terms in s.

$s = \dfrac{r^2 t}{1 - r^2}$ Dividing both sides by $(1 - r^2)$ to make s the subject.

Q4 a $x = \frac{3}{5}$ or 0.6   **b** $t = \pm\sqrt{\dfrac{1 - x}{1 + x}}$

Comments

a) $x = \dfrac{1 - t^2}{1 + t^2}$

$x = \dfrac{1 - \left(\frac{1}{2}\right)^2}{1 + \left(\frac{1}{2}\right)^2}$ Substituting $\frac{1}{2}$ for t.

$x = \dfrac{\frac{3}{4}}{\frac{5}{4}} = \dfrac{3}{5}$

ANSWERS AND SOLUTIONS

b) $x = \dfrac{1 - t^2}{1 + t^2}$

$x(1 + t^2) = 1 - t^2$ Multiplying both sides by $(1 + t^2)$.

$x + xt^2 = 1 - t^2$ Expanding the brackets.

$xt^2 + t^2 = 1 - x$ Collecting together terms in t on one side only.

$t^2(x + 1) = 1 - x$ Factorising the terms in t^2.

$t^2 = \dfrac{1 - x}{1 + x}$ Dividing both sides by $x + 1$ to make t^2 the subject.

$t = \pm\sqrt{\dfrac{1 - x}{1 + x}}$ Taking the square root of both sides to make t the subject.

Q5 a $N = \dfrac{(L + W) \times H}{6}$

    b $\dfrac{PH}{12}$

Comments

a) $L + W$

$(L + W) \times H$

$\dfrac{(L + W) \times H}{6}$

$N = \dfrac{(L + W) \times H}{6}$

b) $P = 2L + 2W$

$P = 2(L + W)$

$L + W = \dfrac{P}{2}$

$N = \dfrac{(L + W) \times H}{6}$

$= \dfrac{P/2 \times H}{6}$

$= \dfrac{PH}{12}$

19 Substitution (page 62)

Q1 33π cm^2

Comments

Substituting $r = 3$ (as the radius is 3 cm) and $l = 8$ (as the slant height is 8 cm) in the equation:
$A = \pi r l + \pi r^2$
$A = \pi \times 3 \times 8 + \pi \times 3 \times 3$ As $r^2 = r \times r$
$A = \pi \times 24 + \pi \times 9$

    Using the fact that
    $\pi \times 24 + \pi \times 9 = \pi \times (24 + 9) = \pi \times 33$
$A = 33\pi$ cm^2

Q2 a $u = 8$ **b** $u = 7.5$ or $7\frac{1}{2}$

Comments

a) Substituting $f = 4$ and $v = 8$ in the formula
$\dfrac{1}{u} = \dfrac{1}{f} - \dfrac{1}{v}$:
$\dfrac{1}{u} = \dfrac{1}{4} - \dfrac{1}{8}$
$\dfrac{1}{u} = \dfrac{1}{8}$ As $\dfrac{1}{4} - \dfrac{1}{8} = \dfrac{1}{8}$
$u = 8$

b) Substituting $f = 3$ and $v = 5$ in the formula
$\dfrac{1}{u} = \dfrac{1}{f} - \dfrac{1}{v}$:
$\dfrac{1}{u} = \dfrac{1}{3} - \dfrac{1}{5}$
$\dfrac{1}{u} = \dfrac{2}{15}$ As $\dfrac{1}{3} - \dfrac{1}{5} = \dfrac{5}{15} - \dfrac{3}{15} = \dfrac{2}{15}$

$u = \dfrac{15}{2}$ Reciprocating both sides.
    $u = 7.5$ or $7\frac{1}{2}$

20 Proportion (page 63)

Q1 a $T = 90$ **b** $W = 4$

Comments

If T is proportional to the positive square root of W then $T \propto \sqrt{W}$ and $T = k\sqrt{W}$.
Since $T = 36$ when $W = 16$ then $36 = k\sqrt{16}$.
$36 = k \times 4$
i.e. $k = 9$
The equation is $T = 9\sqrt{W}$.
a) When $W = 100$ then:
    $T = 9\sqrt{100}$
      $= 9 \times 10$
      $= 90$
a) When $T = 18$ then $18 = 9\sqrt{W}$
    $\sqrt{W} = 2$
      $W = 4$ as $\sqrt{4} = 2$

Q2 a $V = \frac{1}{9}$

    b $\dfrac{3}{1000}$ or 0.003 or 3×10^{-3}

Comments

If V varies inversely as the cube of Y then $V \propto \dfrac{1}{Y^3}$ and
$V = \dfrac{k}{Y^3}$.
Since $V = \frac{3}{8}$ when $Y = 2$ then:
$\dfrac{3}{8} = \dfrac{k}{2^3}$
$\dfrac{3}{8} = \dfrac{k}{8}$
$k = 3$
The equation is $V = \dfrac{3}{Y^3}$.

200

a) When $Y = 3$ then:

$V = \dfrac{3}{3^3} = \dfrac{3}{27}$

$= \dfrac{1}{9}$ Cancelling down.

b) When $Y = 10$ then:

$V = \dfrac{3}{10^3} = \dfrac{3}{1000}$ or 0.003 or 3×10^{-3}

Q3 a $y = \dfrac{25}{16}x^2$

   b $6\frac{1}{4}$ or 6.25

   c $\pm 2\frac{2}{5}$ or ± 2.4

Comments

a) $y \propto x^2$ so $y = k\,x^2$

When $x = 4$, $y = 25$

so $25 = k\,4^2$

$25 = k\,16$

$k = \frac{25}{16}$

so $y = \frac{25}{16} \times x^2$

b) When $x = 2$, $y = \frac{25}{16} \times 2^2$

$y = \frac{25}{4} = 6\frac{1}{4}$ or 6.25

c) When $y = 9$

$9 = \frac{25}{16} \times x^2$

$x^2 = 9 \times \frac{16}{25}$

$x = \dfrac{9 \times 16}{25}$

$x = \pm \frac{12}{5} = \pm 2\frac{2}{5}$ or ± 2.4

21 Solving equations (page 65)

Q1 a $x = 3.5$ **b** $x = 1.5$ or $1\frac{1}{2}$

   c $z = 9$ **d** $y = 5$

   e $x = 7$ **f** $x = 5$

   g $y = 27$ **h** $x = 7$

Comments

a) $3x = 10.5$ Subtracting 4.5 from both sides.

        $x = 3.5$ Dividing both sides by 3.

b) $x = \frac{30}{20} = 1.5$ or $1\frac{1}{2}$

c) $27 = 3z$ Multiplying both sides by z.

        $z = 9$ Dividing both sides by 3.

d) $3y = 20 - y$ Subtracting 5 from both sides.

        $4y = 20$ Adding y to both sides.

        $y = 5$ Dividing both sides by 4.

e) $8x - 12 = 44$ Expanding the brackets.

       $8x = 56$ Adding 12 to both sides.

        $x = 7$ Dividing both sides by 8.

f) $4x + 1 = 3x + 6$ Expanding the brackets.

     $4x = 3x + 5$ Subtracting 1 from both sides.

        $x = 5$ Subtracting $3x$ from both sides.

g) $y + 3 = 30$ Multiplying both sides by 10.

        $y = 27$ Subtracting 3 from both sides.

h) $6x - 12 - 4x - 2 = 0$

Remember the $-$ sign outside the second bracket.

    $2x - 14 = 0$ Collecting like terms.

       $2x = 14$ Adding 14 to both sides.

        $x = 7$ Dividing both sides by 2.

Q2 25, 26 and 27

Comments

Let the three consecutive numbers be x, $x + 1$ and $x + 2$, then:

$x + (x + 1) + (x + 2) = 78$

     $3x + 3 = 78$ Collecting like terms.

       $3x = 75$ Subtracting 3 from both sides.

        $x = 25$ Dividing by 3.

So the numbers are 25, 26 and 27.

Q3 $x = 25$

Comments

The angles of a triangle add up to $180°$ so:

$x° + 2x° + (3x + 30)° = 180°$ and $x = 25$

Q4 a $\$(16x + 16)$

   b (i) $16x + 16 = 72$

         (ii) $\$3.50$ and $\$5.50$

Comments

a) Total cost $= 8 \times x + 8 \times (x + 2) = 8x + 8x + 16$

             $= 16x + 16$

b) (i) $16x + 16 = 72$

    (ii) $16(x + 1) = 72$

        $x + 1 = 4.5$ Dividing both sides by 16.

        $x = 3.5$ Subtracting 1 from each side.

    Cost of a cup $= \$x = \$3.50$

    (Remember to include the zero, as this is money.)

    Cost of a mug $= \$x + 2 = \$5.50$

    (Remember to include the zero, as this is money.)

22 Simultaneous equations (page 68)

Q1 **a** $x = 4$ and $y = 2$

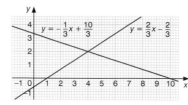

b $x = 12$ and $y = 3$

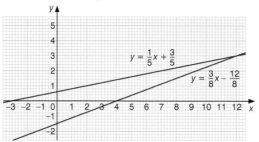

c $x = \frac{10}{7}$ or $1\frac{3}{7}$ and $y = \frac{3}{7}$

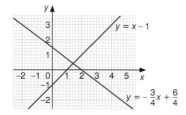

Comments

a) $x + 3y = 10$
$2x - 3y = 2$
(i) Graphical method
Plot $y = -\frac{1}{3}x + \frac{10}{3}$ and $y = \frac{2}{3}x - \frac{2}{3}$.
Intersect at (4, 2).
(ii) Substitution method
Substitute $x = 10 - 3y$ in the second equation.
(iii) Elimination method
Add the two equations to eliminate the term in y.

b) $x = 5y - 3$
$3x - 8y = 12$
(i) Graphical method
Plot $y = \frac{1}{5}x + \frac{3}{5}$ and $y = \frac{3}{8}x - \frac{12}{8}$.
Intersect at (12, 3).
(ii) Substitution method
Substitute $x = 5y - 3$ in the second equation.
(iii) Elimination method
Rewrite the first equation as $x - 5y = {}^{-}3$ and then $3x - 15y = {}^{-}9$ (multiplying by 3). Subtract the two equations to eliminate the term in x.

c) $x - 1 = y$
$3x + 4y = 6$
(i) Graphical method
Plot $y = x - 1$ and $y = \frac{-3}{4}x + \frac{6}{4}$.
Intersect at $(\frac{10}{7}, \frac{3}{7})$.
(ii) Substitution method
Substitute $y = x - 1$ in the second equation.
(iii) Elimination method
Rewrite the first equation as $x - y = 1$ and then $4x - 4y = 4$ (multiplying by 4). Add the two equations to eliminate the term in y.

Q2 $x = 4.5, y = -3$

Comment

$6x - 2y = 33$ ①
$4x + 3y = 9$ ②
①× 3 $18x - 6y = 99$
②× 2 $8x + 6y = 18$
Adding: $26x = 117$
⇒ $x = 4.5$
Substituting in ①: $6x - 2y = 33$
$6 \times 4.5 - 2y = 33$
$27 - 2y = 33$
$-2y = 6$
$y = -3$

Q3 16 and 20

Comments

Let the two numbers be x and y (say).
$x + y = 36$ As their sum is 36.
$x - y = 4$ As their difference is 4.
Solving these simultaneous equations by the elimination method and adding the two equations:
$(x + y) + (x - y) = 36 + 4$
$2x = 40$
$x = 20$
Substituting in the first equation:
$x + y = 36$
$20 + y = 36$ As $x = 20$.
$y = 16$
So the two numbers are 20 and 16.

Q4 The cost of a skirt is $8.00 and the cost of a shirt is $16.50.

The cost of a skirt and a shirt is $24.50.

Comments

Let t be the cost of one skirt and s be the cost of one shirt.

$2t + s = 32.50$ As the cost of two skirts and a shirt is $32.50.

$t + 2s = 41.00$ As the cost of one skirt and two shirts is $41.00.

Solving these simultaneous equations by the substitution method:

Using $2t + s = 32.50$ you can write $s = 32.50 - 2t$.

Substituting this value of s into the second equation:

$t + 2s = 41$ 41 is the same as 41.00

$t + 2(32.50 - 2t) = 41$ Substituting $s = 32.50 - 2t$.

$t + 65 - 4t = 41$ Expanding the brackets.

$-3t = {}^-24$ Collecting like terms on each side.

$t = 8$ Dividing both sides by $^-3$.

You can now use $s = 32.50 - 2t$ with $t = 8$ to find s.

$s = 32.50 - 2t$

$s = 32.50 - 2 \times 8$ As $t = 8$.

$s = 16.50$

The cost of a skirt is $8.00 and the cost of a shirt is $16.50.

A skirt and a shirt together cost $24.50.

Q5 **a** $x = 0.2, y = 0.2$ and $x = 2, y = 20$

b $x = 3, y = 4$ and $x = 4, y = 3$

Comments

a) To solve the simultaneous equations, substitute the value of $y = 11x - 2$ into $y = 5x^2$.

$11x - 2 = 5x^2$ Substituting $y = 11x - 2$.

$5x^2 - 11x + 2 = 0$ Collecting terms on one side.

$(5x - 1)(x - 2) = 0$ Factorising the quadratic equation.

Either $x = 0.2$ or $x = 2$.

If $x = 0.2$ then $y = 0.2$. As $y = 5x^2$.

If $x = 2$ then $y = 20$ As $y = 5x^2$ again.

b) To solve the simultaneous equations, use $x + y = 7$ to substitute the value $y = 7 - x$ into $x^2 + y^2 = 25$.

$x^2 + (7 - x)^2 = 25$ Substituting $y = 7 - x$.

$x^2 + (49 - 14x + x^2) = 25$ Expanding the brackets.

$x^2 + 49 - 14x + x^2 = 25$ Expanding the brackets.

$2x^2 - 14x + 24 = 0$ Collecting terms on one side.

$x^2 - 7x + 12 = 0$ Dividing throughout by 2.

$(x - 3)(x - 4) = 0$ Factorising the quadratic.

Either $x = 3$ or $x = 4$.

If $x = 3$ then $y = 4$. As $y = 7 - x$.

If $x = 4$ then $y = 3$. As $y = 7 - x$ again.

Q6 **a** $x^2 + y^2 = 25$

If the line cuts the curve, the x-value will be given by:

$x^2 + 6^2 = 25$

$\Rightarrow x^2 + 36 = 25$

$\Rightarrow x^2 = -11$

This is impossible, since you cannot take the square root of a negative number. Bill is wrong.

b $x = 3, y = 4$ or $x = -1.4$ and $y = -4.8$

Comments

b) $x^2 + y^2 = 25$

$y = 2x - 2$

Substitute for y in the first equation.

$x^2 + (2x - 2)^2 = 25$

$x^2 + (4x^2 - 8x + 4) = 25$ $(2x - 2)^2 = (2x - 2)(2x - 2)$
$= 4x^2 - 8x + 4$

$5x^2 - 8x + 4 = 25$

$5x^2 - 8x - 21 = 0$

$(5x + 7)(x - 3) = 0$ Factorising.

$5x + 7 = 0$ or $x - 3 = 0$

$\Rightarrow x = -1.4$ $\Rightarrow x = 3$

If $x = -1.4$, $y = 2x - 2 = -4.8$

If $x = 3$, $y = 2x - 2 = 2 \times 3 - 2 = 6 - 2 = 4$

23 Quadratic equations (page 71)

Q1 **a** $x = 5$ and $x = 7$ **b** $x = 6$ and $x = -\frac{1}{2}$

c $x = 1$ and $x = -5$

Comments

a) $(x - 5)(x - 7) = 0$ Either $(x - 5) = 0$ or $(x - 7) = 0$

The solutions are $x = 5$ and $x = 7$.

b) $(x - 6)(2x + 1) = 0$ Either $(x - 6) = 0$ or $(2x + 1) = 0$

The solutions are $x = 6$ and $x = -\frac{1}{2}$.

c) $x^2 + 4x + 5 = 0$

$(x - 1)(x + 5) = 0$ Either $(x - 1) = 0$ or $(x + 5) = 0$

The solutions are $x = 1$ and $x = {}^-5$.

Q2 **a** $(x - 2)(x - 5) = 0$ or $x^2 - 7x + 10 = 0$
   b $(x + 3)(5x - 1) = 0$ or $5x^2 + 14x - 3 = 0$

Comments

Reverse the above process to find the factors.

a) $x = 2$ and $x = 5$
   Either $(x - 2) = 0$ or $(x - 5) = 0$
   $(x - 2)(x - 5) = 0$ or $x^2 - 7x + 10 = 0$

b) $x = {}^-3$ and $x = \frac{1}{5}$
   Either $(x + 3) = 0$ or $(x - \frac{1}{5}) = 0$
   $x - \frac{1}{5} = 0$ gives $5x - 1 = 0$ Multiplying both
                                            sides by 5.
   $(x + 3)(5x - 1) = 0$ or $5x^2 + 14x - 3 = 0$

Q3 $x = 6$ and $x = {}^-1$

Comments

$x^2 - 5x + 2 = 8$
$x^2 - 5x - 6 = 0$ Writing in the form
                     $ax^2 + bx + c = 0$.
$(x - 6)(x + 1) = 0$ Factorising.
Either $(x - 6) = 0$ or $(x + 1) = 0$.
The solutions are $x = 6$ and $x = {}^-1$.

Q4 width = 8 metres, length = 12 metres

Comments

Let the width be x centimetres, then the length is
$(x + 4)$ centimetres.
   Area $= x(x + 4) = 96$
        $x^2 + 4x = 96$ Expanding the brackets.
   $x^2 + 4x - 96 = 0$ Writing in the form
                     $ax^2 + bx + c = 0$.
   $(x - 8)(x + 12) = 0$ Factorising Either $x = 8$ or
                          $x = {}^-12$.
But a width of $^-12$ centimetres is impossible so
ignore this value. Since the length is 4 cm greater
than the width, this gives width = 8 cm and
length = 12 cm.

Q5 **a** $x = 0.414$ or $x = {}^-2.41$ (3 s.f.)
   b $x = 4.56$ or $x = 0.438$ (3 s.f.)

Comments

a) Comparing $x^2 + 2x - 1 = 0$ with the general
   form $ax^2 + bx + c = 0$:
   $a = 1, b = 2, c = {}^-1$.
   $x = \dfrac{{}^-2 \pm \sqrt{2^2 - 4 \times 1 \times {}^-1}}{2 \times 1}$
   $x = \dfrac{{}^-2 \pm \sqrt{8}}{2}$
   $x = \dfrac{{}^-2 + 2.828\,427\,125}{2}$
   or $x = \dfrac{{}^-2 - 2.828\,427\,125}{2}$

   $x = 0.414$ or $x = {}^-2.414$ (3 s.f.)

b) The equation $2x^2 = 10x - 4$ needs to be
   rearranged in order to compare it with the
   general form $ax^2 + bx + c = 0$.
   $2x^2 = 10x - 4$
   $2x^2 - 10x + 4 = 0$
   Comparing $2x^2 - 10x + 4 = 0$ with the
   general form $ax^2 + bx + c = 0$:
   $a = 2, b = {}^-10, c = 4$.
   $x = \dfrac{{}^-10 \pm \sqrt{({}^-10)^2 - 4 \times 2 \times 4}}{2 \times 2}$
   $x = \dfrac{10 \pm \sqrt{68}}{4}$ Remember that $- \times - = +$
                                   and $({}^-10)^2 = 100$.
   $x = \dfrac{10 + 8.246\,211\,251}{4}$
   or $x = \dfrac{10 - 8.246\,211\,251}{4}$
   $x = 4.56$ or $x = 0.438$ (3 s.f.)

Q6 width = 4 metres, length = 8 metres

Comments

Let the width be x metres, then the length is
$(x + 4)$ metres.
Area $= x(x + 4) = 32$
$x^2 + 4x = 32$
$x^2 + 4x - 32 = 0$
Comparing $x^2 + 4x - 32 = 0$ with the general
form $ax^2 + bx + c = 0$:
$a = 1, b = 4, c = -32$.
$x = \dfrac{{}^-4 \pm \sqrt{4^2 - 4 \times 1 \times {}^-32}}{2 \times 1} = \dfrac{{}^-4 \pm \sqrt{144}}{2}$
$x = \dfrac{{}^-4 + 12}{2} = 4$ or $x = \dfrac{{}^-4 - 12}{2} = {}^-8$

But a width of $^-8$ metres is impossible so ignore
this value. Since the length of the room is 4 m
greater than the width: width = 4 m, length = 8 m.
The fact that the square root worked out to be
an exact number ($\sqrt{144} = 12$) suggests that
the quadratic equation $x^2 + 4x - 32 = 0$ could
have been factorised which would have made the
problem a lot easier and quicker. As a rule, you
should always use factorising rather than the
formula, if you can.

Q7 $x = 10.0990$ (4 d.p.)

Comments

Using $x_{n+1} = 10 + \dfrac{1}{x_n}$ and $x_1 = 5$:

$x_2 = 10 + \dfrac{1}{x_1} = 10 + \dfrac{1}{5} = 10.2$

$x_3 = 10 + \dfrac{1}{x_2} = 10 + \dfrac{1}{10.2} = 10.098\ 039\ 22$

$x_4 = 10 + \dfrac{1}{x_3} = 10 + \dfrac{1}{10.098\ 039\ 22} = 10.099\ 029\ 13$

$x_5 = 10 + \dfrac{1}{x_4} = 10 + \dfrac{1}{10.099\ 029\ 13} = 10.099\ 019\ 42$

Since $x_5 = x_4$ to 4 d.p. then a root of the equation is 10.0990 (4 d.p.).

Q8 a $x_2 = 0.75$ $x_3 = 1.043\ 478\ 3$ $x_4 = 0.992\ 805\ 7$
b The value of x_n would seem to be tending towards an answer of 1.

c $x = \dfrac{6}{x+5}$

$x(x+5) = 6$
$x^2 + 5x = 6$
$x^2 + 5x - 6 = 0$
d $x = 1$ or $x = {}^-6$

Comments

a) Using $x_n + 1 = \dfrac{6}{x_n + 5}$ and $x_1 = 3$:

$x_2 = 0.75$ $x_3 = 1.043\ 478\ 3$ $x_4 = 0.992\ 805\ 7$
b) The value of x_n would seem to be tending towards an answer of 1 as n becomes very large.
c) The quadratic equation is found by rearranging:

$x = \dfrac{6}{x+5}$

$x(x+5) = 6$ Multiplying both sides by $(x+5)$.
$x^2 + 5x - 6 = 0$ Expanding and rearranging.
d) Factorising the left-hand side of the equation:
$x^2 + 5x - 6 = (x-1)(x+6)$
giving $(x-1)(x+6) = 0$.
So the solutions of the quadratic equation $x^2 + 5x - 6 = 0$ are $x = 1$ and $x = {}^-6$.

24 Inequalities and graphs (page 74)

Q1 a $x \leqslant 3$

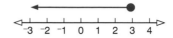

b $x > 5$

Comments

a) $4x + 2 \leqslant 17 - x$

$4x \leqslant 15 - x$ Subtracting 2 from both sides.

$5x \leqslant 15$ Adding x to both sides.

$x \leqslant 3$ Dividing both sides by 5.

b) $18 - 6x < 3 - 3x$

$18 \leqslant 3 + 3x$ Adding $6x$ to both sides.

$15 < 3x$ Subtracting 3 from both sides.

$5 < x$ Dividing both sides by 3.

$x > 5$ Rewriting the inequality to take x to the left-hand side.

Q2 a $-1, 0, 1, 2, 3$ **b** $x \leqslant \frac{2}{3}$

Comments

a)

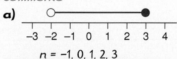

$n = -1, 0, 1, 2, 3$

b) $3x + 2 \leqslant 4$

$3x \leqslant 2$ Subtracting 2 from each side.

$x \leqslant \frac{2}{3}$ Dividing both sides by 3.

Q3 a $y \geqslant x$ **b** $y < 7x + 2.5$
c $y \leqslant {}^-x^2$ and $y \geqslant {}^-4$

Comments

a) $y \geqslant x$
Values can be taken either side of the given line to ascertain the required region.
b) $y < 7x + 2.5$
The dotted line shows that the line is **not** included in the required region.
c) $y \leqslant {}^-x^2$ and $y \geqslant {}^-4$
Both inequalities must be satisfied to give the required region.

Q4 The maximum value for $x + y$ which satisfies all of these conditions is 9 at the points on the line between $(2, 7)$ and $(8, 1)$ on the graph.

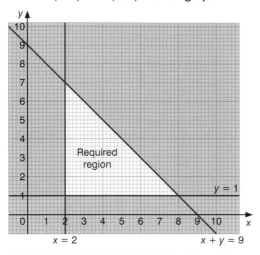

Comments

Draw lines $x = 2$, $y = 1$ and $x + y = 9$ to identify the required region.

Q5 a

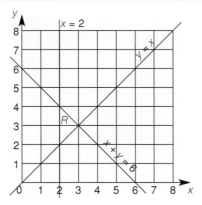

b $(2, 2), (2, 3), (2, 4), (3, 3)$

Comments

a) Remember to identify the required region.

Q6

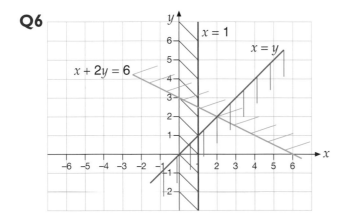

Comments

Draw lines $x = 1$, $y = x$ and $x + 2y = 6$ to identify the required region.

25 Patterns and sequences (page 77)

Q1 a $3, 5, 7, 9, 11, ...$ **b** $^-5, ^-2, 1, 4, 7, ...$

   c $^-2, ^-2, 0, 4, 10, ...$ **d** $\frac{1}{2}, \frac{2}{3}, \frac{3}{4}, \frac{4}{5}, \frac{5}{6}, ...$

Comments

a) $2 \times 1 + 1 = 3, 2 \times 2 + 1 = 5, 2 \times 3 + 1 = 7, ...$

b) $3 \times 1 - 8 = ^-5, 3 \times 2 - 8 = ^-2, 3 \times 3 - 8 = 1, ...$

c) $1 \times 1 - 3 \times 1 = ^-2, 2 \times 2 - 3 \times 2 = ^-2,$
   $3 \times 3 - 3 \times 3 = 0, ...$

d) $\frac{1}{1+1} = \frac{1}{2}, \frac{2}{2+1} = \frac{2}{3}, \frac{3}{3+1} = \frac{3}{4}, ...$

Q2 nth term $= 5n - 2$

Comments

As the differences are constant then a linear rule can be applied to the terms to find the nth term. Each term is the previous term $+ 5$ so try $5n$ first.

Term	1	2	3	4
Sequence	3	8	13	18
Try $5 \times$ (term number)	5	10	15	20
Difference	$^-2$	$^-2$	$^-2$	$^-2$
The difference is always $^-2$.				
So try $5 \times$ (term number) $- 2$.	3	8	13	18

So the nth term is $5 \times n - 2$ or $5n - 2$.

Q3 $5n + 1$

Comment

As the differences are constant then a linear rule can be applied to the terms to find the nth term. The difference between terms is 5; use 5 as multiplier.

Term number, n	1	2	3	4	5
Sequence	6	11	16	21	26
$5 \times$ term number	5	10	15	20	25
Difference	1	1	1	1	1
The difference is always 1.					
So try $5 \times$ (term number) $+ 1$.	6	11	16	21	26

So the nth term is $5n + 1$.

Q4 a 10th term $= \frac{40}{11}$ **b** 100th term $= \frac{400}{101}$

   c The value gets closer and closer to 4.

Comments

a) 10th term $= \frac{4 \times 10}{10 + 1}$ **b)** 100th term $= \frac{4 \times 100}{100 + 1}$

   $= \frac{40}{11}$ $= \frac{400}{101}$

c) Trying out increasing values of n, you should see that the value gets closer and closer to 4.

26 Interpreting graphs (page 80)

Q1

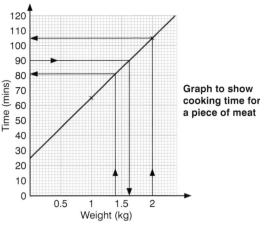

Graph to show cooking time for a piece of meat

a 105 minutes   **b** 81 minutes   **c** 1.62 or 1.63 kg

Comments

Reading from the graph:

a) A piece of meat weighing 2 kilograms would take 105 minutes to cook.

b) A piece of meat weighing 1.4 kilograms would take 81 minutes to cook.

c) A piece of meat which takes $1\frac{1}{2}$ hours to cook would weigh 1.62 or 1.63 kilograms. Converting $1\frac{1}{2}$ hours to 90 minutes.

Q2 a 24 minutes   **b** He was back home
   c 0 and 40 minutes   **d** 15 km/h
   e 84 minutes

Comments

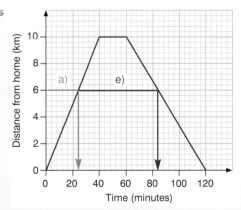

a) Show lines.

b) Back home as line meets axis.

c) This is the point of the graph with the steepest gradient.

d) Distance = 5 km

time = 20 minutes = $\frac{1}{3}$ hour

so speed = $\frac{distance}{time}$

$= \dfrac{5}{\frac{1}{3}}$

= 15 km/hour

e) At 14 km he was 6 km from home (he went 10 km away from, then turned around and came 4 km back towards home)

Q3 a 15 kilometres   **b** 15 kilometres per hour
   c 44 minutes   **d** 1.19 p.m.
   e 20 kilometres per hour
   f 2.03 p.m.   **g** 5.2 or 5.3 kilometres

Comments

Reading from the given graph:

a) The first cyclist travels 15 kilometres before the first stop.

b) Distance travelled = 15 kilometres

Time taken = 1 hour

So speed = 15 kilometres per hour

speed = distance ÷ time

c) The first cyclist stops for 44 minutes. Each small square represents 2 minutes.

d) The second cyclist overtakes the first cyclist at 1.19 p.m.

e) Distance travelled = 10 kilometres

Time taken = 30 minutes

So speed = distance ÷ time

$= 10 \div \frac{1}{2}$ As 30 minutes = $\frac{1}{2}$ hour.

= 20 kilometres per hour

f) The second cyclist arrives at the destination at 2.03 p.m.

g) The greatest distance between the two cyclists is 5.2 kilometres to 5.3 kilometres (when the second cyclist arrives at the destination).

Q4 a, b

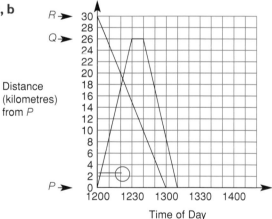

c 19 kilometres

Comments

a) Add points on graph and join with straight lines.

b) Remember that goods train leaves R so is 30 kilometres from P at 12.00. Add points and join with straight lines.

c) The trains cross at the intersection of the graph when distance = 19 km.

27 Linear graphs and coordinates (page 84)

Q1 The lines are all parallel and have the same gradient.

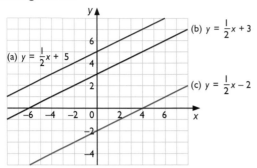

(a) $y = \frac{1}{2}x + 5$

(b) $y = \frac{1}{2}x + 3$

(c) $y = \frac{1}{2}x - 2$

Comments

Parallel lines have the same gradient and lines with the same gradient are parallel.

In this case the gradient, $m = \frac{1}{2}$.

Q2 a $y + 3x = 5$ **b** $x = 2y + 6$

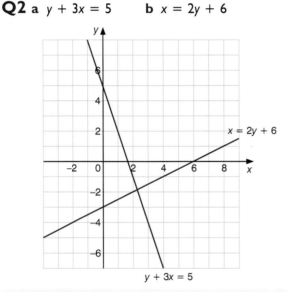

$y + 3x = 5$

$x = 2y + 6$

Comments

To sketch the graphs it is helpful to find the value of m (the gradient) and c (the cut-off on the y-axis, or y-intercept).

a) $y + 3x = 5$ Rearranging the formula to get it in the form $y = mx + c$.

$y = {}^-3x + 5$ Subtracting $3x$ from both sides.

$m = {}^-3$ and $c = 5$

b) $x = 2y + 6$ Rearranging the formula to get it in the form $y = mx + c$.

$x - 6 = 2y$ Subtracting 6 from both sides.

$2y = x - 6$ Turning the formula around.

$y = \frac{1}{2}(x - 6)$ Multiplying both sides by $\frac{1}{2}$ (or dividing both sides by 2).

$y = \frac{1}{2}x - 3$ Multiplying out the bracket.

$m = \frac{1}{2}$ and $c = {}^-3$.

Q3 $(-\frac{1}{2}, 3\frac{1}{2})$

Comment

Midpoint $= \left(\frac{5-6}{2}, \frac{3+4}{2}\right)$

Q4 $\frac{-1}{11}$

Comment

Gradient $= \frac{y_2 - y_1}{x_2 - x_1} = \frac{4 - 3}{-6 - 5} = \frac{1}{-11}$

Q5 a $y = \frac{1}{2}x - 4$ **b** $y = -\frac{5}{3}x - 5$

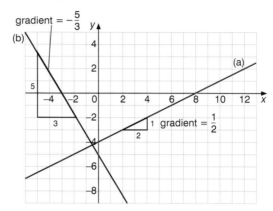

Comments

a) From the graph you can see that $m = \frac{1}{2}$ and $c = {}^-4$.

so $y = mx + c$

$y = \frac{1}{2}x - 4$

b) From the graph you can see that $m = {}^-\frac{5}{3}$ and $c = {}^-5$.

so $y = mx + c$

$y = {}^-\frac{5}{3}x - 5$

Q6 $y = 2x + 6$

Comments

The straight line is parallel to AB so the gradient is the same, 2.

The straight line passes through $(0, 6)$ so the cut-off is 6.

$y = mx + c$ where $m = 2$ and $c = 6$

$y = 2x + 6$

Q7 a 8   **b** $y = \frac{1}{2}x + p$ (where $p \neq 1$)

Comments

a) $y = \frac{1}{2}x + 1$

When $y = 5$, $5 = \frac{1}{2}x + 1$

$4 = \frac{1}{2}x$

$8 = x$

b) Any line of the form $y = \frac{1}{2}x + p$, where p is any number except 1, would be correct.

28 Quadratic graphs (page 87)

Q1

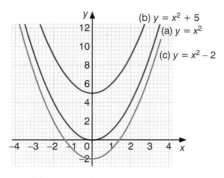

(b) $y = x^2 + 5$
(a) $y = x^2$
(c) $y = x^2 - 2$

Comments

Remember to check your graph. For example, when $x = 0$ calculate the value of y.

Q2 **a** Minimum = $(3, ^-4)$

b i) $x = 1$ and $x = 5$ ii) $x = 0$ and $x = 6$

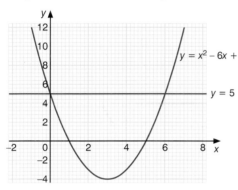

$y = x^2 - 6x + 5$

$y = 5$

Comments

From the graph you can see that:

a) the coordinates of the minimum value of $x^2 - 6x + 5$ are $(3, ^-4)$

b) i) the values of x when $x^2 - 6x + 5 = 0$ will lie on $y = x^2 - 6x + 5$ and $y = 0$, so the values $x = 1$ and $x = 5$ satisfy the equation $x^2 - 6x + 5 = 0$

 ii) the values of x when $x^2 - 6x + 5 = 5$ will lie on $y = x^2 - 6x + 5$ and $y = 5$, so the values $x = 0$ and $x = 6$ satisfy the equation $x^2 - 6x + 5 = 5$.

Q3

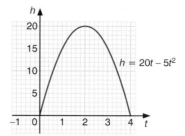

$h = 20t - 5t^2$

Maximum height = 20 metres

Comments

From the graph, the maximum height occurs at the point $(2, 20)$ so the maximum height is 20 metres (which occurs when the time is 2 seconds).

29 Gradients and tangents (page 89)

Q1 **a** gradient = 4
b gradient = $^-4$
c gradient = 10
d gradient = 0

Comments

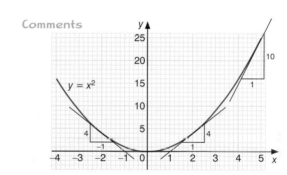

$y = x^2$

Q2 **a** 12
b 48
c 3
d 27

30 Functions (page 92)

Q1 **a** i) 7   ii) −1   iii) 3/2
b i) 4   ii) 2   iii) 1/5

Comments

Given that $f(x) = 5 - 2x$ and $g(x) = 1/x$

a) (i) $f(-1) = 5 - 2(-1) = 7$

 (ii) $g(-1) = 1/(-1) = -1$

 (iii) $g(2/3) = 1/2/3 = 3/2$

b) (i) $5 - 2x = -3$

$5 = -3 + 2x$

$8 = 2x$

$x = 4$

(ii) $1/x = \frac{1}{2}$

$x = 2$

(iii) $1/x = 5$

$x = 1/5$

Q2 a 0

b >10

c −5

Comments

a) $f : x \mapsto 1/x$ cannot include $x = 0$

b) $g : x \mapsto \sqrt{(10-x)}$ cannot include $x > 10$

c) $h : x \mapsto 2/(x+5)$ cannot include $x = -5$

Q3 a (i) 1

(ii) -1

b (i) $1/(x-2)^3$

(ii) $1/(x^3 - 2)$

(iii) $(x-2)/(5-2x)$

c (i) 2

(ii) $\sqrt[3]{2}$

(iii) 5/2

Comments

$f : x \mapsto x^3$ and $g : x \mapsto 1/(x-2)$

a) (i) $fg(3) = f(1) = 1$

(ii) $gf(1) = g(1) = -1$

b) (i) $fg(x) = f(1/(x-2)) = (1/(x-2))^3 = 1/(x-2)^3$

(ii) $gf(x) = g(x^3) = 1/(x^3 - 2)$

(iii) $gg(x) = g(1/(x-2))$ $= \dfrac{1}{(1/(x-2) - 2)}$

$= \dfrac{1}{(1 - 2(x-2))/(x-2)}$

$= \dfrac{x-2}{1 - 2(x-2)}$

$= \dfrac{x-2}{1 - 2x + 4}$

$= \dfrac{x-2}{5 - 2x}$

c) (i) $fg(x) = 1/(x-2)^3$ is not defined when $x = 2$

(ii) $gf(x) = 1/(x^3 - 2)$ is not defined when $x = \sqrt[3]{2}$

(iii) $gg(x) = (x-2)/(5-2x)$ is not defined when $x = 5/2$

Q4 $p : x \mapsto (x+5)^2$ has a range with $p(x) \geq 0$ for $\{x : x$ is any number$\}$

$q : x \mapsto 5 - x$ has a range with $q(x) < 5$ for $\{x : x > 0\}$

Q5 a − 1/3

b $5/x - 2$

Comments

The function f(x) is defined as $f(x) = 5/(x+2)$

a) If $f(x) = 3$ then $5/(x+2) = 3$ and $x = -1/3$

b) Let $y = 5/(x+2)$ replace $f(x)$ with y and

$y(x+2) = 5$ change the subject

$yx + 2y = 5$

$yx = 5 - 2y$

$x = \dfrac{5 - 2y}{y}$

So $f^{-1}(x) = \dfrac{5 - 2x}{x}$ or $5/x - 2$ replace y with x to complete the inverse

Q6 a (i) 5

(ii) 0

b $\dfrac{x+1}{2}$

c (i) $\dfrac{3}{2x-1}$

(ii) $x \neq \dfrac{1}{2}$

Comments

a) (i) $f(3) = 2 \times 3 - 1 = 5$

(ii) $fg(6) = f(\frac{3}{6}) = f(\frac{1}{2}) = 2 \times \frac{1}{2} - 1 = 0$

b) Let $y = 2x - 1$

$2x - 1 = y$

$2x = y + 1$

$x = \dfrac{y+1}{2}$

so $f^{-1}(x) = \dfrac{x+1}{2}$

c) (i) $gf(x)$

$= g(2x - 1)$

$= \dfrac{3}{2x-1}$

(ii) $2x - 1 \neq 0$

$2x \neq 1$

$x \neq \dfrac{1}{2}$

31 Calculus (page 96)

Q1 **a** $2x - 7$ **b** $10x - 8$
     c $3x^2 - 16x + 3$ **d** $3x^2/5 - 6x/4 = 3x^2/5 - 3x/2$
     e $2x + 10$ **f** $-3x^{-4} + 8x^{-3} - 3x^{-2}$

Comments

e) as $(x+5)^2 = x^2 + 10x + 25$

Q2 **a** $\frac{dy}{dx} = 2x - 2$ **b** $\frac{dy}{dx} = 2x - 1$

     c $\frac{dy}{dx} = -2x^{-2} - 6x^{-3}$

Comments

b) as $(x-3)(x+2) = x^2 - x - 6$
c) as $2/x + 3/x^2 = 2x^{-1} + 3x^{-2}$

Q3 **a** gradient = 13   **b** gradient = 1
     c $6x - 2$ **d** gradient = -14

Comments

a) $\frac{dy}{dx} = 6x - 5$
When $x = 3$, $\frac{dy}{dx} = 6 \times 3 - 5 = 13$ so gradient = 13

b) $\frac{dy}{dx} = 3 - 2x^{-2}$ at the point $(1, 0)$
When $x = 1$, $\frac{dy}{dx} = 3 - 2 \times 1^{-2} = 3 - 2 \times 1 = 1$
so gradient = 1

c) $\frac{dy}{dx} = 6x - 2$ at the point $(-2, 11)$
When $x = -2$, $\frac{dy}{dx} = 6x - 2 - 2 = -14$ so gradient = -14

Q4 **a** $2x - 12$ **b** gradient = -6
     c $(6, -1)$

Comments

b) At $(3, 8)$, gradient = $2 \times 3 - 12$ (as $x=3$) so gradient = -6

c) The turning point occurs when $\frac{dy}{dx} = 0$
so $2x - 12 = 0$ or $x = 6$
When $x = 6$, $y = 6^2 - 12 \times 6 + 35$ so $y = -1$ and the coordinate is $(6, -1)$

Q5 **a** $2x - 5$
     b $(2.5, -0.25)$
     c The turning point is a minimum as the shape of $y = x^2 - 5x + 6$ is

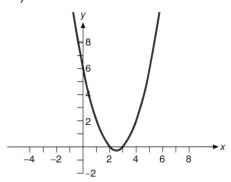

Comments

a) $\frac{dy}{dx} = 2x - 5$

b) The turning point occurs when $\frac{dy}{dx} = 0$
so $2x - 5 = 0$ or $x = 2.5$
When $x = 2.5$, $y = 2.5^2 - 5 \times 2.5 + 6$ so $y = -0.25$
and the coordinate is $(2.5, -0.25)$

Q6 **a** -8
     b $t = 6$

Comments

a) The rate of change is the same as the differential so $\frac{dT}{dt} = 2t - 12$
After 2 seconds, $\frac{dT}{dt} = 2 \times 2 - 12 = -8$

b) The temperature is at its minimum when $\frac{dT}{dt} = 0$
so $2t - 12 = 0$ so $t = 6$

Q7 **a** $t = 1$ second
     b $8 - 16t$
     c $t = \frac{1}{2}$ second
     d -40 m/s

Comments

a) The car passes through the origin when $s = 0$
so $8(t - t^2) = 0$
$8t(1 - t) = 0$ ie when $t = 0$ and $t = 1$

b) $\frac{ds}{dt} = 8 - 16t$ as $s = 8(t - t^2) = 8t - 8t^2$

c) The maximum distance occurs when $\frac{ds}{dt} = 0$ so
$8 - 16t = 0$ or $t = \frac{1}{2}$ second

d) The speed of the car is given by $\frac{ds}{dt}$
when $t = 3$, $\frac{ds}{dt} = 8 - 16 \times 3 = -40$ m/s

Q8 Velocity = $3t^2 + 8t - 5$
When $t = 2$, velocity = $3 \times 2^2 + 8 \times 2 - 5$
= 2.3 m/s.
Acceleration = $\frac{dv}{dt} = 6t + 8$
When $t = 2$, acceleration = $6 \times 2 + 8 = 20$ m/s^2.

Q9 **a** $6x^2 - 6x - 72$
     b $(-3, 135)$ and $(4, -208)$

Comments

a) $\frac{dy}{dx} = 6x^2 - 6x - 72$

b) The turning points occur when $\frac{dy}{dx} = 0$ so that
$6x^2 - 6x - 72 = 0$
$x^2 - x - 12 = 0$ dividing throughout by 6
$(x + 3)(x - 4) = 0$ so $x = -3$ and $x = 4$
When $x = -3$, $y = 2 \times (-3)^3 - 3 \times (-3)^2 - 72 \times (-3) = 135$
so coordinate is $(-3, 135)$
When $x = 4$, $y = 2 \times 4^3 - 3 \times 4^2 - 72 \times 4 = -208$ so
coordinate is $(4, -208)$
So coordinates of turning points are $(-3, 135)$ and $(4, -208)$

SHAPE, SPACE AND MEASURES
32 Geometric terms (page 107)

Q1 $b = 54°, b = 79°, c = 63°$

> **Comments**
>
> $a = 54°$ Angles of a triangle add up to 180°.
> $b = 79°$ Angles of a triangle add up to 180°,
> the base angles of an isosceles triangle
> are equal.
> $c = 63°$ Angles of a quadrilateral add up to 360°.

Q2 287°

> **Comment**
> This angle is
> $180° - 138° = 42°$
>
> This angle is
> $180° - 65° - 42° = 73°$
> (Angle sum of the triangle.)
>
> $A = 360° - 73° = 287°$

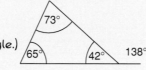
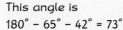

Q3 The smallest angle = 40°

> **Comments**
> The angles of a triangle add up to 180° so
> $2x + 3x + 4x = 180°$
> $\qquad 9x = 180°$
> $\qquad\quad x = 20°$
> The smallest angle = $2x = 2 \times 20° = 40°$

Q4   **a** Area of triangle = 27 cm²
    b Area of rhombus = 36.7 cm² (3 s.f.)
    c Area of polygon = 35 cm²

> **Comments**
> **a)** Area of triangle
> $\quad = \frac{1}{2} \times$ base $\times$ perpendicular height
> $\quad = \frac{1}{2} \times 9 \times 6 \ = 27$ cm²
> **b)** Area of rhombus = base $\times$ perpendicular height
> $\quad = 7.2 \times 5.1$ Perpendicular height is 5.1 cm
> $\qquad\qquad\qquad\qquad\qquad$ (not 7.2 cm).
> $\quad = 36.72 = 36.7$ cm² (3 s.f.)
> Rounding to an appropriate degree of
> accuracy.
> **c)** Area of polygon
> $\quad =$ area of rectangle + area of triangle
> $\quad = 8 \times 3.5 + \frac{1}{2} \times 3.5 \times 4$
> $\qquad\quad$ As length of rectangle = $12 - 4 = 8$ cm.
> $\quad = 28 + 7 = 35$ cm²

Q5 $a = 18°$ $b = 117°$
      $c = 63°$ $d = 63°$

> **Comments**
> $a = 18°$ Angles on a straight line add up to 180°.
> $b = 117°$ Vertically opposite angle.
> $c = 63°$ Angles on a straight line add up to 180°.
> $d = 63°$ Vertically opposite angle or angles on
>   a straight line add up to 180°.

Q6 Your answer should look something like this.

Let the angles of the triangle ABC be α, β and γ.

$\alpha + \beta + \gamma = 180°$ Angle sum of a triangle.
$\gamma = 180° - \alpha - \beta$ Rearranging the formula.
$\angle ACE = 180° - \angle ACB$
$\angle ACE = 180° - \gamma$
$\qquad = 180° - (180° - \alpha - \beta)$ From above.
$\qquad = \alpha + \beta$

As $\angle ACE$ is the exterior angle of the triangle,
then the exterior angle is equal to the sum of
the interior opposite angles of the triangle.

Q7 $a = 117°$ $b = 68°$ $c = 49°$ $d = 87°$
      $e = 87°$ $f = 87°$ $g = 87°$ $h = 93°$

> **Comments**
> $a = 117°$ Interior angles between parallel lines
>   add up to 180°. ($180° - 63° = 117°$)
> $b = 68°$ Interior angles between parallel lines
>   add up to 180°. ($180° - 112° = 68°$)
> $c = 49°$ Angles in a triangle add up to 180°.
>   ($180° - 63° - 68° = 49°$)
> $d = 87°$ Corresponding angles between parallel
>   lines.
> $e = 87°$ Corresponding angles between parallel
>   lines (the other pair).
> $f = 87°$ Vertically opposite angle to angle e.
> $g = 87°$ Alternate angle between parallel lines
>   with angle f.
> $h = 93°$ Angles on a straight line add up to 180°.

Q8 Each interior angle = 144°

> **Comments**
> A decagon is a ten-sided shape.
> Use the formula.
> Angle sum of an n-sided polygon = $(n - 2) \times 180°$
> Angle sum of a ten-sided polygon = $(10 - 2) \times 180°$
> $\qquad\qquad\qquad\qquad\qquad\qquad = 8 \times 180°$
> $\qquad\qquad\qquad\qquad\qquad\qquad = 1440°$
> As the polygon is a regular polygon then all the
> interior angles are equal so $1440° \div 10 = 144°$.

Q9 The exterior angle of a regular hexagon = 60°.

Comments

A hexagon is a six-sided shape.

Using the formula:

angle sum of an n-sided polygon = (n − 2) × 180°

angle sum of a 6-sided polygon

$\qquad$ = (6 − 2) × 180°

$\qquad$ = 4 × 180°

$\qquad$ = 720°

As the polygon is regular, then
all the interior angles are equal.

Each interior angle = 720° ÷ 6 = 120°

The exterior angle = 180° − 120° = 60°

(as angles on a straight line add up to 180°).

Q10 a 60° $\qquad$ **b** 120°

Comments

a) The interior angle of an equilateral triangle is
180° ÷ 3 = 60°.

b) The angle sum of angle sum of
an n-sided polygon = (n − 2) × 180°
For a hexagon, this is 720°.
As this is a regular hexagon,
all the angles are equal, so one
interior angle is 720° ÷ 6 = 120°.

33 Constructions (page 113)

Q1

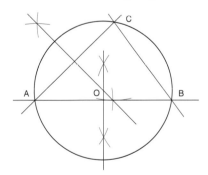

Comments

Accurate construction will result in the circle
circumscribing (completely enclosing) triangle
ABC and passing through the points A, B and C of
the triangle.

Q2

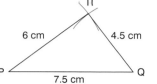

The triangle PQR
is right-angled.

Comments

You should follow the instructions given under the
heading 'Constructing a triangle given three sides'.

Q3

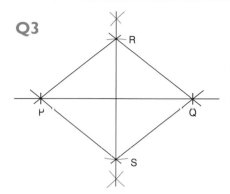

The special
name given
to this
quadrilateral is
'rhombus'.

Comments

Accurate construction will result in a rhombus PRQS.

Q4 a 270° $\quad$ **b** 300° $\quad$ **c** 165° $\quad$ **d** 023°

Comments

a)

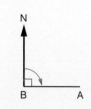

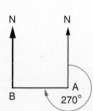

b)

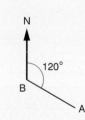

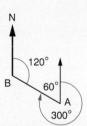

c)

d)

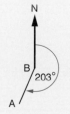

Q5 225°

Comments

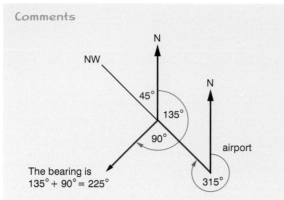

The bearing is
135° + 90° = 225°

A south-west direction is equivalent to a bearing of 225°.
As the two north lines are parallel you can use the fact
that interior angles between parallel lines add up to 180°.

Q6 a $22\frac{1}{2}$ miles   **b** 7.2 inches

Comments

a) If 1 inch represents 5 miles then $4\frac{1}{2}$ inches
represents $4\frac{1}{2} \times 5$ miles $= 22\frac{1}{2}$ miles.

b) As 5 miles represents 1 inch then 1 mile
represents $\frac{1}{5}$ inch   Dividing both sides by 5.
36 miles represents $36 \times \frac{1}{5}$ inches = 7.2 inches.

Q7 The distance between them is 5.1 miles.

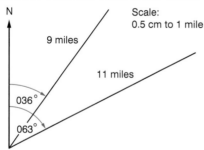

Scale:
0.5 cm to 1 mile

9 miles

11 miles

036°

063°

Comments

After two hours the explorers travel 9 miles on a
bearing of 036° and 11 miles on a bearing of 063°.
The distance between them is 2.55 cm which
converts to 5.1 miles, using the given scale.

Q8 a 222°   **b** 243°

Comments

a) Bearing of B from
P = 360° − 138° = 222°

b) Interior opposite
angle = 180° − 63°
= 117°
Bearing of P from
A = 360° − 117° = 243°
Always draw a diagram to help you with
questions like this.

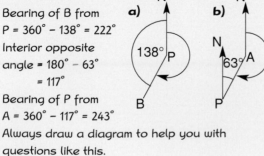

34 Angle properties of circles
(page 117)

Q1 $a = 93°$ As opposite angles of a cyclic
quadrilateral add up to 180°.

$b = 45°$ As opposite angles of a cyclic
quadrilateral add up to 180°.

$c = 90°$ As the angle in a semicircle is 90°.

$d = 90°$ As the angle in a semicircle is 90°.

$e = 96°$ As the angle subtended by an arc at the
centre is twice that subtended at the
circumference.

$f = 39°$ As the angles subtended by the same
arc at the circumference are equal.

$g = 40°$ As vertically opposite angles are equal
and the angles of a triangle add up to
180°.

$h = 122°$ As opposite angles of a cyclic
quadrilateral add up to 180°.

$i = 90°$ As the angle in a semicircle is 90°.

$j = 32°$ As the angles of a triangle add up to
180°.

$k = 32°$ As j and k are alternate angles between
two parallel lines.

Q2 a BC = 10.4 cm (3 s.f.)
b ∠BAC = 71.4° (3 s.f.)
c ∠ABC = 18.6° (3 s.f.)

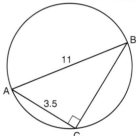

Comments

a) Drawing a diagram helps to see the
situation clearly.
∠ACB = 90° As the angle in a semicircle is 90°.
$AB^2 = AC^2 + BC^2$
Applying Pythagoras' theorem to triangle ABC.
$11^2 = 3.5^2 + BC^2$ so BC = 10.428 327 cm

b) Using $\cos \theta = \frac{\text{length of adjacent side}}{\text{length of hypotenuse}}$:
$\cos BAC = \frac{3.5}{11}$ so ∠BAC = 71.446 995°

c) ∠ABC = 18.553 005°
As the angles of a triangle add up to 180°.

Q3 a 27°   **b** 63°

Comments

a) ∠ACE = 90°   The tangent is perpendicular
∠ACB = 90° − 63°   to the radius at the point of
= 27°   contact.

b) ∠ABC = 90°   The angle in the semicircle is 90°.
∠BAC = 180° − 90° − 27°
= 63°   Angle sum of the triangle.

Q4 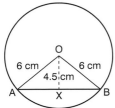 AB = 7.94 cm (3 s.f.)

35 Pythagoras' theorem in two dimensions (page 119)

Q1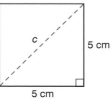

The length of a diagonal = $\sqrt{50}$ cm

Comments

Drawing a diagram helps to see the situation
clearly. Let O be the centre of the circle, OX be
the perpendicular bisector of the chord.
For the right-angled triangle OAX:
$6^2 = 4.5^2 + AX^2$ Applying Pythagoras' theorem to
                    the right-angled triangle.
AX = 3.968 627
AB = 2 × AX = 2 × 3.968 627 = 7.937 254
AB = 7.94 cm (3 s.f.)

Comments

Drawing a diagram helps to see the situation.
Using Pythagoras' theorem:
$a^2 + b^2 = c^2$
$5^2 + 5^2 = c^2$ Substituting values for a and b.
$c^2 = 50$ Squaring 5 and adding.
$c = \sqrt{50}$ Taking square roots to find c.
The length of a diagonal = $\sqrt{50}$ cm

Q5 a 60°   **b** 35°
   c Yes. If ∠CAD = 65°, ∠BAD = 90°, the angle
      in the semicircle.

Comments

a) ∠ABC = 120°   Supplementary angles -
                    on a straight line.

   ∠ADC = 60°   Opposite angles of a
                    cyclic quadrilateral.

b) ∠BDC = 25°   Angles subtended by the
                    same arc, CB.

   ∠ADB = 35°   ∠ADB = ∠ADC − ∠BDC

c) If ∠CAD = 65°, then ∠BAD = 65° + 25° = 90°.
   So ∠BAD is the angle in a semicircle, which
   means that BD must be a diameter.

Q6 a ∠PXC = 61°   **b** ∠PYC = 61°

Comments

a) ∠PXC = 61°   ∠PXC = ∠CPT by the alternate
                    segment theorem.

b) ∠PYC = 61°   ∠PYC = ∠PXC as these are
                    angles subtended by the same
                    arc PC.

Q7 a ∠COP = 76°
   b ∠CPT = 38°
   c ∠OCP = 52°

Comments

a) ∠COP = 76°   The angle subtended by the arc
                    PC at the centre is twice that
                    subtended at the circumference.

b) ∠CPT = 38°   ∠CPT = ∠CDP by the alternate
                    segment theorem.

c) ∠OCP = 52°   ∠OCP = ∠OPC as they are base
                    angles of the isosceles
                    triangle COP where ∠COP = 76°.

Q2 Area of triangle
    = 15.6 cm² (3 s.f.)

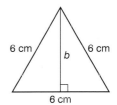

Comments

The triangle can be split into two right-angled
triangles to find the height. Drawing a diagram
helps to see the situation.
Using Pythagoras' theorem:
$a^2 + b^2 = c^2$
$3^2 + b^2 = 6^2$ Length of the hypotenuse is 6 cm.
$9 + b^2 = 36$ Squaring individual lengths.
$b^2 = 36 − 9$ Making the height the subject.
$b^2 = 27$
b = 5.196 152 4 Taking square roots to find b.
Area of triangle = $\frac{1}{2}$ × base × perpendicular height
              = $\frac{1}{2}$ × 6 × 5.196 152 4
              = 15.588 457
              = 15.6 cm² (3 s.f.)

Q3 Distance = 29.2 km (3 s.f.)

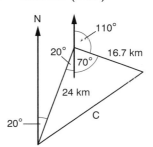

Comments

Drawing a diagram helps to see the situation. Since the diagram includes a right-angled triangle you can use Pythagoras' theorem.

$a^2 + b^2 = c^2$

$16.7^2 + 24^2 = c^2$ Substituting values for a and b.

$c^2 = 854.89$ Squaring and adding.

$c = 29.238\,502$ Taking square roots to find c.

Distance = 29.2 km (3 s.f.)

36 Sine, cosine and tangent in right-angled triangles (page 124)

Q1   a $a = 6.16$ cm (3 s.f.)   b $b = 9.15$ cm (3 s.f.)
     c $c = 3.00$ cm (3 s.f.)

Comments

a) $\sin 38° = \dfrac{a}{10}$ $a = 6.16$ cm (3 s.f.)

b) $\cos 49° = \dfrac{6}{b}$ $b = \dfrac{6}{\cos 49°} = 9.15$ cm (3 s.f.)

c) $\tan 15° = \dfrac{c}{11.2}$ $c = 3.00$ cm (3 s.f.)

Q2   a $a = 40.6°$ (3 s.f.)   b $b = 42.8°$ (3 s.f.)
     c $c = 52.3°$ (3 s.f.)

Comments

a) $\tan a = \dfrac{6}{7}$ $a = \tan^{-1} \dfrac{6}{7}$

    $a = \tan^{-1} 0.857\,142\,8\ldots = 40.6°$ (3 s.f.)

b) $\cos b = \dfrac{11}{15}$ $b = \cos^{-1} \dfrac{11}{15}$

    $b = \cos^{-1} 0.733\,333\,3\ldots = 42.8°$ (3 s.f.)

c) $\sin c = \dfrac{3.8}{4.8}$ Converting 48 mm to 4.8 cm.

    $c = \sin^{-1} \dfrac{3.8}{4.8} = \sin^{-1} 0.791\,666\,6\ldots$

    $c = 52.3°$ (3 s.f.)

Q3   39.8° (3 s.f.)

Comments

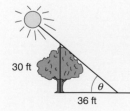

Let the required angle be θ.

$\tan \theta = \dfrac{30}{36}$

$\theta = 39.805\,571° = 39.8°$ (3 s.f.)

30 ft

36 ft

Q4   9.51 m

Comments

$\cos 41° = \dfrac{AB}{12.6}$

$AB = 12.6 \cos 41° = 9.509\,340\,711 = 9.51$ (2 s.f.)

Q5   a   11.7 m   b   36.9°

Comments

a)   In triangle DEG:

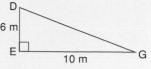

    $DG^2 = 6^2 + 10^2$

         $= 36 + 100 = 136$

    Using Pythagoras' theorem.

    $DG = \sqrt{136} = 11.661\,903\,79 = 11.7$ m (3 s.f.)

b)   In triangle EFG:

    $\cos x° = \dfrac{8}{10} = 0.8$ Using cosine = $\dfrac{\text{adjacent}}{\text{hypotenuse}}$.

    $x° = \cos^{-1} 0.8 = 36.869\,897\,65° = 36.9°$ (1 d.p.)

37 Sine and cosine rules (page 128)

Q1   a $a = 57.6$ mm (3 s.f.)
     b $B = 70.9°$ or $109.1°$ (1 d.p.)
     c $C = 45.8°$ (1 d.p.)
     d $D = 75.6°$ or $104.4°$ (1 d.p.)

Comments

a)   Using the cosine rule:

    $a^2 = 47^2 + 35^2 - (2 \times 47 \times 35 \times \cos 88°)$

    Substituting the given lengths and taking care with the $- 2\,bc \cos A$ term.

    $a = 57.612\,331$

b)   Using the sine rule and both sides.

    $\dfrac{a}{\sin A} = \dfrac{b}{\sin B}$ or $\dfrac{\sin A}{a} = \dfrac{\sin B}{b}$

    $\dfrac{\sin B}{3.9} = \dfrac{\sin 58°}{3.5}$ Substituting the given values.

    $\sin B = 3.9 \times \dfrac{\sin 58°}{3.5}$ Multiplying both sides by 3.9.

    $B = 70.903\,321°$ or $B = 109.096\,679°$

c)   Using the cosine rule:

    $\cos C = \dfrac{4.6^2 + 5.1^2 - 3.8^2}{2 \times 4.6 \times 5.1}$ Substituting the given lengths.

    $C = 45.767\,605°$

d)   Using the sine rule and reciprocating both sides:

    $\dfrac{\sin D}{110} = \dfrac{\sin 25°}{48}$ Substituting the given values.

    $\sin D = 110 \times \dfrac{\sin 25°}{48}$ Multiplying both sides by 110.

    $\sin D = 0.968\,500\,1$

    $D = 75.580\,895°$ or $104.4191°$

    As $\sin D$ has two possible solutions here.

Q2 a Area = 4.36 m² (3 s.f.)
   b Area = 111 cm² (3 s.f.)

Comments

a) Area of a triangle = $\frac{1}{2}ab \sin C$
    = $\frac{1}{2} \times 3.6 \times 4.7 \times \sin 31° = 4.3572221$

b) Area of a triangle = $\frac{1}{2}ab \sin C$
    = $\frac{1}{2} \times 16 \times 16 \times \sin 60°$
    As the angles of an equilateral triangle are all 60°.
    = 110.85125

Q3

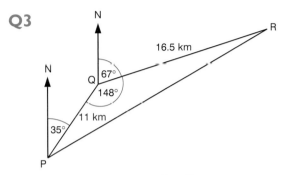

Distance = 26.5 km (3 s.f.)
Bearing = 054° (to the nearest whole degree)

Comments

By drawing a diagram of the situation you can see that PR represents the required distance and that the bearing can be found from the angle QPR.
The bearing of P from Q is 215° and the angle PQR = 148°, as 215° − 67° = 148°.
Using the cosine rule on the triangle PQR:
$a^2 = b^2 + c^2 - 2bc \cos A$
$PR^2 = 11^2 + 16.5^2 - (2 \times 11 \times 16.5 \times \cos 148°)$
Substituting the given lengths and taking care with the − 2bc cos A term.
PR = 26.478132
So the distance = 26.5 km (3 s.f.).
To find angle QPR, using the sine rule in the form
$\frac{\sin A}{a} = \frac{\sin B}{b}$:
$\frac{\sin QPR}{QR} = \frac{\sin 148°}{PR}$
$\frac{\sin QPR}{16.5} = \frac{\sin 148°}{26.478132}$ Substituting the given lengths and ∠PQR.
$\sin QPR = 16.5 \times \frac{\sin 148°}{26.478\,132}$ Multiplying both sides by 16.5.
$\sin QPR = 0.330\,222\,23$
∠QPR = 19.282265°
Required bearing = 35° + 19.282265°
    Bearing = 35° + angle QPR
        = 54.282265°
        = 054° (to the nearest whole degree)
Remember to write it in the bearing form and round to an appropriate degree of accuracy.

Q4 a 27.6° (3 s.f.)   **b** 25.6 cm² (3 s.f.)

Comments

a) $\frac{\sin \angle ABC}{7.5} = \frac{\sin 30°}{8.1}$ Using the sine rule.
   $\sin \angle ABC = 7.5 \times \frac{\sin 30°}{8.1}$
          = 0.462 962 963
   So ∠ABC = 27.578 467 98° = 27.6° (3 s.f.)

b) ∠BAC = 180° − 30° − 27.578 467 98° = 122.421 532°
   Area of △ABC = $\frac{1}{2} \times 8.1 \times 7.5 \times \sin 122.421\,532°$
           = 25.640 342 43 = 25.6 cm² (3 s.f.)

38 Three-dimensional trigonometry (page 130)

Q1 a AF = $5\sqrt{5}$ cm

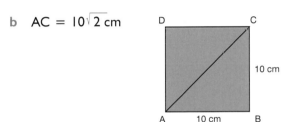

b AC = $10\sqrt{2}$ cm

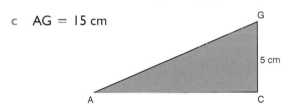

c AG = 15 cm

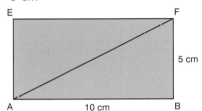

Comments

a) Drawing a diagram helps to see the situation clearly.
   $AF^2 = AB^2 + BF^2$ Using Pythagoras' theorem on the right-angled triangle ABF.
   $AF^2 = 10^2 + 5^2$ As BF = CG.
   $AF^2 = 125$
   $AF = \sqrt{125}$ Taking square roots on both sides.
   $AF = 5\sqrt{5}$ cm In its lowest terms.

b) Drawing a diagram helps to see the situation clearly.
   $AC^2 = AB^2 + BC^2$ Using Pythagoras' theorem on the right-angled triangle ABC.
   $AC^2 = 10^2 + 10^2$
   $AC^2 = 200$
   $AC = \sqrt{200}$ Taking square roots on both sides.
   $AC = 10\sqrt{2}$ cm In its lowest terms.

c) Drawing a diagram helps to see the situation clearly.

$AG^2 = AC^2 + CG^2$ Using Pythagoras' theorem on the right-angled triangle ACG.

$AG^2 = (10\sqrt{2})^2 + 5^2$

$AG^2 = 200 + 25$

$AG^2 = 225$

$AG = \sqrt{225}$ Taking square roots on both sides.

$AG = 15$ cm

$XS = \dfrac{30}{\tan 26°}$ Rearranging the equation.

$XS = 61.509\,115$

$WS^2 = WX^2 + XS^2$ Using Pythagoras' theorem on the right-angled triangle WXS.

$WS^2 = 48.010\,036^2 + 61.509\,115^2 = 6088.3348$

$WS = 78.027782$ Taking square roots.

$WS = 78.0$m (3 s.f.) Rounding to an appropriate degree of accuracy.

Q2 $25\sqrt{10}$ cm²

Comments

Draw a diagram to see the situation clearly.

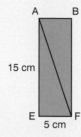

15 cm

5 cm

$AF^2 = AE^2 + EF^2$ Using Pythagoras' theorem on the right-angled triangle AEF.

$AF^2 = 15^2 + 5^2 = 250$

$AF = \sqrt{250}$ Taking square roots on both sides.

$AF = 5\sqrt{10}$ cm

Area of ADGF = AF × FG   As the plane is a rectangle.

$\quad = 5\sqrt{10} \times 5$

$\quad = 25\sqrt{10}$ cm²

Q3 WS = 78.0m (3 s.f.)

Comments

To find WS, you need to find WX and XS.

30 m

from above

32°

26°

$\tan 32° = \dfrac{YX}{WX}$ Using tangent on the right-angled triangle WXY.

$\tan 32° = \dfrac{30}{WX}$ As the height YX = 30.

$WX = \dfrac{30}{\tan 32°}$ Rearranging the equation.

$WX = 48.010\,036$

$\tan 26° = \dfrac{XY}{XS}$ Using tangent on the right-angled triangle XYS.

$\tan 26° = \dfrac{30}{XS}$ As the height YX = 30.

Q4 a 9.11 cm (3 s.f.)   b 19.2° (1 d.p.)

Comments

a) Draw a diagram to make the situation clear.

From the base rectangle, ABCD:

$AC^2 = AB^2 + BC^2$

Using Pythagoras' theorem.

$AC^2 = 5^2 + 7^2 = 25 + 49 = 74$

$AC = \sqrt{74}$

Leaving as a square root.

In triangle ACG:

$AG^2 = AC^2 + CG^2$

Using Pythagoras' theorem.

$AG^2 = 74 + 9 = 83$

$AG = \sqrt{83}$

$\quad = 9.110\,433\,579 = 9.11$ cm (3 s.f.)

5 cm

7 cm

3 cm

$\sqrt{74}$ cm

b) From the diagram, $\tan GAC = \dfrac{3}{\sqrt{74}}$.

$\tan GAC = 0.348\,742\,916$

$\angle GAC = \tan^{-1} 0.348\,742\,916$

$\quad = 19.225\,855\,75°$

$\angle GAC = 19.2°$ (1 d.p.)

Q5 x = 8

Comment

For the shaded triangle, the length of the base is half the diagonal of the base, a square of side 2x.

If the length of the diagonal is d, then:

$d^2 = (2x)^2 + (2x)^2 = 4x^2 + 4x^2 = 8x^2$

$d = \sqrt{8x^2} = 2\sqrt{2x^2}$ As $\sqrt{8} = \sqrt{4} \times 2 = \sqrt{4} \times \sqrt{2} = 2\sqrt{2}$

So half the diagonal is $\sqrt{2}x$ cm.

In the shaded triangle:

$(8\sqrt{3})^2 = x^2 + (\sqrt{2}x)^2$

$64 \times 3 = x^2 + 2x^2$

$64 \times 3 = 3x^2$

$64 = x^2$

$x = \pm 8$

So x = 8, as the length must be positive.

39 Mensuration (page 134)

Q1 a

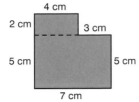

Area = 43 cm²

b

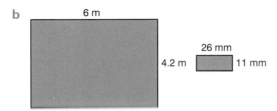

Area = 252 000 cm² or 25.2 m² (3 s.f.)

Comments

a) Drawing a diagram helps to see the situation clearly.
Area = 4 × 2 + 5 × 7 = 8 + 35 = 43 cm²

b) Drawing a diagram helps to see the situation clearly.
Area = 600 × 420 − 2.6 × 1.1
Writing all lengths in the same units.
= 252 000 − 2.86
= 251 997.14
= 252 000 cm² (3 s.f.) or 25.2 m² (3 s.f.)
if all units are converted into metres.

Q2

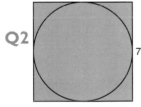

Area of waste
= 10.5 cm²
Percentage waste
= 21.5% (3 s.f.)

Comments

Drawing a diagram helps to see the situation clearly.
Area of waste = area of square − area of circle
= 7 × 7 − π × 3.5²
= 10.515 49 cm²
= 10.5 cm² (3 s.f.)

Percentage waste = $\frac{10.515\,49}{49}$ × 100%

As original area = 49 cm².
= 21.460 184%
= 21.5% (3 s.f.)

Q3 Diameter = 22.6 m (3 s.f.)

Comments

Area of pond = πr²
πr² = 400
$r^2 = \frac{400}{\pi}$
r² = 127.323 95
r = √127.323 95
r = 11.283 792
d = 2 × 11.283 792   As diameter = 2 × radius.
d = 22.567 583
d = 22.6 m (3 s.f.)
An answer correct to 3 s.f. or 2 s.f. would seem most appropriate in view of the original data.

Q4

Area of surface of washer
= 27π mm²

Comments

Area of washer = outside area − inside area
= π × 6² − π × 3²
= 36π − 9π
= 27π mm²

Q5

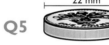

Volume of the coin
= 363π mm³

Comments

Volume = πr²h   As the shape is a cylinder.
= π × 11² × 3   As the radius is 11 mm.
= π × 363
= 363π mm³

Q6 42 cm³

Comments

Volume of prism = area of cross-section × length
This information is given on the examination paper.
= ($\frac{1}{2}$ × base × height) × length   The cross-
= ($\frac{1}{2}$ × 3 × 4) × 7   section is a
= 6 × 7   triangle.
= 42 cm³

Q7 a 503 cm³

b The greatest length inside the cylinder will be from a point on the rim at the top to an opposite point on the bottom. This length is 12.8 cm (1 d.p.), which is less than 13 cm, the length of the pencil.

Comments

a) Volume = $\pi r^2 h$

$\qquad$ = $\pi \times 4^2 \times 10$

$\qquad$ = 502.654 824 6

$\qquad$ = 503 cm³ (3 s.f.)

b)

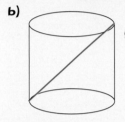
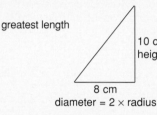

greatest length

10 cm height

8 cm

diameter = 2 × radius

$x^2 = 8^2 + 10^2$ $\qquad$ Using Pythagoras' theorem.

$\quad$ = 64 + 100 = 164

$x = \sqrt{164}$

$\quad$ = 12.806 248 47

$\quad$ = 12.8 cm (1 d.p.)

Q8 Volume of the sphere is 36π cm³

Comments

Surface area = $4\pi r^2 = 36\pi$

$\qquad\qquad \pi r^2 = 9\pi$ $\quad$ Dividing both sides by 4.

$\qquad\qquad\quad r^2 = 9$ $\quad$ Dividing both sides by π.

$\qquad\qquad\qquad r = 3$ $\quad$ Taking the square root on both sides.

Volume = $\frac{4}{3}\pi r^3$

$\qquad$ = $\frac{4}{3}\pi \times 3^3$

$\qquad$ = 36π cm³

Q9 a Ratio of their surface areas = 9 : 25

b Ratio of their volumes = 27 : 125

Comments

If the ratio of corresponding lengths = 3 : 5 then

ratio of corresponding areas = $3^2 : 5^2$

ratio of corresponding volumes = $3^3 : 5^3$.

a) Ratio of their surface areas = $3^2 : 5^2 = 9 : 25$

b) Ratio of their volumes = $3^3 : 5^3 = 27 : 125$

Q10 Curved surface area = 10 485 mm²

Comments

If the height of the similar cone is three times that of the original then the area of the similar cone is 3^2 (= 9) times that of the original. Curved surface area = 9 × 1165 mm² = 10 485 mm².

Q11 3200 cm³

Comment

The ratio of the surface areas = 450 : 800 = 9 : 16

$\qquad\qquad\qquad\qquad\qquad\qquad\qquad = 3^2 : 4^2$.

So the ratio of corresponding lengths is 3 : 4.

The ratio of their volumes is $3^3 : 4^3 = 27 : 64$

So 27 : 64 = 1350 : y or $\frac{27}{64} = \frac{1350}{y}$

So the volume of y is = $\frac{1350 \times 64}{27}$ = 3200 cm³.

40 Arc, sector and segment (page 138)

Q1 Arc length = 6π cm

$\qquad$ Sector area = 27π cm²

Comments

Arc length = $\frac{120}{360} \times 2 \times \pi \times 9$

$\qquad\qquad$ = 6π cm

Sector area = $\frac{120}{360} \times \pi \times 9^2$

$\qquad\qquad$ = 27π cm²

Q2 Area = 74.3 cm²

Comments

Area of segment = area of sector − area of triangle

Area of sector = $\frac{120}{360} \times \pi r^2 = \frac{120}{360} \times \pi \times 11^2$

$\qquad\qquad$ = 126.710904

Area of triangle = $\frac{1}{2}ab\sin\theta$

$\qquad\qquad$ = $\frac{1}{2} \times 11 \times 11 \times \sin 120°$

$\qquad\qquad$ Where a and b are equal to the radius of the circle.

$\qquad\qquad$ = 52.394 537

Area of segment = area of sector AOB − area of ΔAOB

$\qquad\qquad$ = 126.710904 − 52.394 537

$\qquad\qquad$ = 74.316 363

$\qquad\qquad$ = 74.3 cm² (3 s.f.)

Q3 41.1° (1 d.p.)

Comments

Drawing a diagram helps to see the situation clearly.

Arc length = $\frac{\theta}{360} \times 2\pi r$

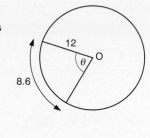

$8.6 = \frac{\theta}{360} \times 2 \times \pi \times 12$

$\theta = 41.061\,975°$

Angle subtended by arc = 41.1° (3 s.f.)

Q4 Arc length = 24π cm, angle = 270°

Comments

Drawing a diagram helps to see the situation clearly.

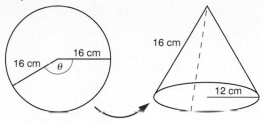

From the diagram you can see that:

i) the radius of the circle is the same as the slant height of the cone (given as 16 cm)

ii) the circumference of the base of the cone is the same as the arc cut out from the circle.

Circumference of the base of the cone

$= 2\pi r$

$= 2 \times \pi \times 12$

$= 24\pi$

Arc length = $\frac{\theta}{360} \times 2\pi r$

$24\pi = \frac{\theta}{360} \times 2 \times \pi \times 16$ As arc length = circumference of base of cone.

$\theta = 270°$ Cancelling π on both sides and working out.

Q5 71.6° (3 s.f.)

Comments

Arc length = $\frac{\theta}{360} \times 2\pi r$

So $15 = \frac{\theta}{360} \times 2 \times \pi \times r$

$\theta = \frac{15 \times 360}{2 \times \pi \times 12} = 71.619\,724\,39 = 71.6°$ (3 s.f.)

41 Symmetry (page 140)

Q1   **a**   C, D, E, H, I, each have a horizontal line of symmetry.

    b   A, H, I each have a vertical line of symmetry.

    c   H, I have both horizontal and vertical lines of symmetry.

    d   B, F, G, J, K have no line symmetry.

    e   H, I have rotational symmetry of order 2.

Comments

It is always important to read the question carefully. The correct types of symmetry must be identified, for maximum marks.

Q2   **a)** A triangular prism has four planes of symmetry (provided the triangle is regular).

    b) A hexagonal prism has seven planes of symmetry (provided the hexagon is regular).

Comments

a)   **b)**

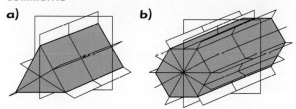

42 Transformations (page 144)

Q1   **a** $(^-3, 4)$ **b** $(3, ^-4)$

    c $(1, 4)$ **d** $(4, 3)$

Comments

A reflection is such that the object and image are the same distance away from the given line.

(a)

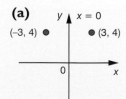

(b)

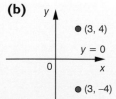

(c)

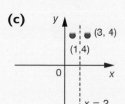

(d)

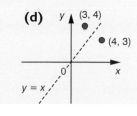

Q2 a, b

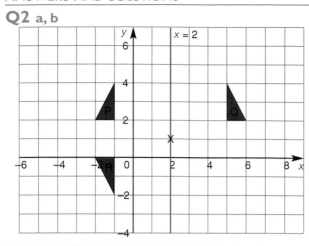

Comments

You might find it helpful to check your answer using tracing paper.

Q3 a

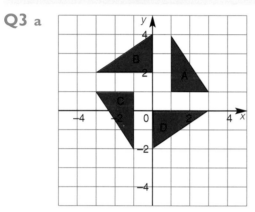

b A rotation through 180° about (0, 1)

Comments

You might find it useful to check your answer using tracing paper.

Q4 The single transformation is a translation of $\begin{pmatrix} -5 \\ 3 \end{pmatrix}$.

Comments

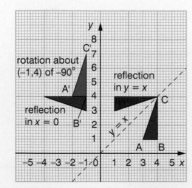

Q5 a   **b**

Comments

An enlargement scale factor $\frac{3}{2}$ makes the image $1\frac{1}{2}$ times larger.

Q6

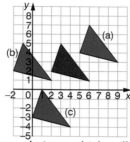

The translations which will return the image to ABC are given by:

a $\begin{pmatrix} -3 \\ -2 \end{pmatrix}$ **b** $\begin{pmatrix} 4 \\ 0 \end{pmatrix}$ **c** $\begin{pmatrix} 2 \\ 5 \end{pmatrix}$

Comments

After a translation of $\begin{pmatrix} a \\ b \end{pmatrix}$ the translation that will return the image to the object is $\begin{pmatrix} -a \\ -b \end{pmatrix}$.

Q7

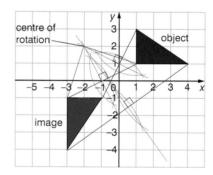

Centre of rotation is $(-2, 2)$.
Angle of rotation is $-90°$.

Comments

To find the centre of rotation you should join corresponding points on the object and image with straight lines and draw the perpendicular bisectors of these lines. The centre of rotation lies on the intersection of these perpendicular bisectors. To find the angle of rotation you should join corresponding points on the object and image to the centre of rotation. The angle between these lines is the angle of rotation.

43 Vectors and vector properties (page 148)

Q1 a $\vec{AC} = 2\boldsymbol{a}$ **b** $\vec{AM} = 3\boldsymbol{b}$
  c $\vec{AF} = \boldsymbol{a} + \boldsymbol{b}$ **d** $\vec{AK} = 2\boldsymbol{a} + 2\boldsymbol{b}$
  e $\vec{GA} = -2\boldsymbol{a} - \boldsymbol{b}$ **f** $\vec{PE} = -3\boldsymbol{a} - 2\boldsymbol{b}$

Comments

Remember that $\mathbf{a} + \mathbf{b} = \mathbf{b} + \mathbf{a}$
and if $\overrightarrow{AB} = \mathbf{a}$ then $\overrightarrow{BA} = {}^-\mathbf{a}$.

Q2 a $|\overrightarrow{AB}| = 5$ units   b $|\overrightarrow{BC}| = \sqrt{26}$ units

c $|\overrightarrow{AC}| = \sqrt{73}$ units

Comments

Using the fact that $|\overrightarrow{AB}| = \sqrt{x^2 + y^2}$

a) $|\overrightarrow{AB}| = \left|\binom{3}{4}\right| = \sqrt{3^2 + 4^2} = \sqrt{25} = 5$

b) $|\overrightarrow{BC}| = \left|\binom{5}{-1}\right| = \sqrt{5^2 + (^-1)^2} = \sqrt{26}$

c) $|\overrightarrow{AC}| = \left|\binom{8}{3}\right| = \sqrt{8^2 + 3^2} = \sqrt{73}$

Q3 a $\overrightarrow{AC} = \mathbf{a} + \mathbf{b}$
b $\overrightarrow{AO} = \mathbf{b}$
c $\overrightarrow{OB} = \mathbf{a} - \mathbf{b}$
d $\overrightarrow{AD} = 2\mathbf{b}$

ACDF is a
parallelogram.

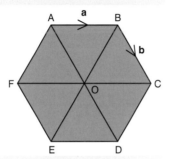

Comments

a) $\overrightarrow{AC} = \overrightarrow{AB} + \overrightarrow{BC} = \mathbf{a} + \mathbf{b}$
b) $\overrightarrow{AO} = \mathbf{b}$
c) $\overrightarrow{OB} = \overrightarrow{OA} + \overrightarrow{AB} = {}^-\mathbf{b} + \mathbf{a} = \mathbf{a} - \mathbf{b}$
d) $\overrightarrow{AD} = 2\mathbf{b}$
$\overrightarrow{AC} = \mathbf{a} + \mathbf{b}$ and $\overrightarrow{FD} = \mathbf{a} + \mathbf{b}$
$\overrightarrow{AF} = \mathbf{b} - \mathbf{a}$ and $\overrightarrow{CD} = \mathbf{b} - \mathbf{a}$
so AC is parallel and equal to FD.
AF is parallel and equal to CD.
Therefore ACDF is a parallelogram.

Q4 a $2(\mathbf{a} + 2\mathbf{c})$
b $\overrightarrow{OM} = \overrightarrow{OC} + \overrightarrow{CM}$
$\overrightarrow{OM} = \overrightarrow{OC} + \frac{1}{2}\overrightarrow{CB}$ As M is the midpoint of $\overrightarrow{CB}$.
$= 6\mathbf{c} + \frac{1}{2} \times 6\mathbf{a}$ As $\overrightarrow{CB} = \overrightarrow{OA}$
$= 3\mathbf{a} + 6\mathbf{c} = 3(\mathbf{a} + 2\mathbf{c})$
Since $\overrightarrow{OM} = 3(\mathbf{a} + 2\mathbf{c})$ and $\overrightarrow{OP} = 2(\mathbf{a} + 2\mathbf{c})$,
$\overrightarrow{OM}$ is parallel to $\overrightarrow{OP}$.
Since they both start at O, they must be along the same line. So OPM is a straight line.

Comments

a) $\overrightarrow{OP} = \overrightarrow{OA} + \overrightarrow{AP}$
$= \overrightarrow{OA} + \frac{2}{3}\overrightarrow{AC}$
$= \overrightarrow{OA} + \frac{2}{3}(\overrightarrow{AO} + \overrightarrow{OC})$ As $\overrightarrow{AC} = \overrightarrow{AO} + \overrightarrow{OC}$
$= 6\mathbf{a} + \frac{2}{3}(-6\mathbf{a} + 6\mathbf{c})$ As $\overrightarrow{AO} = -\overrightarrow{OA}$
$= 6\mathbf{a} - 4\mathbf{a} + 4\mathbf{c}$
$= 2\mathbf{a} + 4\mathbf{c}$
$= 2(\mathbf{a} + 2\mathbf{c})$

STATISTICS

44 Collecting and representing data (page 156)

Q1 a **Sales of coloured socks**

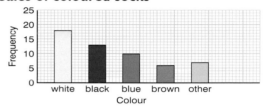

b Sales of coloured socks

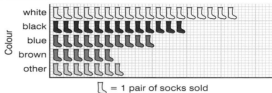

Q2

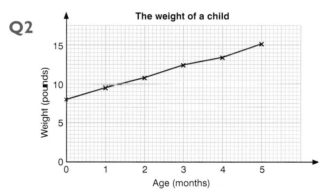

Q3

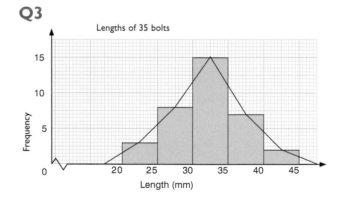

Q4

Courses followed by 250 students

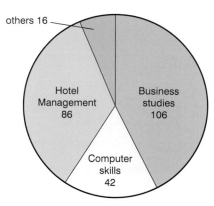

others 16

Hotel Management 86

Business studies 106

Computer skills 42

45 Histograms – unequal class intervals (page 160)

Q1

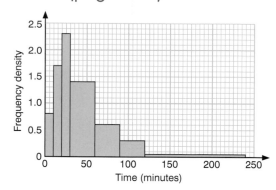

Comments

The pie chart needs to be drawn to represent 250 people. There are 360° in a full circle so each person is represented by 360° ÷ 250 = 1.44° of the pie chart.

Course	Number	Angle	
Business studies	106	106 × 1.44° =	153°
Hotel management	42	42 × 1.44° =	60°
Computer skills	86	86 × 1.44° =	124°
Others	16	16 × 1.44° =	23°
			360°

All angles are rounded to the nearest degree. The angles do not work out exactly, so they have to be rounded to the nearest whole number.

Q5 a train   b walking   c 36°
      d 30   e 15

Comments

a) Train (from the pie chart)

b) Walking (from the pie chart)

c) 10% × 360° = 36°

The number travelling by bus or by car = 45% × 100 = 45 people

Number who travelled by bus is twice the number who travelled by car.

d) Travelled by bus: $\frac{2}{3} \times 45 = 30$

e) Travelled by car: $\frac{1}{3} \times 45 = 15$

Comments

Completing the table:

Time (t minutes)	Frequency	Class width	Frequency density
0 ⩽ t < 10	8	10	0.8
10 ⩽ t < 20	17	10	1.7
20 ⩽ t < 30	23	10	2.3
30 ⩽ t < 60	42	30	1.4
60 ⩽ t < 90	18	30	0.6
90 ⩽ t < 120	9	30	0.3
120 ⩽ t < 240	3	120	0.025

The histogram is shown in the answer.

Q2

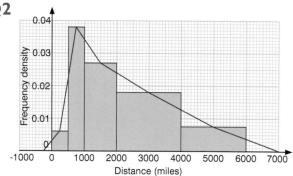

Comments

Completing the table:

Distance (miles)	Frequency	Class width	Frequency density
0–500	3	500.5	0.005 994
501–1000	19	500	0.038
1001–2000	27	1000	0.027
2001–4000	36	2000	0.018
4001–6000	15	2000	0.0075

The histogram and frequency polygon are shown in the answer.

Note: The boundaries on the first interval are 0 and 500 so the class width = 500.5.

Q3

Distance (miles)	0–	5–	10–	15–	20–	30–50
Number of lecturers	1	8	13	10	12	6

You should check that the total number of lectures is 50.

Comments

Reading from the histogram and working backwards:

Distance (miles)	0–	5–	10–	15–	20–	30–50
Class width	5	5	5	5	10	20
Frequency density	0.2	1.6	2.6	2.0	1.2	0.3
Number of lecturers	1	8	13	10	12	6

where number of lectures = class width × frequency density.

Q4

Time (t minutes)	Frequency
$0 < t \leqslant 10$	20
$10 < t \leqslant 15$	18
$15 < t \leqslant 30$	45
$30 < t \leqslant 50$	52
Total	135

Comments

Calculate the information from the graph as follows.

Time (t minutes)	Frequency
$0 < t \leqslant 10$	$10 \times 2 = 20$
$10 < t \leqslant 15$	$5 \times 3.6 = 18$
$15 < t \leqslant 30$	$15 \times 3 = 45$
$30 < t \leqslant 50$	$20 \times 2.6 = 52$
Total	135

Remember to check that your total really is 135.

46 Measures of central tendency (page 166)

Q1
a Science fiction books
b Class 2
c Apples

Comments
a) Science Fiction books – greatest number of pictures
b) Class 2 – longest bar
c) Apples – largest angle/sector area

Q2 Median = 2

Comments

To find the median of a frequency distribution you need to find the cumulative frequency.

Number of goals	Frequency	Cumulative frequency
0	4	4
1	8	12
2	11	23
3	7	30
4	3	33
5	0	33
6	1	34

Median value = $\frac{1}{2}(34 + 1) = 17\frac{1}{2}$th value which is 2.

Q3 17.6 years (3 s.f.)

Comments

Age (years) x	Frequency f	Frequency × age fx
17	23	391
18	13	234
19	4	76
20	0	0
21	1	21
	$\Sigma f = 41$	$\Sigma fx = 722$

Mean = $\frac{\Sigma fx}{\Sigma f} = \frac{722}{41} = 17.609756$

= 17.6 years (3 s.f.)

Q4 a $12 < t \leqslant 16$

c Kemal is incorrect as 25 out of 31 of the readings are above 12 minutes.

Comments

a) The frequency is 31 so the middle value is the 16th value. The 16th value appears in the $12 < t \leqslant 16$ class interval.

Q5 23 kg to an appropriate degree of accuracy.

Comments

Weight (kg)	Mid-interval value x	Frequency f	Frequency × mid-interval value fx
0–10	5	11	55
10–20	15	18	270
20–30	25	16	400
30–40	35	11	385
40–50	45	5	225
50–60	55	2	110
		$\Sigma f = 63$	$\Sigma fx = 1445$

For the group frequency distribution:

$$\text{mean} = \frac{\Sigma fx}{\Sigma f} = \frac{1445}{63} = 22.936508$$

$$= 23 \text{ kg to an appropriate degree of accuracy.}$$

Q6 $9.61 to an appropriate degree of accuracy.

Comments

Amount ($)	Mid-interval value x	Frequency f	Frequency × mid-interval value fx
0 and less than 5	2.5	12	30
5 and less than 10	7.5	15	112.5
10 and less than 15	12.5	8	100
15 and less than 20	17.5	7	122.5
20 and less than 25	22.5	3	67.5
		$\Sigma f = 45$	$\Sigma fx = 432.5$

For the group frequency distribution:

$$\text{mean} = \frac{\Sigma fx}{\Sigma f} = \frac{432.5}{45} = 9.611\,111\,1$$

47 Measures of spread and cumulative frequency diagrams (page 171)

Q1 a 13 seconds

b 12 seconds

Comments

a) (i) 4 12 13 17 18 20 22 24 25 30 34

LQ median UQ

(ii) Interquartile range = UQ − LQ = 25 − 13 = 12

Q2

Median = 41

Interquartile range = $11\frac{1}{2}$

Comments

Time (t minutes)	Frequency	Cumulative frequency
$20 \leqslant t < 25$	3	3
$25 \leqslant t < 30$	7	10
$30 \leqslant t < 35$	15	25
$35 \leqslant t < 40$	18	43
$40 \leqslant t < 45$	22	65
$45 \leqslant t < 50$	17	82
$50 \leqslant t < 55$	8	90
$55 \leqslant t < 60$	2	92

The cumulative frequencies must be plotted at the upper class boundaries (i.e. 25, 30, 35, 40, etc.)

From the graph: median = 41

upper quartile = 46

lower quartile = $34\frac{1}{2}$

Interquartile range = upper quartile − lower quartile

$$= 46 - 34\frac{1}{2} = 11\frac{1}{2}$$

Q3

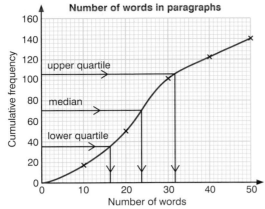

Number of words in paragraphs

a Median = 24, interquartile range = 16
b Percentage of paragraphs over 35 words = 19%

Comments

Number of words per paragraph	Number of paragraphs	Cumulative frequency
1–10	17	17
11–20	33	50
21–30	51	101
31–40	21	122
41–50	18	140

The cumulative frequencies must be plotted at the upper class boundaries (i.e. 10, 20, 30, etc.) as the number of words is discrete in this instance.

a) From the graph: median = 24
upper quartile = 32
lower quartile = 16

Interquartile range
= upper quartile − lower quartile
= 32 − 16 = 16

b) Number of paragraphs under 35 words in length = 114
Number of paragraphs over 35 words in length
= 140 − 114 = 26
Percentage of paragraphs over 35 words in length
$= \frac{26}{140} \times 100 = 19\%$ (to 2 s.f.)

Q4 a 52   **b** 44   **c** 16

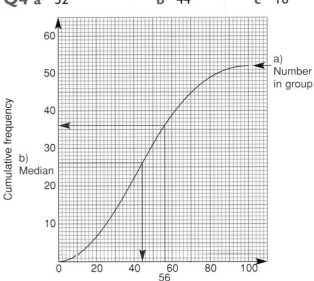

a) Number in group

b) Median

Mark

Comments
a) Take care with this sort of question. The answer is the highest value for cumulative frequency on the graph, not the axis.
c) 36 had a score of 56 and under, so 52 − 36 − 16 passed the exam.

48 Probability (page 175)

Q1 a Number of blue balls = 16
b Number of red balls = 23
c Number of green balls = 11

Comments
a) Number of blue balls = 32% × 50 = 16
b) Number of red balls = 0.46 × 50 = 23
c) Number of green balls = 50 − (16 + 23)
= 11   As the remaining balls are green.

Q2 p(late) = 0.35

Comments
p(late) = 1 − p(not late)
= 1 − (0.2 + 0.45) Total probability = 1.
= 0.35

Q3

		Die				
		1	2	3	4	5	6
Coin	H	H1	H2	H3	H4	H5	H6
	T	T1	T2	T3	T4	T5	T6

a $\frac{1}{12}$ **b** $\frac{1}{4}$

227

Comments

From the possibility space diagram, there are 12 possible outcomes.

a) p(a head and a one) = $\frac{1}{12}$ As only one outcome gives this result.

b) p(a tail and an odd number)

= $\frac{3}{12}$ As three outcomes give this result.

= $\frac{1}{4}$ Cancelling down to its lowest terms.

Q4

		Second die			
		1	2	3	4
First die	1	2	3	4	5
	2	3	4	5	6
	3	4	5	6	7
	4	5	6	7	8

a $\frac{1}{16}$ b $\frac{3}{16}$ c 0

The most likely outcome is a 5.

Comments

From the possibility space diagram, there are 16 possible outcomes.

a) p(total of 2) = $\frac{1}{16}$ As only one outcome gives this result.

b) p(total of 6) = $\frac{3}{16}$ As three outcomes give this result.

c) p(total of 9) = 0 As there is no possibility of getting a total of 9.

The most likely outcome is a 5.

Q5 40

Comments

p(number greater than 4) = $\frac{2}{6}$ = $\frac{1}{3}$

Expected frequency = 120 × $\frac{1}{3}$ = 40

Q6 1 car (rounding to an appropriate degree of accuracy)

Comments

Expected number of cars

= 1037 × 0.062% = 1037 × $\frac{0.062}{100}$

= 0.642 94

= 1 car (rounding to an appropriate degree of accuracy)

49 The addition and multiplication rules (page 179)

Q1 a $\frac{1}{3}$ b $\frac{1}{2}$ c $\frac{1}{2}$

Comments

a) p(5 or 6) = p(5) + p(6)

As the events are mutually exclusive.

= $\frac{1}{6}$ + $\frac{1}{6}$ = $\frac{2}{6}$ = $\frac{1}{3}$

b) p(even number)

= p(2 or 4 or 6)

As the events are mutually exclusive.

= p(2) + p(4) + p(6)

= $\frac{1}{6}$ + $\frac{1}{6}$ + $\frac{1}{6}$ = $\frac{3}{6}$ = $\frac{1}{2}$

c) p(factor of 8) = p(1 or 2 or 4)

As the factors of 8 are 1, 2 4 and 8.

= p(1) + p(2) + p(4)

As the events are mutually exclusive.

= $\frac{1}{6}$ + $\frac{1}{6}$ + $\frac{1}{6}$ = $\frac{3}{6}$ = $\frac{1}{2}$

Q2 a $\frac{1}{11}$ b $\frac{2}{11}$ c $\frac{4}{11}$

Comments

a) p(letter P) = $\frac{1}{11}$

b) p(letter B) = $\frac{2}{11}$

c) p(letter B or letter I) = p(letter B) + p(letter I)

= $\frac{2}{11}$ + $\frac{2}{11}$ = $\frac{4}{11}$

As the events are mutually exclusive.

Q3

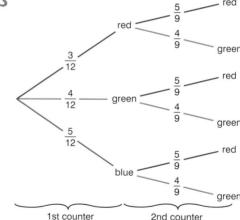

1st counter   2nd counter

Comments

See the tree diagram.

Q4 a 0.176   **b** 0.144

Comments

a) p(lights and brakes)
   = p(lights) × p(brakes)   As the events are
                             independent.
   = 0.32 × 0.55 = 0.176

b) The probability that the car fails because of
   its lights only is equal to the probability that
   the car fails because of its lights and does
   not fail because of the brakes.
   The probability that a car will fail its MOT
   because of the brakes is 0.55.
   The probability that a car will not fail its MOT
   because of the brakes is 0.45.   (1 − 0.55)
   p(car fails because of its lights only)
   = 0.32 × 0.45 = 0.144

Q5 a   0.000 225 or 2.25 × 10⁻⁴
   b   0.029 55

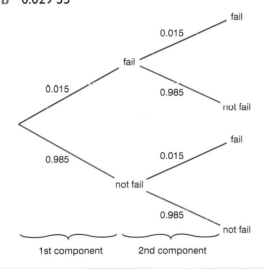

Comments

a) p(both components will fail) = p(fail and fail)
   = p (fail) × p(fail) As the events are
   independent.
   = 0.015 × 0.015
   = 0.000 225 or 2.25 × 10⁻⁴

b) The probability that exactly one component will
   fail is equivalent to the probability that the first
   component fails and the second doesn't or the
   first component doesn't and the second fails.
   = p(fails and doesn't fail or doesn't fail and
     fails)
   = p(fails and doesn't fail) + p(doesn't fail and
     fails) As the events are mutually exclusive.
   = p(fails) × p(doesn't fail)
     + p(doesn't fail) × p(fails)
                 As the events are independent.
   = 0.015 × 0.985 + 0.985 × 0.015
                 As p(doesn't fail) = 1 − p(fail)
   = 0.029 55

50 Multiplication rule for dependent events (page 181)

Q1 a $\frac{3}{8}$ **b** $\frac{1}{8}$ **c** $\frac{1}{2}$

Comments
A diagram helps to see the situation clearly.

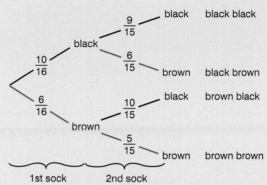

a) p(black and black) = $\frac{10}{16} \times \frac{9}{15} = \frac{3}{8}$

b) p(brown and brown) = $\frac{6}{16} \times \frac{5}{15} = \frac{1}{8}$

c) Reading from the tree diagram p(socks are
   different colours)
   = p(black and brown or brown and black)
   = $\frac{10}{16} \times \frac{6}{15} + \frac{6}{16} \times \frac{10}{15} = \frac{1}{2}$

Q2 Probability = $\frac{1}{64}$

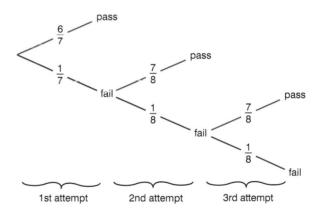

Comments
p(passing on third attempt)
= p(fail and fail and pass)
= $\frac{1}{7} \times \frac{1}{8} \times \frac{7}{8} = \frac{1}{64}$

Q3 $\frac{33}{50}$

Comments

For each attempt: $p(\text{black}) = \frac{3}{10}$

$p(\text{red}) = \frac{5}{10}$

$p(\text{green}) = \frac{2}{10}$

$p(\text{two are the same colour})$

$= 1 - p(\text{all three are different colours}$

$\quad + \text{all three are the same colour})$

$= 1 - [p(BRG) + p(BGR) + p(RBG) + p(RGB) + p(GBR)$

$\quad p(GRB) + p(BBB) + p(RRR) + p(GGG)]$

$= 1 - [6 \times \frac{3}{10} \times \frac{5}{10} \times \frac{2}{10} + \frac{3}{10} \times \frac{3}{10} \times \frac{3}{10} + \frac{5}{10} \times \frac{5}{10} \times \frac{5}{10} + \frac{2}{10} \times \frac{2}{10} \times \frac{2}{10}]$

$= 1 - [6 \times \frac{30}{1000} + \frac{27}{1000} + \frac{125}{1000} + \frac{8}{1000}]$

$= 1 - [\frac{180 + 27 + 125 + 8}{1000}]$

$= 1 - [\frac{340}{1000}]$

$= \frac{660}{1000}$

$= \frac{33}{50}$

EXAM PRACTICE

Paper 3H Higher Tier

1 $3\frac{8}{15}$

> **Comments**
> $5\frac{1}{5} - 1\frac{2}{3} = \frac{26}{5} - \frac{5}{3}$ Converting to improper fractions.
>
> $= \frac{78}{15} - \frac{25}{15}$ Writing as equivalent fractions with a common denominator.
>
> $= \frac{53}{15} = 3\frac{8}{15}$ Rewriting as a mixed number.

2 $8 \times 10^1 \, \text{km}^2$ (square kilometres)

> **Comments**
> **b)** Area per head of population $= \dfrac{4 \times 10^{11}}{5 \times 10^9}$
> $= 0.8 \times 10^2 = 8 \times 10^1 \, \text{km}^2$, leaving the answer in standard form.

3

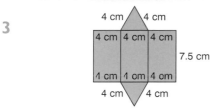

Not full size

> **Comments**
> The net should be drawn, using the fact that the cross-section is an equilateral triangle. The lengths should be drawn to the required accuracy of ±1mm and the angles are drawn to the required accuracy of ±1°.

4   0.06 or 0.09

> **Comments**
> Rounding as $\dfrac{30 \times 0.09}{15 \times 3} = 0.06$
>
> or $\dfrac{30 \times 0.09}{10 \times 3} = 0.09$

5 $y = 5x - 7$

> **Comments**
> Substituting the points (2, 3) and (1, ⁻2) in the equation $y = mx + c$:
> $3 = 2m + c$
> $^-2 = 1m + c$
> The process of elimination is applied to the two equations which are subtracted to produce:
> $5 = m$
> This value is then substituted into the first equation to give $c = {}^-7$.

6   **a)** 37   **b)** nth term $= n^2 + 1$
    c) 100th term $= 10\,001$

> **Comments**
> **a)**   2   5   10   17   26   37 ...
> Differences   +3   +5   +7   +9   +11
> **b)** The differences are all odd numbers. Each term is one more than a square number.
> **c)** 100th term $= 100^2 + 1 = 10\,001$

7 $2\pi r(h + r)$

> **Comments**
> $2\pi r$ is a common factor and is taken outside the brackets.

8

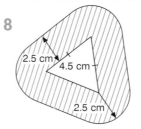

2.5 cm   4.5 cm   2.5 cm   Not full size

> **Comments**
> The locus should be constructed with ruler and compasses, and angles should be measured accurately. The curved areas at the ends are parts of circles.

9   **a)** $2^3 \times 5^2$

> **Comments**
> **a)** 200

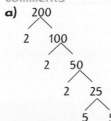

> **b)** 600

> **Comments**
> **b)** Multiples of 75 are 75, 150, 225, 300, 375, 450, 525, 600, ...
>
> Multiples of 200 are 200, 400, 600, ...

10 **a)** (5, 3)

Comments

b) Midpoint $= \left(\dfrac{2+8}{2}, \dfrac{1+5}{2} \right)$

$= \left(\dfrac{10}{2}, \dfrac{6}{2} \right)$

$= (5, 3)$

b) 7.21 (3 s.f.) cm

Comments

b) A diagram might help

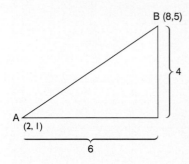

$AB^2 = 4^2 + 6^2$

$AB^2 = 16 + 36$

$AB^2 = 52$

$AB = \sqrt{52}$

$AB = 7.211102551 \dots$

11 **a) (i)** 1, 3
   (ii) 1, 2, 3, 4, 5
   b) ∈ means "is a member of" so 3 is a member
   of set A.

Comments

A∩B is the intersection of {1, 2, 3, 4} and {1, 3, 5}

A∪B is the union of {1, 2, 3, 4} and {1, 3, 5}

12 The expression $\frac{4}{3}\pi$ is a constant and r^2 gives
   units of length $\times$ length $=$ area so the
   expression cannot represent the volume of a
   sphere.

13 **a)** 19   **b)** 20
   c) Median = 30 and interquartile range = 21
   d) In the second test the interquartile range is
   greater so the marks are more spread out.

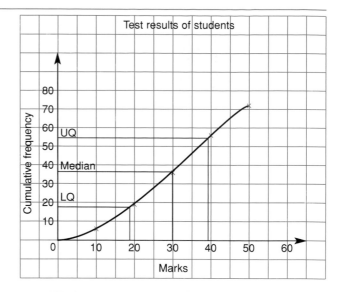

Comments

a) 19   from table
b) 20   56 – 36

Marks	Cumulative frequency	Frequency
⩽ 10	6	6
⩽ 20	19	13
⩽ 30	36	17
⩽ 40	56	20
⩽ 50	72	16

When plotting the cumulative frequency
diagram, remember to plot the points at
the upper class boundaries
(i.e. 10, 20, 30, 40 and 50).

c) Median = 30
   Lower quartile = 18
   Upper quartile = 39
   Interquartile range = 39 – 18 = 21
   Always show your working, so that the
   examiner can see where your answers come
   from.

d) The conclusions should be stated clearly.

14 $x = 4$ and $y = 3$

Comments

The process of elimination is applied to the two
equations which are added to produce:

$7x = 28$ and $x = 4$

This value is then substituted into the first
equation to give $y = 3$.

15 a)

			red		
		1	2	3	4	5
blue	5	5	10	15	20	25
	6	6	12	18	24	30
	7	7	14	21	28	35
	8	8	16	24	32	40
	9	9	18	27	36	45

b) p(square number) = $\frac{4}{25}$

c) p(final score is less than 20) = $\frac{12}{25}$

Comments

a) Using an appropriate grid helps to show the final scores.

b) Results can be read from the table.

c) Results can be read from the table.

16 a) $x + 2$ **b)** $4x + 14$

     c) $1\frac{1}{2}$ or 1.5

Comments

a) From the diagram, the short side is $x + 2$ metres long.

b) Perimeter = $(x + 2) + (x + 5) + (x + 2) + (x + 5)$

         = $4x + 14$

c) $4x + 14 = 20$

   $4x = 6$ Subtracting 14 from both sides.

   $x = \frac{6}{4} = \frac{3}{2} = 1\frac{1}{2}$ or 1.5

17 a) $\angle ROP = 138°$ **b)** $\angle RSP = 69°$

     c) $\angle RQP = 111°$

Comments

a) $\angle OPT = \angle ORT = 90°$

As the tangents to a circle are perpendicular to the radius at the point of contact.

$\angle ROP = 360° - (42° + 90° + 90°)$

As the angles of quadrilateral RTPO add up to 360°.

     $\angle ROP = 138°$

b) $\angle RSP = \frac{1}{2} \times \angle ROP$

The angle subtended at the circumference of a circle equals half of the angle subtended at the centre.

c) $\angle RQP = 180° - \angle RSP$

Opposite angles of cyclic quadrilateral RQPS add up to 180°.

     $\angle RQP = 180° - 69° = 111°$

Remember that the diagrams in these questions will not be drawn accurately so you should not attempt to reach solutions by using measuring instruments.

18 $0.\dot{2}3\dot{4} = \frac{26}{111}$

Comments

A rational number can be expressed in the form $\frac{p}{q}$ where p and q are integers.

$$1000 \times 0.\dot{2}3\dot{4} = 234.234234...$$
$$1 \times 0.\dot{2}3\dot{4} = 0.234234...$$
$$999 \times 0.\dot{2}3\dot{4} = 234$$
$$0.\dot{2}3\dot{4} = \frac{234}{999} = \frac{26}{111} \quad \text{Cancelling down.}$$

As $0.\dot{2}3\dot{4} = \frac{26}{111}$ then $0.\dot{2}3\dot{4}$ must be a rational number.

19 a) 4   **b)** 2

     c) 83.3% (3 s.f.)

Comments

b) $\sqrt{40} = \sqrt{4 \times 10} = \sqrt{4} \times \sqrt{10} = 2\sqrt{10}$ so $k = 2$

c) Area = $\dfrac{(\sqrt{5} + \sqrt{20}) \times \sqrt{8} - \sqrt{5} \times \sqrt{2}}{(\sqrt{5} + \sqrt{20}) \times \sqrt{8}} \times 100$

Multiplying by 100 to convert to a percentage.

$$= \frac{\sqrt{5}\sqrt{8} + \sqrt{20}\sqrt{8} - \sqrt{5}\sqrt{2}}{\sqrt{5}\sqrt{8} + \sqrt{20}\sqrt{8}} \times 100$$

$$= \frac{\sqrt{40} + \sqrt{160} - \sqrt{10}}{\sqrt{40} + \sqrt{160}} \times 100$$

$$= \frac{2\sqrt{10} + 4\sqrt{10} - \sqrt{10}}{2\sqrt{10} + 4\sqrt{10}} \times 100$$

as $\sqrt{160} = \sqrt{16} \times \sqrt{10} = 4\sqrt{10}$

$$= \frac{5\sqrt{10}}{6\sqrt{10}} \times 100$$

$$= \frac{5}{6} \times 100$$

$$= 83.3\% \text{ (3 s.f.)}$$

20 a) 0.162 m³

Comments

Ratio of height = 1:3

Area = $1^2 : 3^2 = 1:9$

Volume = $1^3 : 3^3 = 1:27$

Volume of large drum = 0.006×27

     = 0.162 m³

b) $43200

Comments

Number of drums = $\dfrac{3240}{0.162} = 20\,000$

Surface area of large drum = 0.2×9

     = 1.8 m²

Cost of one drum = $1.8 \times \$1.20$

     = $2.16

Cost of 20 000 drums = $20\,000 \times \$2.16$

     = $43\,200

21

Price (P) in dollars ($)	Frequency
$0 < P \leqslant 5$	40
$5 < P \leqslant 10$	60
$10 < P \leqslant 20$	60
$20 < P \leqslant 40$	40

Comment

Remember that the area represents the frequency for the histogram.

Price (P) in dollars ($)	Frequency
$0 < P \leqslant 5$	$5 \times 8 = 40$
$5 < P \leqslant 10$	$5 \times 12 = 60$
$10 < P \leqslant 20$	$10 \times 6 = 60$
$20 < P \leqslant 40$	$20 \times 2 = 40$

22 $p = \dfrac{q}{s - 1}$

Comments

$s = \dfrac{p + q}{p}$

$sp = p + q$ Multiplying both sides by p.

$sp - p = q$ Subtracting p from both sides.

$p(s - 1) = q$ Factorizing the left-hand side.

$p = \dfrac{q}{s - 1}$ Dividing both sides by $(s - 1)$.

23 $\dfrac{2x - 1}{(x + 3)(x - 4)}$

Comments

A common denominator is $(x + 3) \times (x - 4)$ so writing each part as an equivalent fraction:

$\dfrac{1}{x + 3} + \dfrac{1}{x - 4}$

$= \dfrac{x - 4}{(x + 3)(x - 4)} + \dfrac{x + 3}{(x + 3)(x - 4)}$ where $\dfrac{1}{x + 3} = \dfrac{x - 4}{(x + 3)(x - 4)}$

$= \dfrac{x - 4 + x + 3}{(x + 3)(x - 4)}$ and $\dfrac{1}{x - 4} = \dfrac{x + 3}{(x + 3)(x - 4)}$

$= \dfrac{2x - 1}{(x + 3)(x - 4)}$

24 a) (i) $\dfrac{dy}{dx} = 2x - 4$

(ii) $(2, -3)$

Comments

Coordinates of turning point are:

$2x - 4 = 0$

$2x = 4$

$x = 2$

When $x = 2$ $y = x^2 - 4x + 1$

                         $= 2^2 - 4 \times 2 + 1$

                         $= -3$

b) The turning point is a minimum and a shape of $y = x^2 - 4x + 1$ is ⌣

c) $x = 2$

Comments

The line of symmetry passes through $(2, -3)$ and is vertical so $x = 2$

Paper 4H

1 24 mph and 36 mph

Comments

Ratio $= 2 : 3 : 5 = 24 : 36 : 60$, as an equivalent ratio found by multiplying by 12. So the speed in the other two lanes is 24 mph and 36 mph.

2 $\dfrac{4}{1}$ or 4

Comments

To find the reciprocal of a number you need to convert the number to a fraction.

The number $0.25 = \dfrac{1}{4}$ and turning the fraction upside-down gives the answer $\dfrac{4}{1}$ or 4.

3

Comments

Always label each sector and include the angles at the centre for further information.

Sum of frequencies $= 120$ so each book gets $360° \div 120 = 3°$.

Angles of pie chart:

Type of book	Frequency	Angle
Sport	12	$12 \times 3° = 36°$
Crime	31	$31 \times 3° = 93°$
Horror	29	$29 \times 3° = 87°$
Romance	34	$34 \times 3° = 102°$
Other	14	$14 \times 3° = 42°$
		Total 360°

Always check that the angles add up to 360°.

4   **a)** 60 kph   **b)** 65.5 kph (3 s.f.)

Comments

a) For speed in kilometres per hour, the time must be expressed in hours.

40 minutes = $\frac{40}{60}$ hours

Between A and B distance travelled = 40 km and time taken = 40 minutes.

So speed = distance ÷ time = $40 ÷ \frac{40}{60}$ = 60 kph

b) Again 110 minutes = $\frac{110}{60}$ hours.

Between A and C distance travelled = 120 km and time taken = 110 minutes.

So speed = distance ÷ time = $120 ÷ \frac{110}{60}$

= 65.454 545 = 65.5 kph (3 s.f.)

5 $x > -\frac{1}{2}$

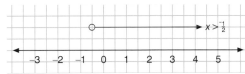

Comments

$2(3 + 2x) > 4$

$6 + 4x > 4$ Expanding the brackets.

$4x > {}^-2$ Subtracting 6 from both sides.

$x > -\frac{1}{2}$ Dividing both sides by 4.

6   1.082 132 8

Comments

Remember to use brackets in the denominator

(281 + 217)

7 $534 000

Comments

After an increase of 8%, $576 720 represents 108% (100% + 8%) of the original value so

108% = $576 720, 1% = $5340 (dividing by 108) and 100% = $534 000.

8 $a = 4.5$

Comments

$(a + 5) + (2a - 1) + (3a - 7) = 24$

$6a - 3 = 24$

$6a = 27$

$a = \frac{27}{6}$

$a = 4.5$

9   **a)** $A = 5030$ cm² (3 s.f.)

b) $r = \sqrt{\frac{A}{4\pi}}$

c) $r = 2.82$ cm (3 s.f.)

Comments

a) $A = 4 \times \pi \times r^2 = 5026.5482$ cm²

b) $A = 4\pi r^2$

$\frac{A}{4\pi} = r^2$ Dividing both sides by 4π.

$r^2 = \frac{A}{4\pi}$ Turning the equation around.

$r = \sqrt{\frac{A}{4\pi}}$ Taking square roots on both sides.

c) $r = \sqrt{\frac{A}{4\pi}} = \sqrt{\frac{100}{4\pi}} = 2.820\ 947\ 9$ cm

10 $20x$

Comments

$(x + 5)^2 - (x - 5)^2 = (x^2 + 10x + 25) - (x^2 - 10x + 25)$

$= x^2 + 10x + 25 - x^2 + 10x - 25$

$= 20x$

11 $\angle PBC = 72°$ Exterior angle of regular pentagon.

$\angle PCB = 72°$ Exterior angle of regular pentagon.

$\angle BPC = 36°$ Angles of a triangle add up to 180°.

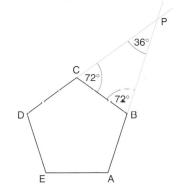

Comments

It is always a good idea to give reasons, so that the examiner can give credit for the methods used, even if the answers are wrong.

External angle of regular pentagon = $\frac{360}{5}$ = 72°.

$\angle PBC = \angle PCB = 72°$ as these are exterior angles.

$\angle BPC = 36°$ as the angles of triangle BPC add up to 180°.

12 **a)** 1×10^{-9} **b)** 2×10^8

Comments

The easiest way to answer this is to use a calculator.

a) 1×10^{-9}

$A = 1$ and $n = -9$

b) 5 nanoseconds $= 5 \times 10^{-9}$ seconds

The number of calculations $= \dfrac{1}{5 \times 10^{-9}}$

$= \dfrac{1}{5} \times \dfrac{1}{10^{-9}}$

$= 0.2 \times 10^9$

$= 2 \times 10^8$

13 **a)** $\angle POS = 67°$ **b)** $\angle OPR = 23°$
    c) $\angle OPS = 23°$

Comments

a) $\angle POS = 67°$ $\angle POS = \angle POR$ as triangle ORP and triangle OSP are congruent (RHS).

b) $\angle OPR = 23°$ $\angle ORP = 90°$ and angles of the triangle RPO = 180°.

c) $\angle OPS = 23°$ $\angle OPS = \angle OPR$ as triangle ORP and triangle OSP are congruent (RHS).

14   Distance $= 1330$ m (3 s.f.)

Comments

Start by drawing a sketch of the situation and completing the given details on the diagram.

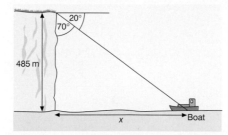

Since the angle of depression is 20° the top angle in the triangle is 70° (as angles forming a right angle add up to 90°). Then from the triangle:

$\tan 70° = \dfrac{x}{485}$

$x = 485 \times \tan 70° = 1332.5265$ m

15 **a)** $\angle ABD = 90° - x$ **b)** $\angle DBE = x$
    c) $\angle BAD = 90° - 2x$

Comments

a) $\angle CDE = 90°$ CE is a diameter and the angle in a semicircle $= 90°$.

$\angle DEC = 90° - x$ As the angles of the triangle DEC add up to 180°.

$\angle DBC = 90° + x$ As opposite angles of a cyclic quadrilateral add up to 180°.
$180° - (90° - x) = 90° + x$

$\angle ABD = 90° - x$ As the angles on a straight line ABC add up to 180°.
$180° - (90° + x) = 90° - x$

b) $\angle DBE = DCE$ As the angles subtended by the same chord DE at the circumference are equal (it would be helpful to draw in the line BE on the diagram).

c) $\angle ACE = 3x$ and $\angle AEC = 90° - x$

$\angle BAD = 180° - \{3x + (90° - x)\}$
As the angles of $\triangle$ ACE add up to 180°.

$\angle BAD = 180° - (3x + 90° - x)$
$= 180° - (2x + 90°) = 180° - 2x - 90°$
$= 90° - 2x$

16   116 cm³ (3 s.f.)

Comments

Volume of sphere $= \dfrac{4}{3}\pi r^3$

Volume of rubber = volume of outer − volume of inner

$= \dfrac{4}{3}\pi \, 5^3 - \dfrac{4}{3}\pi \, (5 - 0.4)^3$

$= \dfrac{4}{3}\pi \, (125 - 4.6^3)$

$= \dfrac{4}{3}\pi \, (125 - 97.336)$

$= 115.8786922...$

$= 116$ cm³ (3 s.f.)

17 **a)** 10–19   **b)** $\dfrac{43}{59}$ **c)** 1340 (3 s.f.)

Comments

a) The 10–19 group has the highest frequency so is the modal class.

b) Probability $= \dfrac{9 + 20 + 14}{9 + 20 + 14 + 5 + 11} = \dfrac{42}{59}$

c) Total number of marks, using mid interval values

$= 9 \times 4\tfrac{1}{2} + 20 \times 14\tfrac{1}{2} + 14 \times 24\tfrac{1}{2} + 5 \times 34\tfrac{1}{2} + 11 \times 44\tfrac{1}{2}$

$= 1335.5$

18 a) 11

b) $a = 4$

c) 4

d) $x < 0$

e) $g^{-1} : x \rightarrow (x - 1)^2$

Comments

a) $f(-4) = 2 \times -4 - 3$

$\qquad = -8 - 3$

$\qquad = -11$

b) $f(a) = 5 \quad$ so $2a - 3 = 5$

$\qquad\qquad\qquad 2a = 8$

$\qquad\qquad\qquad a = 4$

c) $gf(6) = g(2 \times 6 - 3)$

$\qquad = g(9)$

$\qquad = 1 + \sqrt{9}$

$\qquad = 1 + 3$

$\qquad = 4$

d) Since $\sqrt{x}$

You cannot take the square root of a negative number, so $x \geqslant 0$

e) Let $y = 1 + \sqrt{x}$

$\sqrt{x} = y - 1$

$x = (y - 1)^2$

$g^{-1} : x \mapsto (x - 1)^2$

19 a) \$2000

b) 2 years 10 months (to nearest month)

Comments

a) Using $v \propto \dfrac{1}{a}$ to write $v = \dfrac{k}{a}$, find the value of k by substituting $v = 7000$ when $a = 1$.
The constant of proportionality $= 7000$ and $v = \dfrac{7000}{a}$.
When $a = 3\frac{1}{2}$, $v = \$2000$.

b) When $v = 2500$, $a = 2.8$ years.
It is important that this is not interpreted as 2 years 8 months as it is closer to 2 years 10 months (to the nearest month).

20 a)

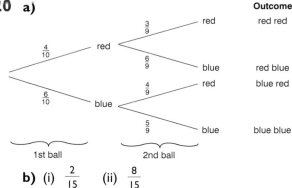

| | 1st ball | 2nd ball | Outcome |

b) (i) $\dfrac{2}{15}$ (ii) $\dfrac{8}{15}$

Comments

b) (i) The probability of obtaining two red balls
$= p(\text{red and red})$
$= \frac{4}{10} \times \frac{3}{9} = \frac{2}{15}$

(ii) The probability of obtaining one ball of each colour
$= p(\text{red and blue or blue and red})$
$= \frac{4}{10} \times \frac{6}{9} + \frac{6}{10} \times \frac{4}{9} = \frac{8}{15}$

21 Area $= 1080$ cm^2 (3 s.f.)

Comments

Area $= \frac{110}{360} \times \pi \times 35^2 - \frac{110}{360} \times \pi \times 10^2$
$= \frac{110}{360} \times \pi \times (35^2 - 10^2)$
$= 1079.9225$

22 B $= (8, 1)$

Comments

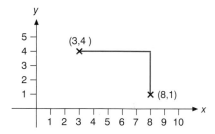

23 Size of angle = 22.2° (1d.p.)

Comment

Diagrams not drawn to scale

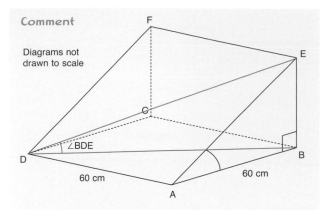

For the triangle BDE, calculate BD and BE to find the angle BDE.

Using Pythagoras' theorem:

$BD^2 = DA^2 + AB^2$

$BD^2 = 60^2 + 60^2$

$BD^2 = 3600 + 3600$

$BD^2 = 7200$

$BD = \sqrt{7200}$

$BD = 84.852\ 813\ 74$

$\tan(BAE) = \dfrac{BE}{AB}$

$\tan 30 = \dfrac{BE}{60}$

$BE = 60 \times \tan 30°$

$BE = 34.641\ 016\ 15$

$\tan BDE = \dfrac{BE}{BD}$

$\tan BDE = \dfrac{34.641\ 016\ 15}{84.852\ 813\ 74}$

$\tan BDE = 0.408\ 248\ 29$

$BDE = 22.207\ 654\ 3°$

$BDE = 22.2°\ (1\text{d.p.})$

24 Maximum = 73.9 mph (3 s.f.)
Minimum = 70.1 mph (3 s.f.)

Comments

Distance = 42 miles. Distance$_{min}$ = 41.5 miles.

Distance$_{max}$ = 42.5 miles.

Time = 35 minutes. Time$_{min}$ = 34.5 minutes.

Time$_{max}$ = 35.5 minutes.

Using speed = $\frac{distance}{time}$, and expressing time in hours:

Speed$_{max}$ = $\dfrac{42.5}{\frac{34.5}{60}}$ = 73.9 mph (3 s.f.)

Speed$_{min}$ = $\dfrac{41.5}{\frac{35.5}{60}}$ = 70.1 mph (3 s.f.)

Index